Elements of Mathematics

Under the Editorship of CARL B. ALLENDOERFER

Elements of Mathematics

James W. Armstrong

Associate Professor of Mathematics, University of Illinois, Urbana

The Macmillan Company / Collier-Macmillan Limited, London

First Printing

Library of Congress catalog card number: 72–80304

The Macmillan Company

Collier-Macmillan Canada, Ltd., Toronto, Ontario

Printed in the United States of America

Preface

As we shall see in the coming chapters, there have been two periods of great mathematical activity. The first of these was the period of Greek mathematics (roughly 600 B.C. to 100 B.C.). Many of the ideas discovered by the ancient Greeks are still being used and studied today. The second period began in the early seventeenth century and has not yet come to a close. The Greek period has been called the Golden Age of Mathematics, but it cannot compare with contemporary mathematical activity. The quantity and quality of current mathematical research is almost overpowering. For example, in 1968 the American Mathematical Society (one of the premier mathematical organizations in the world) published reviews of more than 10,000 original pieces of mathematical research and the number grows each year at such a rate that the backlog of papers waiting to be published is reaching crisis proportions. But perhaps even more startling is a set of figures published recently by the National Academy of Sciences. In the academic year 1954–55 there were awarded in the United States 4034 undergraduate degrees in mathematics as compared with 22,589 in engineering, 10,516 in the physical sciences, and 9050 in the biological sciences. Forecasted for 1976 are 65,000 undergraduate degrees in mathematics as compared with 46,000 in engineering, 35,000 in the physical sciences, and 53,000 in the biological sciences! As these figures clearly indicate, mathematics not only is now an important force in our lives, but will grow in importance over the coming years. Equally clearly these figures imply a growing need for the nonmathematician to make himself aware of at least some of the major ideas and problems of mathematics. It is to help meet this end that this book has been written.

In the coming ten chapters we shall introduce the student to the basic aspects of seven or eight of the most important ideas in mathematics. These are ideas that run through most parts of mathematics and that provide the bases for the four or five single most important parts of mathematics. Of necessity the discussions of these ideas will be conducted on rather straightforward intuitive levels and so will be limited in depth, but even so the basic ideas show through clearly.

Every effort has been made to bypass the usual computational and manipulative aspects of mathematics and some chapters involve almost no computation at all. In those few instances where a minimum of computation is absolutely necessary we have included beforehand sufficient preliminary work in the techniques. The student is not required or asked to bring more into his classroom than a willingness to look at some old and some new ideas with an unprejudiced mind.

Of necessity the chapters in a book must be linearly ordered whether their content calls for such an ordering or not. Such is the case with these chapters. The teacher will find that there are a number of possible alternate arrangements of the chapters, and I would like to point out a few of these alternatives. The book should probably begin with Chapter 1. (Incidentally, note that the first two sections of this chapter are expository and so are quite different from the other sections of this and the other chapters.) Chapter 4, set theory, can be interchanged with Chapter 3. Another possibility is to move Chapter 4 between Chapters 1 and 2. If this is done, then a certain amount of care should be exercised in covering Sections 4.3 and 4.4 (including their exercises) for there are terms used in these two sections which are first introduced in Chapter 2. Thus the most reasonable orderings of these chapters are 1-2-3-4, 1-2-4-3, and 1-4-2-3. Chapter 5 should follow the first four chapters and should precede the last five chapters. Chapters 6, 7, 8, and 10 comprise another block of material. Chapter 10 is really a continuation and development of the ideas introduced in Chapter 6 and so either of the orderings 6-7-8-10 or 6-10-7-8 is reasonable. Chapter 9, probability, can be used anywhere, perhaps most reasonably sometime after Chapter 6. This chapter can be used to provide a change of pace anywhere in the coverage of ideas in Chapters 6, 7, 8, and 10. Teachers are invited to try their own orderings of chapters, but are advised to take some care in assigning exercises if such changes are made. It is even possible to rearrange the book by sections, but this would involve considerably more attention to possible later difficulties. More information in this regard is contained in the Teacher's Manual.

The teacher will find a number of starred exercises in the book. The star does *not* indicate an exercise of more than average difficulty. In fact, many of the starred exercises are quite easy. What the star indicates is that the exercise deals with an idea which has not been discussed in the body of the text or that it deals with an idea introduced in a previous exercise. The starred exercises may be used as source material for lectures if the teacher desires. At any rate, these exercises should be examined before they are assigned routinely as homework.

I want to acknowledge the assistance of Professors Carl B. Allendoerfer of the University of Washington and Donald R. Sherbert of the University of Illinois. These mathematicians read the manuscript in its early stages and made many substantial and important suggestions and recommendations. Also, I would like to express my thanks to Professors Leslie Peek of Mercer University and Carolyn C. Styles of San Diego Mesa College, who read the finished manuscript and made many valuable suggestions. Mr. Harry Conn of The Macmillan Company deserves much of the credit for this book because of his wholehearted assistance throughout its development.

I also acknowledge The Granger Collection for use of the portrait of George Boole; Frederick Lewis, Inc., for the photograph of Bertrand Russell; and Scripta Mathematica for all other portraits of mathematicians.

Contents

Elements of Mathematics

1 Logical Foundations

IT IS APPROPRIATE that we should begin our study of the underlying ideas of modern mathematics with an examination of the logical foundation for those ideas. To do this we must first beat a quick retreat back to the time of the ancient Greeks and then work our way forward again to about our own time. We shall begin with a discussion of the axiomatic method and conclude with a look at elementary symbolic logic.

1.1 Axiomatic Mathematics, I

The characteristic of modern mathematics that so dramatically differentiates it from the other sciences is that mathematics is presented as an axiomatic study while the other sciences are axiomatic only to the extent that they utilize mathematics. So let us begin by a brief examination of axiomatic mathematics.

Exactly when, where, and by whom axiomatic or deductive reasoning was first used in mathematics is unknown although there are conjectures that it might have been a Greek of the fifth century B.C. named Thales of Miletus. It is likely that until this time mathematics did not exist as we know it today but instead consisted of unrelated and empirically derived ideas about numbers and simple geometric objects such as circles and right triangles. The first specific evidence of an axiomatic treatment of a part of mathematics is contained in an elementary textbook concerned with geometry, algebra, and number theory called *Elements* written by a Greek, Euclid of Alexandria, about 300 B.C. Probably you have heard of Euclid only as a geometer although the real significance of his textbook lies not so much in the geometry that it contains as in the way that this geometry was presented. Euclid was, as far as we know, the first writer of mathematical literature to employ the axiomatic or deductive method of reasoning and it is for this reason that he is famous.

Axiomatic or deductive reasoning is the key to modern mathematics. The key to **deductive reasoning** is the idea that the truth of a statement must be shown to follow logically from the truth of other statements that have already been shown to be true by this method. Loosely speaking, the truth of a new statement must be deduced from the truth of old statements.

This is in contrast to the other method of reasoning called **inductive reasoning**. When we establish the "truth" of a statement by making a generalization based upon a limited number of observations or experiments, we are using inductive reasoning.[1] But inductive reasoning has one great fault: We have no guarantee that an event that has taken place in the same way each time we observed it will continue to take place in that same way in the future. Also, it may be that our observation was faulty or that we did not correctly interpret what we observed. It is because the theories of physics, for example, are based for the most part on inductive reasoning that every so often physical theories must be revised so as to agree with new observations made since the last time the theory was formulated. Generally speaking, inductive reasoning plays a great role in the nonmathematical sciences and plays relatively little role in mathematics. Deductive reasoning, on the other hand, plays a relatively small role in the nonmathematical sciences but plays a great role in mathematics.

But insistence upon deductive reasoning in mathematics does present a problem. If the truth of each statement must be based upon the truth of previously proved statements, how was the *first* statement proved true? When trying to prove the first statement there are no previously proved statements available upon which to base the truth of the first statement. The answer is that it could not have been proved true at all and so it can only have been assumed to be true. Thus every study that involves deductive reasoning must necessarily involve a number of statements which are accepted as being true without proof. These statements are called **postulates** or **axioms**. The axioms are the statements that are used to prime the deductive pump. After the pump has been primed, it can begin producing other true statements. When Euclid wrote his *Elements*, he started with these five postulates:

[1] This is sometimes called the "scientific method."

1. A line can be drawn from any point to any other point.
2. A segment can be extended continuously to a line.
3. A circle can be drawn with any point as center and any segment as radius.
4. All right angles are equal.
5. Given a line ℓ and a point P not belonging to ℓ, there can be drawn through P exactly one line that is parallel to ℓ.[2] (Fig. 1.1.)

Figure 1.1

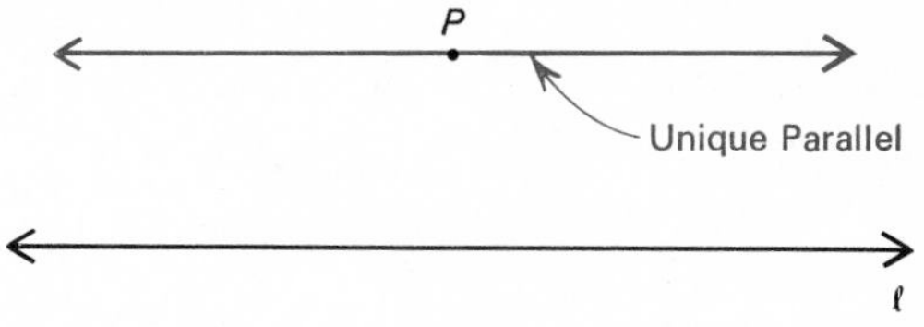

On the basis of the above five postulates (together with additional postulates that were introduced as needed) Euclid deductively built up a geometry that we call Euclidean geometry and with which you are familiar to a greater or lesser degree. Each statement which is called true in this geometry is either one of the postulates (which are assumed to be true) or one of the proved statements (which are variously called theorems, propositions, lemmas, or corollaries).

Now some discretion must be exercised in the choice of the statements to be called axioms. Among a number of other criteria we want the list of axioms to be as concise as possible and we want each axiom to express as primitive an idea as possible. In other words we do not want to assume more than we really have to assume. But most important of all we want the collection of axioms to be **consistent**. By this we mean that we do not want the axioms to give rise to logical contradictions. For example, we would not want to choose axioms which would eventually give rise to both the statements, "The sum of the angles of a triangle is 180°" and "The sum of the angles of a triangle is less than 180°." Euclid's geometry is consistent in the sense that the axioms do not give rise to logical contradictions. But there were serious errors in his deductive presentation. One of these was his failure to recognize the fact that he could not hope to give a definition to each and every concept with which he dealt. If you will reflect for a moment upon the fact that

[2] By a parallel to l through P we mean a line passing through P that does not intersect l. Incidentally, this statement is a simplified version of Euclid's original more complicated statement.

definitions of new concepts are phrased in terms of previously defined concepts, then you will see that, just as we needed axioms to get the statement-proving process started, we need undefined concepts to get the concept-defining process started. Because we cannot hope to find a definition for the first concept in terms of previously defined concepts, this first concept (along with a few others) must be taken without definition. Euclid missed this fact and attempted to define every concept. As a consequence many of his definitions lack any real power as definitions. For example, he defined a line as "that which is breadthless length" without having previously defined what he meant by "length" and by "breadth." Such definitions are of no value whatsoever.

Finally, by a **deductive** (or axiomatic) **system** we mean a part of mathematics that has been organized along the following lines. First of all, we have selected a number of concepts that we feel are very primitive and that we agree to accept without definition. These are the undefined concepts of the system. Secondly, we have selected some statements concerning these undefined concepts that we feel express very primitive truths about the undefined concepts and that we are going to accept without proof. These are the axioms of the system. Then, using the undefined concepts and axioms we can begin the process of defining new concepts in terms of the undefined concepts and establishing the truth of new statements about these concepts on the basis of the axioms. The resulting deductive system therefore consists of four basic parts: undefined concepts, axioms, defined concepts, and theorems. One of the goals of mathematics is to present every part of mathematics in the form of such a deductive system.

Exercises 1.1

1. In your everyday life which do you use more often, inductive or deductive reasoning? Give some examples of conclusions you have reached inductively. Have these conclusions held up under the weight of subsequent events? Can you find any examples of deductive reasoning in your everyday life? If so, can you identify the axioms upon which you based one of these deductive arguments?
2. We have pointed out that the axioms are statements about the undefined concepts. So by examining Euclid's first five axioms you should be able to identify some undefined concepts. (For example, Axiom 1 involves the undefined concepts of *point* and *line*.) Make a list of the undefined concepts involved in these first five axioms.

3. Make a careful and thorough dictionary search for the meanings of the terms you listed in the preceding exercise. You should run into difficulties because of the very primitive nature of these concepts. You should also run into some circular definitions (that is, concepts ultimately defined in terms of themselves.)
4. Now assume that you have taken all the terms you found in Exercise 2 as undefined. Use a dictionary and search for new terms (for example, rectangle?) that are definable in terms of these undefined concepts. Locate at least a couple of these defined concepts.

1.2 Axiomatic Mathematics, II

Euclid chose his axioms with care and to him each of them represented what he might have called an "absolute truth" or a "self-evident truth" or an "undeniable truth." This view was held for two thousand years and it was not until the early nineteenth century that the possibility of absolute and undeniable truth was called into question. We shall trace through this story in this section.

Euclid believed that he had chosen as axioms statements that were not only very primitive in what they said but also expressed ideas that must be undeniable. For him there could be no question but that each of these axioms was true of the material world and so there was no reason why they should not be accepted as axioms. But the fifth postulate, which is called the **Unique Parallel Postulate**, did seem to be somehow "different" from the other axioms. The Unique Parallel Postulate seemed more sophisticated than the other axioms; it seemed to express a higher order of truth. In fact, this fifth postulate looked more like a theorem than an axiom. The question was, could the fifth postulate be proved on the basis of the other postulates? If it could be then the fifth postulate would be dependent upon the other postulates. But if it could not be proved on the basis of the other postulates then it would be independent of them. So the question was, is the fifth postulate independent of or dependent upon the other axioms? As far as we can tell this question was attacked continuously from Euclid's time to about the year 1825.

One of the men who tried to decide this question was Janos Bolyai (Hungarian, 1802–1860), a professional soldier and the son of a mathematician. Bolyai was working hard on the problem when his father wrote to him, "For God's sake, I beseech you, give it up. Fear it no less than sensual passion because it, too, may take all your time, and deprive you of your health, peace of mind, and happiness in life." Clearly working on the question of dependence of the Unique Parallel Postulate was losing its fascination for some mathematicians after 2000 years. What was needed was a new insight into the problem.

About this same time Karl Friedrich Gauss (German, 1777–1855), the greatest mathematician of his time and one of the greatest mathematicians of all time, had been working on the problem. A professor from the University of Kazan, Nikolai Ivanovitch Lobachevski (Russian, 1793–1856) was working on it also. These three men had never met (although they were known to each other), but they were all to come to just about the same conclusion at just about the same time. Let us continue the story with Lobachevski.

Lobachevski became convinced that the Unique Parallel Postulate was in fact independent of the other axioms. To test out this conjecture he replaced the Unique Parallel Postulate with the following contradictory postulate:

Nikolai Ivanovitch Lobachevski (1793-1856)

Multiple Parallel Postulate: *Given a line ℓ and a point P not belonging to ℓ, there can be drawn through P infinitely many lines that are parallel to ℓ.* (Fig. 1.2.[3])

Figure 1.2

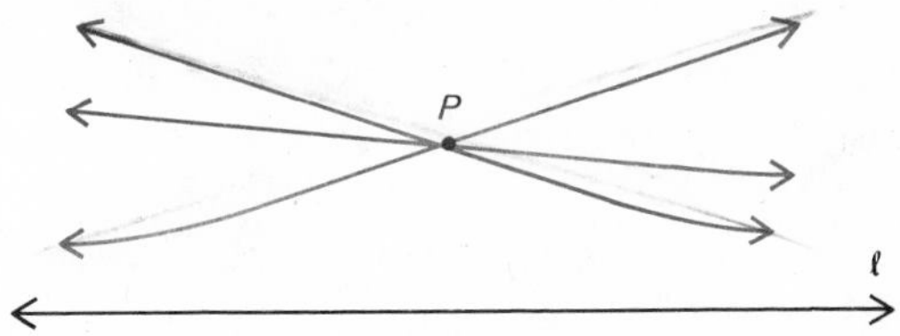

Lobachevski's reasoning was this: If the Unique Parallel Postulate were in fact independent of Euclid's other axioms, then replacing it with this new postulate should *not* produce an inconsistent geometry. On the other hand, if the Unique Parallel Postulate were dependent upon the other axioms, then replacing it with this new axiom would introduce a contradiction into the resulting deductive system. That is, the statement, "Through *P* there is only one parallel" would be provable from the other axioms, whereas the statement "there are infinitely many parallels through *P*" would be an axiom and these two statements would contradict each other. Hence the resulting deductive system would be inconsistent. So Lobachevski made the replacement, introducing his Multiple Parallel Postulate, and then went on to prove that the resulting deductive system was *not* inconsistent. This meant that the Unique Parallel Postulate was independent of the other axioms. Finally after some two thousand years the independence of Euclid's fifth postulate had been established.

The deductive system that results from the assumption of Euclid's axioms (except for his Unique Parallel Postulate) together with the Multiple Parallel Postulate is called **Lobachevskian geometry**. (As a matter of fact both Gauss and Bolyai had come to the same conclusions as had Lobachevski, but the main credit for the invention of this new non-Euclidean geometry is usually given to Lobachevski.) But even to its creator Lobachevskian geometry appeared so unnatural that he referred to it as "imaginary geometry."

[3] This figure only hints at the true situation. Because of the smallness of the figure it has been necessary to make the infinitely many parallels appear to bend, but in actuality they do not bend at all. In order to understand the figure it is essential that you tear yourself away from the traditional understanding that there is only one such parallel. This is difficult to do, for the assumption that there is only one such parallel line is bred into us from birth.

Thus the question of independence of the Unique Parallel Postulate had been solved and in the process a new kind of geometry had been invented. Here things rested for a number of years until the German mathematician Georg Riemann (1826–1866) invented another new non-Euclidean geometry that is called **Riemannian Geometry**. Riemannian geometry is based upon the assumption of Euclid's axioms (except for the Unique Parallel Postulate) plus the following axiom:

No Parallels Postulate: *Given a line ℓ and a point P not belonging to ℓ there cannot be drawn any lines through P which are parallel to ℓ* (Figure 1.3[4]).

Figure 1.3

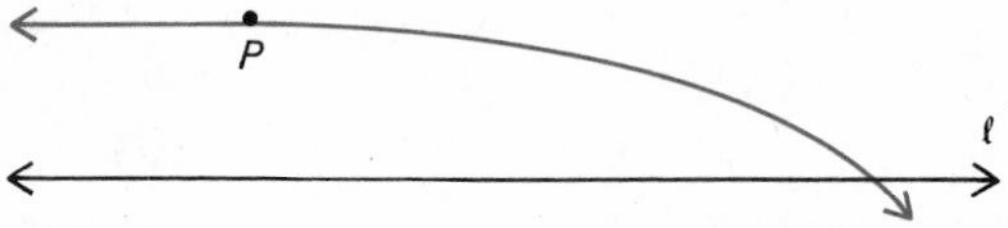

The geometry based upon this set of axioms is also internally consistent. There were now three distinct geometries, Euclid's (unique parallels), Lobachevski's (infinitely many parallels) and Riemann's (no parallels). From a purely axiomatic point of view each of these three geometries is as good as the other two, for all three geometries are internally consistent in the sense that none of them is capable of giving rise to a contradiction. The natural question now is, which of these geometries is the "correct" one in terms of being a "correct" abstraction of our physical environment? We cannot answer this question. The fact is that if we consider only "local" problems—that is, problems dealing with distances similar to those here on earth, say problems in which distances do not exceed a few million miles—then these geometries give so nearly the same results that we cannot distinguish between them using our best measuring devices. For example, in Euclidean geometry the sum of the angles of a triangle is exactly 180°, in Lobachevskian geometry this angle sum is always greater than 180°, while in Riemannian geometry the angle sum is always less than 180°. Theoretically, to determine the "correct" geometry all we have to do is construct a triangle and measure the sum of its angles and then we will know which geometry is the "real" geometry. But in order to be able to make this determination with the measuring instruments available to us

[4] The lines do not really bend as shown here. Because of the smallness of the illustration it is necessary to make them bend in order to have the point of intersection be a point on the page.

we would have to work with a triangle the sides of which were not measured in miles but in light-years. It is doubtful that we will ever be able to make such a determination and find out which of these geometries is "correct."

But, as Riemann realized, the invention of these non-Euclidean geometries has deeper significance than the question of which one represents our physical environment. The fact that each of these geometries is internally consistent has forced mathematicians and philosophers to renounce the notion of "absolute truth" or "undeniable truth" or "self-evident truth." For if, as Euclid thought, his axioms were undeniable truths, this would mean that the non-Euclidean geometries are based axiomatically upon statements contrary to fact and it would then follow that these geometries would have to be internally inconsistent. But it has been proved they are not internally inconsistent. So we must reject the idea that there are any statements about geometry that can be called absolute truths. We now understand that truth is not an attribute that a statement has or does not have in any absolute sense. A statement that is true in one deductive system may be false in another. (For example, the statement "The sum of the angles of a triangle is 180°" is a true statement in Euclidean geometry but is false in the non-Euclidean geometries.) Thus in order to say that a particular statement is true we must know that the statement follows from the axioms of that system in a logically valid way. Thus by "truth" we really mean "validity." That is, a statement is true (in a given deductive system) provided that the statement can be derived in a logically valid way from the axioms of that system.

As long as mathematicians could regard the axiomatic foundations of mathematics as being undeniable truths there was no reason to be excessively critical of those foundations. But with the destruction of the notion of absolute truth it became clear that mathematicians would have to spend at least a part of their time examining and re-examining the axiomatic foundations of mathematics.

1.3 Introduction to Symbolic Logic

Logic was first studied in a systematic way by the ancient Greeks, who used it to provide a logical framework in which to do mathematics. But following the period of Greek mathematics the development of logic languished for nearly two thousand years. The next great surge took place in the middle of the nineteenth century with the invention of symbolic logic. We shall discuss elementary symbolic logic in this and the next three sections.

The logic studied by the Greeks is called **Aristotelian logic** after Aristotle (about the fourth century B.C.), who was its most famous student. Aristotle produced a list of fourteen syllogisms that he felt summed up the major ideas of logic. For example, one of these syllogisms is

All heroes are men.
All men are mortal.
Hence,
All heroes are mortal.

The other syllogisms dealt with statements of the form, "Some men are mortal," "No men are mortal," and so on. These syllogisms were examples of all the known ways to draw a conclusion (when such a conclusion was possible) from two given statements.

The fourteen syllogisms of Aristotle, plus another five that were added by medieval logicians, represented logic for about two thousand years. To study logic essentially meant to study these nineteen syllogisms. Then in 1848 the English mathematician George Boole (1815–1864) published a little book in which he used symbols to facilitate the study of logic in much the same way that symbols are used in algebra. Moreover, Boole organized his study of what we today call symbolic logic along the lines of a deductive system. He selected undefined concepts and axioms and used these to build up the system of symbolic logic.

Just as algebra is the study of the ways that numbers can be compared and operated upon, **symbolic logic** is the study of ways that statements can be compared and operated upon. We shall leave the concept of "statement" undefined except to say that a statement is either true or false, but cannot be both true and false at the same time. We may accept this as an axiom concerning the undefined concept of "statement".

Example 1: "Help!" is not a statement in the sense of symbolic logic because it is neither true nor false. The statement "Two plus two equals four" is a true statement and so is one of the statements with which symbolic logic deals. So too is the false statement "Two plus two equals six."

Expressed as simply as possible, symbolic logic is the study of how statements can be constructed from given statements and how the truth value (that is, the truth or falsity) of the newly constructed statements can be determined from the truth values of the statements from which they were constructed. For example, suppose we are given two statements that we shall label p and q. (Note the use of symbols to denote these statements. This is typical of symbolic logic.) We can use these statements to form the compound statement "p and q". We symbolize this statement by $p \wedge q$. (Note the use of a symbol $\wedge$ to represent the word "and". "$\wedge$" is used to denote "and" in symbolic logic in the same way that "+" is used to denote "added to" in algebra.) Now that we have constructed our new statement, $p \wedge q$, how can we determine its truth value in terms of the truth values of the given statements p and q? By common agreement, the compound statement $p \wedge q$ is true if both p and q are themselves true and is false in all other cases. This information is contained in the table shown in Table 1–1.

Table 1–1

p	q	$p \wedge q$
T	T	T
T	F	F
F	T	F
F	F	F

The word "and" is called a **logical connective** and the statement that results from combining two statements using this word is called a **conjunction**. A logical connective is a way of using old statements to produce new statements and corresponds to the operations of addition, multiplication, etc., in arithmetic. There are three other basic connectives, two of which we shall discuss now. The third will be discussed in the next section.

If p and q are statements, we can form the compound statement "p or q" which is called the **disjunction** of p and q. The symbol representing disjunction is "$\vee$" and so we write $p \vee q$ for "p or q." We agree that the statement $p \vee q$ will be true if one or both of p and q is true, but will be false when both p and q are false. See Table 1–2.

Table 1–2

p	q	$p \vee q$
T	T	T
T	F	T
F	T	T
F	F	F

The conjunction and disjunction connectives operate upon pairs of statements, but the **negation connective** operates upon only one statement. Given a statement p we may form the statement "Not p" or "p is false." This statement is symbolized by $\sim p$ and is called the **negation** of p. The statements p and $\sim p$ have opposite truth values as shown in Table 1–3.

Table 1–3

p	$\sim p$
T	F
F	T

These three logical connectives (together with a fourth discussed in Section 1.4) can be used in combination to construct more complex statements. For example, using the conjunction and negation connectives we can construct the compound statement $\sim p \vee q$ from statements p and q. The truth value of such a compound statement can be most easily determined by constructing tables like those shown earlier. The table for this statement is shown in Table 1–4.

Example 2: Find statements p and q such that the statement $\sim p \vee q$ is false.

Table 1–4

p	q	$\sim p$	$\sim p \vee q$
T	T	F	T
T	F	F	F
F	T	T	T
F	F	T	T

SOLUTION: From Table 1–4 we see that the only way $\sim p \vee q$ can be false is for p to be true and q to be false. So let p be the statement "The moon is not made of Camembert" and let q be the statement "Three is less than two". Then $\sim p \vee q$ is the statement "Either the moon is made of Camembert or three is less than two."

The tables that we have been using are called **truth tables**. Their principal value is that they provide a routine and generally easy way to determine the truth values of compound statements.

Example 3: When is the statement $\sim p \vee (p \wedge \sim q)$ true?

SOLUTION: The truth table for this statement is shown in Table 1–5. From this table we can see that the given statement is true in all cases except when p is true and q is true.

Table 1–5

p	q	$\sim p$	$\sim q$	$p \wedge \sim q$	$\sim p \vee (p \wedge \sim q)$
T	T	F	F	F	F
T	F	F	T	T	T
F	T	T	F	F	T
F	F	T	T	F	T

Exercises 1.3

1. Let p and q denote the statements given below:

p: $2 = 3 + 7$.

q: Ethelred was a king of England.

(a) Form the statement $(p \vee q)$. Is this statement true or false?

(b) Form the statement $\sim(q \vee p)$. What is the truth value of this statement?

2. Let p represent the statement "I like school" and q represent the statement "I like to study." Render each of the following statements in words.
(a) $\sim p \wedge \sim q$.
(b) $p \wedge \sim q$.
(c) $\sim p \vee \sim q$.
(d) $\sim p \vee q$.
(e) $\sim(p \wedge \sim q)$.
(f) $\sim(p \vee q)$.
3. Ethelbert likes school but he does not like to study. Which of the six statements in the preceding exercise would Ethelbert regard as being true?
4. Ethelred neither likes school nor likes to study. Which of the six statements in Exercise 2 would he regard as being true?
5. As in Example 3 construct a truth table that shows the truth values of the compound statement $p \wedge (\sim p \vee q)$.
6. Construct a truth table for the statement $(p \wedge \sim q) \vee (p \wedge q)$. Find specific examples of statements p and q for which this statement is true.

1.4 Implications

The fourth logical connective is used more often than the other three and is, unfortunately, more complicated too. We shall study it in this section.

If we are given statements p and q we can combine them into the statement "If p, then q" by which we mean "If p is true, then q is true." This statement is called an **implication** and is symbolized by $p \rightarrow q$. The statement p is called the **hypothesis** of the implication $p \rightarrow q$, and q is called its **conclusion.**

Example 1: From the given statements "$2 + 2 = 5$" and "3 is greater than 2" we can form the two implications:

If $2 + 2 = 5$, then 3 is greater than 2.

and

If 3 is greater than 2, then $2 + 2 = 5$.

Although in everyday usage the hypothesis and conclusion of an implication generally have some material relationship to each other, this need not be the case in symbolic logic. Any two statements can be made into an implication and that implication is either true or false. For example, the implication "If $2 + 2 = 789$, then Grover Cleveland pitched for the White Sox" is an implication that we would probably regard as being nonsense in everyday language but this implication is completely meaningful in symbolic logic. In fact, it is even true! For the axiom that establishes the truth value of an implication in terms of the truth values of its hypothesis and conclusion is the following: The implication $p \to q$ is false if p is true and q is false but is true in all other cases. The full story is told in Table 1–6. If this situation appears strange it is only because in everyday language we do not generally allow ourselves to get involved with implications whose hypotheses or conclusions we know to be false. Generally speaking, the average person is familiar only with implications whose hypotheses and conclusion he believes to be true not because that is the only kind of implication there is, but because that is the only kind he ever uses.

Table 1–6

p	q	$p \to q$
T	T	T
T	F	F
F	T	T
F	F	T

Example 2: Which of these implications are false?
1. If $3 = 5$, then 2 is less than 0.
2. If 2 is less than 0, then $3 = 7 + 4$.
3. If 6 is less than 7, then gold is heavy.
4. If $2 + 4 = 7$, then $2 + 2 = 5$.

SOLUTION: None of these implications is false. The only way an implication can be false is that its hypothesis be true while its conclusion is false and none of these has a true hypothesis and a false conclusion.

Perhaps the most common error made regarding implications is a person's thinking that because he has proved that the implication $p \to q$ is true, he has proved that the statement q is true. It is very important to clearly understand that saying that $p \to q$ is true says nothing definitive about the truth values of p and q except that it is not true that both p is true and q is false.

Given an implication $p \to q$ if we interchange the hypothesis and conclusion we obtain a new implication, $q \to p$, which is called the **converse** of the original implication. From the truth table shown in Table 1–7 we can see that the truth values of an implication and its converse are not identical. There are

Table 1–7

p	q	$p \to q$	$q \to p$
T	T	T	T
T	F	F	T
F	T	T	F
F	F	T	T

times when an implication is true but its converse is false. This will be the case whenever the hypothesis of the implication is false and its conclusion is true. Thus the true statement, "If $2 + 2 = 5$, then $3 = 3$" has a false converse: "If $3 = 3$, then $2 + 2 = 5$."

Of particular importance are statements p and q such that both $p \to q$ and $q \to p$ are true at the same time. When this is the case we write $p \leftrightarrow q$ or "p if and only if q". In this case the statements p and q are said to be **logically equivalent**.

Example 3: The statements "$2 + 2 = 5$" and "$3 = 4$" are logically equivalent because each of the implications

$$(2 + 2 = 5) \to (3 = 4)$$

and

$$(3 = 4) \to (2 + 2 = 5)$$

is true. Thus any two false statements are logically equivalent. Also, any two true statements are logically equivalent because if p and q are both true, then each of the implications $p \to q$ and $q \to p$ is true.

To test whether two statements are logically equivalent all we need to do is to construct truth tables for the statements and compare their truth values. If these truth values are identical, then the statements are logically equivalent.

Example 4: Prove that $\sim(p \wedge q)$ and $\sim p \vee \sim q$ are logically equivalent.

SOLUTION: We use the truth table in Table 1–8. Since the entries in the columns under the statements $\sim(p \wedge q)$ and $\sim p \vee \sim q$ are identical, these statements are equivalent.

Table 1–8

p	q	$p \wedge q$	$\sim(p \wedge q)$	$\sim p$	$\sim q$	$\sim p \vee \sim q$
T	T	T	F	F	F	F
T	F	F	T	F	T	T
F	T	F	T	T	F	T
F	F	F	T	T	T	T

The equivalence $\sim(p \wedge q) \leftrightarrow \sim p \vee \sim q$ is known as the first **De Morgan Law**. The second De Morgan Law is the equivalence $\sim(p \vee q) \leftrightarrow \sim p \wedge \sim q$ (which we leave for you to prove by using truth tables). These equivalences are named after the English mathematician Augustus De Morgan (1806–1871), who along with Boole shares the major credit for the invention of symbolic logic. The first De Morgan Law states that the denial of conjunction is a disjunction and the second law states that the denial of a disjunction is a conjunction.

Example 5: The first De Morgan Law states that to say that the statement "$2 = 4$ *and* $2 = 1 + 1$" is false is equivalent to saying "$2 \neq 4$ *or* $2 \neq 1 + 1$." If Ethelbert promised to love *and* honor his new wife, and if he was lying, then *either* he didn't love her *or* he didn't honor her. The second De Morgan Law tells us that if it is false that "$4 = 5$ *or* $2 + 2 = 5$" then "$4 \neq 5$ *and* $2 + 2 \neq 5$." If Ethelred promised his bride that he would *either* take her to New York *or* to New Orleans for their honeymoon, and if he lied, then he didn't take her to New York *and* he didn't take her to New Orleans.

Exercises 1.4

1. Make a truth table that proves that the statements $p \to q$ and $\sim p \vee q$ are logically equivalent. Use this fact to explain why the statements "If it rains today, then the ground will get wet" and "Either it will not rain today or the ground will get wet" express the same idea.

2. If the implication $p \to q$ and its converse are both true, then how do the truth values of p and q compare? If the implication and its converse have opposite truth value, how do the truth values of p and q compare? (*Hint:* Use Table 1–7).

3.* Use a truth table to prove that the statements $p \to q$ and $\sim q \to \sim p$ are logically equivalent. The implication $\sim q \to \sim p$ is called the **contrapositive** of the implication $p \to q$.

4. Because (by Exercise 3) the contrapositive $\sim q \to \sim p$ of an implication $p \to q$ is logically equivalent to the implication itself, we can replace an implication by its contrapositive whenever we feel it would be convenient to do so. Replace each of these statements by its contrapositive. Which statement do you think is easier to understand, the given implication or its contrapositive?

(a) If $x + 3 = 7$, then $x = 4$.

(b) If $x + 3 \neq 7$, then $x \neq 4$.

(c) If it rains, then the ground will get wet.

(d) If the diagonals of a rectangle do not intersect at right angles, then that rectangle is not a square.

(e) If a number is not a multiple of two, then it is not an even number.

5.* Make a truth table for the statement $(p \to q) \vee \sim q$. Note that the entries in the column under this statement are all T's. This means that this statement is true no matter what the truth values of the component statements p and q might be. Such statements are called **tautologies**. Make truth tables for the following statements and prove that each is a tautology.

(a) $p \vee (p \to q)$.

(b) $(p \to q) \vee (p \to \sim q)$.

(c) $(p \wedge q) \vee (p \to \sim q)$.

6.* Which of these statements are tautologies?

(a) $p \to (p \wedge q)$.

(b) $(p \to q) \vee (q \to p)$.

(c) $(p \wedge \sim q) \vee (q \wedge \sim p)$.

7. Make a truth table that proves the second De Morgan Law.

8.* The **inverse** of an implication is obtained by negating both hypothesis and conclusion. E.g., the inverse of $p \to q$ is $\sim p \to \sim q$. Find an example of an implication whose inverse is true.

9. Use the De Morgan Laws to replace each of these false statements with a true statement.

(a) $2 < 3$ and $2 > 3$.

(b) The next president will both a Democrat and a Republican.

(c) The solution of the equation $x + 3 = 5$ is either 6 or 7.

(d) Either Henry Clay was president or he was born in Kentucky.

1.5 Arguments

The mathematical proof of a theorem is a demonstration using logical arguments that the truth of that theorem follows from the established truth of previously proven theorems and the assumed truth of the axioms. In this section we shall discuss two of the most important and useful of these logical arguments.

Logical arguments are based upon the assumption of certain statements called "hypotheses." One assumes the hypotheses and then argues from them using laws of logic so as to obtain the statement that is the conclusion of the argument. For example, Aristotle's syllogism,

(1) All heroes are men.

(2) All men are mortal.

Therefore,

(3) All heroes are mortal.

argues from the assumption of statements (1) and (2) as hypotheses and using a law of logic arrives at the conclusion (3). We must emphasize, however, that this argument does not establish the truth of any one of the statements (1), (2), or (3). Indeed, in some arguments all the hypotheses as well as the conclusion will be false statements. What the argument does do is to prove that the statement

$$[(1) \wedge (2)] \rightarrow (3)$$

is true.

But what law of logic has permitted us to draw conclusion (3) from the assumption of hypotheses (1) and (2)? By using truth tables we can prove that the statement

$$[(p \rightarrow q) \wedge (q \rightarrow r)] \rightarrow (p \rightarrow r)$$

is true no matter which statements p, q, and r represent. This statement is called the **law of syllogism**. If we rewrite Aristotle's argument we can see how this law of syllogism was used to establish its validity:

(1) If a thing is a hero, then that thing is a man.

(2) If a thing is a man, then that thing is mortal.

Therefore

(3) If a thing is a hero, then that thing is mortal.

We prove the law of syllogism by constructing a truth table (refer to Table 1–9). Observe that the entries in the right-most column are all T's. This means that the law of syllogism is true no matter what the truth values of its component statements p, q, and r might be.

Table 1–9

p	q	r	$p \to q$	$q \to r$	$(p \to q) \wedge (q \to r)$	$p \to r$	$[(p \to q) \wedge (q \to r)] \to (p \to r)$
T	T	T	T	T	T	T	T
T	T	F	T	F	F	F	T
T	F	T	F	T	F	T	T
T	F	F	F	T	F	F	T
F	T	T	T	T	T	T	T
F	T	F	T	F	F	T	T
F	F	T	T	T	T	T	T
F	F	F	T	T	T	T	T

The law of syllogism is a way to "glue" two implications together in the case that the conclusion of one is the same as the hypothesis of the other. By repeated applications of this law a string of implications can be combined.

Example 1: Assume the following statements as hypotheses:

1. If a man smokes, then he will get cancer.
2. If a man gets cancer, then he must go to the hospital.
3. If a man goes to the hospital, then he must pay large bills.
4. If a man must pay large bills, then he must work longer hours.
Hence,
5. If a man smokes, then he must work longer hours.

When we make this argument we do not assert that any of the hypotheses are true or that the conclusion is true (although in everyday situations we probably wouldn't bother with the argument unless these statements were believed to be true), but we do assert that the implication

$$[(1) \wedge (2) \wedge (3) \wedge (4)] \to (5)$$

is true. The symbolic form of this argument is

(1) $p \to q$

(2) $q \to r$

(3) $r \to s$

(4) $s \to t$

Therefore,

(5) $p \to t$

The law of syllogism is the basis for many logical arguments used in mathematics. Another law that is the basis for many arguments is the **law of detachment**:

$$[p \wedge (p \rightarrow q)] \rightarrow q.$$

This law asserts that if we assume the truth of the implication $p \rightarrow q$ as a hypothesis and if we also assume the truth of p as another hypothesis, then we must accept the truth of the conclusion q as well.

Example 2: If we accept the truth of the statement "If John gets married, then he is going to be a very busy fellow" and "John got married last Saturday," then we are forced to accept the truth of the statement "John is a very busy fellow."

Example 3: If we add a fifth hypothesis to the argument in Example 1, "I smoke," then we may draw the conclusion that "I must work longer hours."

The symbolic form of the arguments in both Example 2 and Example 3 is

(1) $p \rightarrow q$

(2) p

Therefore,

(3) q

Table 1–10 shows that the law of detachment is true no matter what the truth values of the component statements p and q might be. This proves that the law of detachment is a valid law of logic.

Table 1–10

p	q	$p \rightarrow q$	$p \wedge (p \rightarrow q)$	$[p \wedge (p \rightarrow q)] \rightarrow q$
T	T	T	T	T
T	F	F	F	T
F	T	T	F	T
F	F	T	F	T

Exercises 1.5

1. Use the laws of syllogism and detachment either together or singly to draw conclusions from the sets of hypotheses given below.
   (a) $(2 < 3) \rightarrow (3 < 4)$.
   $2 < 3$.
   $(3 < 4) \rightarrow (4 < 5)$.
   (b) If horses give milk, then people ride on cows.
   If people ride on cows, then they will get sore.
   If people get sore, then they get mad.
   (c) $p \rightarrow q$.
   $q \rightarrow r$.
   p.
   $r \rightarrow s$.
   (d) $(p \wedge q) \rightarrow (p \vee q)$.
   $(r \rightarrow s) \rightarrow (p \wedge q)$.
   $r \rightarrow s$.
2. From the hypotheses "If $x + 3 = 5$, then $x = 2$" and "If $x = 2$, then $x + 1 = 3$" can you draw the conclusion "$x + 1 = 3$"? What conclusion can you draw? What additional hypothesis do you need in order to be able to draw the conclusion "$x + 1 = 3$"?
3.* The implication

$$[(p \rightarrow q) \wedge (\sim q)] \rightarrow \sim p$$

is called the law of **modus tollendo tollens.** This law is also the basis for many arguments. Use it to draw a conclusion from the given hypotheses.

(a) $(2 + 2 = 5) \rightarrow (2 = 3)$.
$2 \neq 3$

(b) It is morning if the sun is on the eastern horizon.
The sun is on the western horizon.

(c) $(3 + 5 < 9) \rightarrow$ (Horses fly).
Horses do not fly.

(d) $(2 + 2 > 5) \rightarrow (3 + 5 < 9)$.
$(3 > 2) \rightarrow (2 \neq 5)$.
$2 = 5$.

4.* Another law of logic is **modus tollendo ponens**:

$$[(\sim p) \wedge (p \vee q)] \rightarrow q.$$

Use this law to draw a conclusion from the given hypotheses.

(a) Cows either give milk or fly.
Cows do not give milk.

(b) $(2 + 2 < 3) \vee (3 < 4)$.
$3 > 4$.
(c) Either Ethelred was king or Ethelbert was not king.
Ethelred was not king.
(d) Either John works at the factory or Mary goes to school.
Either John does not work at the factory or Harry is retired.
Harry works at the factory.

5. There are many other laws of logic but the ones we have studied in the text (syllogism and detachment) together with two laws in Exercises 3 and 4 (modus tollendo tollens and modus tollendo ponens) are sufficient to enable you to draw a conclusion from each set of hypotheses given below. Do so and explain where you use any of these laws in drawing your conclusion.

(a) If $x \neq 0$, then $x \neq y$.
Either $x = y$ or horses fly.
Horses do not fly.
(b) Either $3 = 4$ or cows fly.
If cows fly, then so do horses.
Horses do not fly.
(c) If horses live in houses, then $x = 0$.
Either horses live in houses or John loves Mary.
If John loves Mary, then Sue is unhappy.
Sue is smiling and singing.
(d) If horses fly, then cows give milk.
If cows give milk, then $2 < 3$.
Either horses fly or John loves Mary.
If John loves Mary, then Sue is unhappy.
Sue is dancing and laughing.

1.6 Universal and Existential Statements

There are two kinds of statements that because of their special internal form are of particular importance in mathematics. In this section we shall discuss these two kinds of statements.

Statements whose general form is "All A's are B's" are called **universal statements**. Such statements may appear in many guises, the following being some of the ways the universal statement "All men are mortal" can be phrased:

1. Every man is mortal.
2. Each man is mortal.
3. If a thing is a man, then that thing is mortal.
4. No matter which man we consider, that man is mortal.
5. There are no men who are not mortal.

To prove a universal statement is false all we need to do is to exhibit an example of its falsity. For example, we can prove that the statement, "Every man is under six feet tall" is false simply by pointing to Wilt the Stilt. An example of the falsity of a universal statement is called a **counterexample** and all that is needed to prove such a statement false is to exhibit a counterexample.

Karl Friedrich Gauss (1777–1855)

The trouble comes when we try to prove that a universal statement is true. A common error is to exhibit a number of instances of the truth of the universal statement and then to think that by so doing we have proved the statement is true. Actually exhibiting such examples does not help at all to prove the statement is true. For example, we can find infinitely many numbers that are even but this does not mean that the universal statement "All numbers are even" is true. In order to prove that a universal statement is true we must somehow prove that no counterexamples can exist. There are a number of ways that this can be done. We shall consider some of them in our work in future chapters.

The second type of statement that we want especially to consider is the existential statement. An **existential statement** asserts the existence of something. For example, the statement "There exists a man who is mortal" is an existential statement. Like universal statements, existential statements may appear in many guises. The existential statement above can also be phrased in these ways:

1. At least one man is mortal.
2. A few men are mortal.
3. Some men are mortal.
4. One or more men are mortal.

In particular, note that "some" and "few" are used synonymously with "at least one" and "one or more." This is in partial variance with the way these words are used in everyday life.

As to proving the truth or falsity of existential statements, existential statements are easier to prove true than to prove false. All that is needed to prove that an existential statement is true is to exhibit an example of its truth. We can prove that the statement "Some men are mortal" is true by giving the name "Grover Cleveland". (The exhibition of more than one example is not necessary. One example of the truth of an existential statement is enough to prove that the statement is true.) But to prove that an existential statement is false we must somehow prove that no examples of its truth are possible. This is in general harder to do. We shall see a few different ways to do this in future chapters.

Let us close this discussion with the observation that the negation of a universal statement is an existential statement and the negation of an existential statement is a universal statement. The following examples should help to make this clear.

Example 1: If it is false that all men are mortal, then what is true? If it is false that some men are mortal, then what is true?

SOLUTION: If it is false that all men are mortal, then there must be a counterexample. This counterexample is a man who is immortal. Hence to say that it is false that all men are mortal is the same as to say that there exists a man who is immortal. If it is false that some men are mortal, then it is impossible to find an example of a man who is mortal. Hence all men are immortal.

Exercises 1.6

1. Rephrase each of the following statements as a statement involving the phrase "Every" or the phrase "There exists."
   (a) Some men work hard and a few men work very hard.
   (b) There are men who do not work hard.
   (c) At least one man works hard but there are no men who do not sleep.
   (d) No matter which number n is, $n + 1 = 1 + n$.
   (e) There is at least one number that when squared is equal to itself.
2. Write out a true existential statement corresponding to each of these false universal statements.
   (a) Every number is greater than zero.
   (b) Every dog barks.
   (c) Every implication has a true converse.
3. Write out a true universal statement corresponding to each of these false existential statements.
   (a) Some implications are neither true nor false.
   (b) There is a man who is totally without value.
   (c) Some true implications have false contrapositives.
4. Search through this book and find two universal and two existential statements. Write out the negation of each statement.
5. Exhibit a counterexample that proves that each of the universal statements in Exercise 2 is false.
6. Exhibit an example that proves each of these existential statements is true.

(a) There exists a number that is greater than 4, is less than 10, and is even.

(b) Some implications have true converses.

(c) Some existential statements are true.

7. When we make a statement of the form "Every *A* is a *B*," are we necessarily implying that there are any *A*'s? That is, does this universal statement assert the existence of any *A*'s?

2 Mathematical Systems

THE STUDY of mathematics consists of the study of many different mathematical systems. You are more or less familiar with a mathematical system called the arithmetic of the whole numbers and with another called Euclidean geometry. These two mathematical systems differ most obviously in that the first deals with numbers and the second deals with geometric objects such as lines and circles. If we were to center our attention too strongly upon the differences between numbers and geometric objects, we would have great difficulty in trying to see the ways that the study of numbers is similar to the study of geometric objects. In the early days of mathematics (say, prior to 1850) the particular objects being studied (numbers, geometric objects, equations, and so forth) received so much focused attention that the similarities between these various mathematical systems went unnoticed. Then, after a time, it became increasingly clear that even though the various parts of mathematics dealt with different kinds of objects, if one were to pay less attention to the particular nature of the objects themselves and concerned himself more with the way that he studied the objects, then he would see patterns to these various studies and that, to a greater or lesser extent, these patterns are similar.

Our objective in this chapter is to inquire into the general structure of these mathematical systems. The particular nature of the objects of the systems (whether they be numbers, geometric objects, equations, or whatever) will be of secondary importance to us here. In subsequent chapters we shall study a number of specific mathematical systems.

2.1 Mathematical Systems, A General Introduction

To introduce the notion of a mathematical system we shall use as our example the mathematical system with which you are probably most familiar, the mathematical system of whole numbers. The whole numbers are the numbers 0, 1, 2, 3, 4, 5, and so on. When we think of doing arithmetic with whole numbers, we naturally first think of these numbers themselves. But what other ideas are involved besides the idea of a whole number? Let us list a few of these other ideas.

1. The idea of one whole number being equal to another.
2. The idea of one whole number being less than another.
3. The idea of one whole number being equal to the square of another.
4. The idea of adding two whole numbers to obtain a third.
5. The idea of multiplying two whole numbers to obtain a third.
6. The idea of dividing one whole number by another to obtain a third.

We can classify these ideas into two groups. The first three ideas have to do with relationships between whole numbers. These ideas involve comparing one whole number with another. The last three ideas are quite different. Each of these involves using given numbers to produce a new number. Thus we see that in studying the system of whole numbers we do two entirely different kinds of things. One of these things is that we compare numbers with each other. We take two numbers and ask in what ways they are related to each other. For instance, in what ways are the numbers 3 and 4 related to each other? Well, 3 is related to 4 in that it *is less than* 4; 3 is related to 4 in that 3 *is equal to one less than* 4; 3 is related to 4 in that it *is greater than the positive square root of* 4; and so on. In fact, these two numbers are related to each other in very many ways indeed.

The second thing we do with numbers is to operate upon them to produce new numbers. For example, how can we operate upon 3 and 4 to produce a new number? We can operate upon 3 and 4 by *adding* them to obtain 7; by *multiplying* them to obtain 12; by *subtracting* 3 from 4 to obtain 1; and so on.

The moral of this is that when we study the arithmetic of whole numbers, we do more than simply look at whole numbers. We *compare* the numbers and we *operate* upon them to produce other whole numbers. This demonstrates that the mathematical system of the whole numbers involves three essentially different ideas:

1. The set of objects of the system (that is, the whole numbers).
2. Relations by means of which these objects may be compared with one another.
3. Operations that can be used to produce new numbers from old numbers.

To further illustrate these three parts of a mathematical system, let us suppose that we were to try to organize the study of, for example, straight lines in the plane into a mathematical system. We have already identified the objects of the system—the straight lines in the plane. What are some of the relations that we might want to investigate? That is, what are some of the important ways that straight lines may be compared? Probably the relations *is parallel to* and *is perpendicular to* spring to mind. In Figure 2.1 the black lines are related to each other by the relation *is parallel to*, while the green lines are related to each other by the relation *is perpendicular to*. Of course, there are many other relations such as *is coincident with*, *forms a* 30° *angle with*, and so on.

Figure 2.1

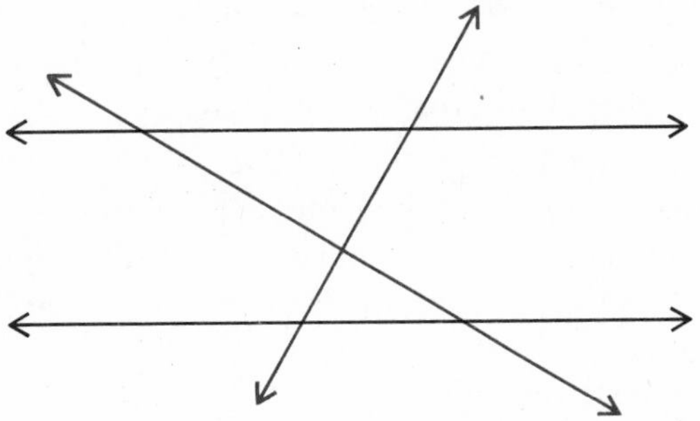

What might be some useful and important operations on straight lines? That is, if you were given two straight lines in the plane, how might you use these lines to produce a third line? Well, if the lines intersect and form an acute angle (an angle less than 90°) then you could use the given pair of lines to produce the line which is the bisector of the acute angle. In Figure 2.2 the green line is the bisector of the acute angle formed by the two black lines.

A mathematical system involves relations and operations and in the coming sections we shall discuss these ideas more thoroughly. Then we shall discuss a mathematical system that is new to you so that you may see these ideas combined in context.

Figure 2.2

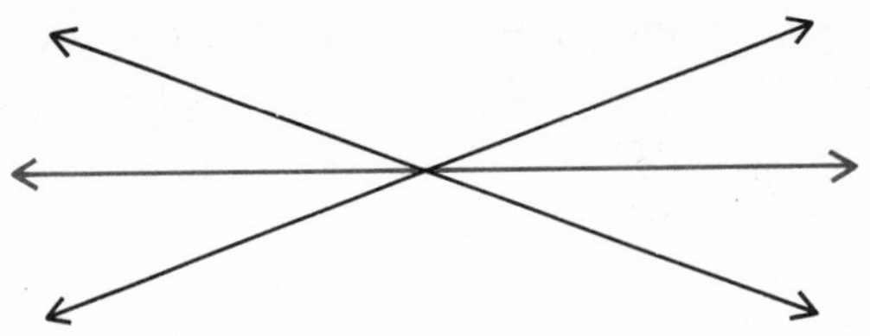

Exercises 2.1

1. Which of the following describe relations on whole numbers and which describe operations? (x and y denote whole numbers.)
   (a) The idea of x being a divisor of y.
   (b) The idea of taking the square root of xy.
   (c) The idea of finding the least common multiple of x and y.
   (d) The idea of multiplying x by itself y times.
   (e) The idea of x being greater than six times y.
   (f) The idea of x being equal to the square root of y.
2. The numbers 5 and 25 may be compared with each other using many different relations. For example, 5 is related to 25 by the relation *is less than.* Name two other relations that relate 5 to 25. Name two relations by which 25 is related to 5.
3. 3 compares to 5 in the same way that 9 compares to 11. What is the relation that is being used here? What number is related to 7 by this relation? To what number is 7 related by this relation? Is 0 related to any whole number by this relation? Is any whole number related to 0 by this relation?
4. Find three different pairs of values for whole numbers x and y if x is related to y by the relation *is less than the square root of.*
5. Name two different relations that would be of interest in the study of triangles in geometry.
6. Draw two different rectangles which are related to each other by the relation *has the same area as.* Is every rectangle related to itself by this relation? If rectangle $\mathscr{R}_1$ is related to rectangle $\mathscr{R}_2$ by this relation, is $\mathscr{R}_2$ related to $\mathscr{R}_1$ also? If rectangle $\mathscr{R}_1$ is related to rectangle $\mathscr{R}_2$ and if $\mathscr{R}_2$ is related to rectangle $\mathscr{R}_3$ by this relation, is rectangle $\mathscr{R}_1$ related to rectangle $\mathscr{R}_3$?
7. Name three relations that might be of interest in a discussion of the men who have been presidents of the United States. (One such relation is *served longer than.*)

8. The number 14 is produced from the numbers 49 and 2 in the same way that 24 is produced from 36 and 4. Describe in words how this operation is performed. What is the effect of this operation upon 25 and 36? Is the effect of the operation upon 25 and 36 the same as the effect of the operation upon 36 and 25?
9. Can the "acute angle bisector" operation discussed in the text be applied to *every* pair of lines in the plane?
10. Describe three different operations that can be used to produce a statement from two given statements. For which of these operations is the effect of operating upon statements p and q the same as the effect upon operating q and p (in the given orders)?
11.* A **unary operation** is an operation that is applied to only one object at a time. Describe a unary operation upon statements. Describe a unary operation upon whole numbers.

2.2 Relations in a Mathematical System

We have said that by a relation on the set of whole numbers we mean a way of comparing whole numbers. For example, the relation *is less than* is a relation on the set of whole numbers since this idea can be used to compare whole numbers. The whole number 3 compares with the whole number 6 using this relation (3 is less than 6) but 7 does not compare with 5 using this relation (7 is not less than 5). Another familiar relation is *equality* of whole numbers. To say that two whole numbers are equal means that they are related to each other by the relation *is equal to*. We usually define equality of whole numbers like this: If n and m are symbols representing two whole numbers, then when we write $n = m$ we mean that n and m represent the whole number. For example, $4 - 1$ and $1 + 2$ are symbols representing the same whole number, and so we write $4 - 1 = 1 + 2$.

The notion of a relation is not restricted just to sets of mathematical objects. The idea is perfectly general and is applied to all kinds of sets of objects.

Example 1: Consider the set of all people and the relation called *is the father of*. Given two people x and y, we can ask the question: "Is x related to y in that x is the father of y?" If x is Edward I of England and y is Edward II, then the answer to this question is yes. If x is Theodore Roosevelt and y is Franklin Roosevelt, then the answer is no. Is anyone related to himself by this relation?

Consider the relation of Example 1 above. Instead of saying

Edward I is related to Edward II by the relation *is the father of*,

we would ordinarily say

Edward I is the father of Edward II,

which may be shortened even more if we simply write

Edward I (father) Edward II,

which may finally be abbreviated ultimately by

Edward I $\mathscr{F}$ Edward II,

if we understand that the symbol $\mathscr{F}$ means *is the father of*. We often abbreviate such statements by using a single symbol in this way. For example, instead of saying "the number named by $1 + 1$ is the same as the number named by $3 - 1$," we employ the special symbol $=$ and write simply $1 + 1 = 3 - 1$. To say that the whole number 3 is less than the whole number 4 we use the special symbol $<$ to mean "is less than" and write the abbreviation $3 < 4$. Since 4 is not less than 3 we write $4 \nless 3$. This use of the stroke to mean "is not related to by the relation $<$" is typical. The symbol $\neq$ means "is not equal to."

Example 2: There is a commonly used relation on the playing cards in a standard 52-card deck. This relation might be called the *has higher rank than* relation. If we temporarily use the symbol $>$ to mean *has higher rank than*, then we can indicate the way that the cards are related to each other by this relation as follows:

$$A > K > Q > J > 10 > 9 > 8 > 7 > 6 > 5 > 4 > 3 > 2.$$

Thus aces are the highest ranking cards and deuces are the lowest ranking cards. The suit of a card plays no role in this relation.

Example 3: Consider the set of all triangles and the relation *is congruent to.* If we use the symbol $\cong$ to denote this relation and if $\mathscr{A}$, $\mathscr{B}$, $\mathscr{C}$, and $\mathscr{D}$ are the triangles shown in Figure 2.3, then the following statements are all true:

$$\mathscr{A} \cong \mathscr{A}, \quad \mathscr{C} \cong \mathscr{D}, \quad \mathscr{A} \not\cong \mathscr{B}, \quad \mathscr{A} \not\cong \mathscr{D}.$$

Figure 2.3

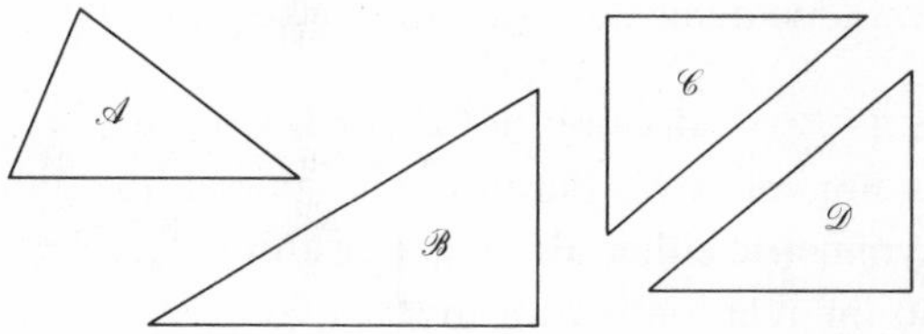

Let us return now to the relation of equality of whole numbers. Recall that to write "$n = m$" means that the symbols n and m represent the same whole number. There are three important properties of this relation that we shall use often in our study.

1. *The Reflexive Property of Equality.* No matter which whole number n represents, n is equal to itself: $n = n$.
2. *The Symmetric Property of Equality.* If we know that $n = m$, then we may conclude that $m = n$.
3. *The Transitive Property of Equality.* If we know that $n = m$ and that $m = p$, then we may conclude that $n = p$.

Because the relation of equality possesses these three properties, we call equality an **equivalence relation.**

Example 4: Consider the set of all lines in the plane and the relation *is parallel to.* This relation is an equivalence relation. First, the relation is reflexive because every line is parallel to itself. Second, the relation is symmetric because if a line ℓ_1 is parallel to a line ℓ_2, then the line ℓ_2 is also parallel to the line ℓ_1. Third, if line ℓ_1 is parallel to line ℓ_2 and if line ℓ_2 is parallel to line ℓ_3, then we may conclude that line ℓ_1 is parallel to line ℓ_3. Therefore the relation is transitive.

Example 5: The relation *is perpendicular to* defined on the set of all lines in the plane is not an equivalence relation because the relation is not reflexive.

That is, it is false that every line is perpendicular to itself. However, the relation is symmetric, because if line ℓ_1 is perpendicular to line ℓ_2, then it follows that line ℓ_2 is perpendicular to line ℓ_1. Why is the relation not transitive?

Example 6: Which of the three properties is possessed by the relation *is less than* defined on the set of whole numbers?

SOLUTION: Because not every whole number is less than itself the relation is not reflexive. Because $x < y$ does not imply $y < x$, the relation is not symmetric either. But if $x < y$ and $y < z$, then it does follow that $x < z$ and so the relation is transitive.

Exercises 2.2

1. Is the relation *is the father of* an equivalence relation?
2. What properties does the relation *is the sibling of* have that neither of the relations *is the brother of* or *is the sister of* has?
3. The relation *is an ancestor of* has only one of the properties of an equivalence relation. Which one is this?
4. Is the relation *is logically equivalent to* an equivalence relation on the collection of all statements?
5. Can you think of a relation defined on people that is reflexive but is neither symmetric nor transitive?
6. What properties does the relation *is equal to or is equal to one more than* defined on the set of whole numbers possess?
7. Consider the set of all professional hockey players. Describe two relations defined on the objects of this set that are symmetric.
8. Look up the words *reflexive*, *symmetric*, and *transitive* in the dictionary. Can you see why these properties were named the way they were?
9. Find a relation on the set of all triangles that is neither reflexive nor symmetric, but is transitive.
10. Which of the three properties does the relation *is equal to one more than or is equal to one less than* defined on the set of all whole numbers possess?

2.3 Operations in a Mathematical System

The third aspect of a mathematical system is the idea of an operation. The concept is not particularly complicated, but perhaps it would be best to begin with a familiar example. On the set of whole numbers there is defined a particular operation called addition. What kind of a process is addition of whole numbers? First, addition works on *pairs* of whole numbers and so is called a *binary* operation. Second, this process may be applied to each and every pair of whole numbers; no matter which whole numbers x and y represent, it makes sense to talk about adding x and y (in that order—first x, then y). Third, not only can the operation be applied to every pair of whole numbers, but the result of this application on any particular pair is always a *single* whole number. For example, the result of operating upon 3 and 5 is the single number 8. So there are these three aspects of the binary operation called addition of whole numbers:

1. It is applied to exactly two whole numbers at a time.
2. It may be applied to every pair of whole numbers regardless of the order in which they are given.
3. It always results in exactly one whole number; that is, the result of the operation is unique.

The process of multiplication is also a binary operation on the whole numbers. This means that no matter which whole numbers x and y represent, the multiplication operation can be applied to x and y (in that order—first x, then y) and that the result is a single whole number. Subtraction of whole numbers, on the other hand, is not a binary operation because subtraction can be applied only to certain pairs of whole numbers. For instance, subtraction can be applied to 5 and 3 (in that order) to give the single number 2, but it cannot be applied to the numbers 3 and 5 (in that order) because $3 - 5$ is not a single whole number. (The result is a single number but it is not a whole number.) Similarly, division of whole numbers is not a binary operation because it is not always possible to apply the process. For example, division cannot be applied to 5 and 0 (given in that order) since $5 \div 0$ is not a whole number. (We shall see later that $5 \div 0$ is a nonsense symbol—it has no meaning at all.)

Now let us generalize from these remarks. By a **binary operation** on a set S of objects, we mean a process that enables us to produce a single object of the set S from any pair of objects of the set S that we might be given. Let us consider some examples of binary operations defined on familiar sets of objects in order to gain an appreciation of the general nature of this idea.

Example 1: The set of objects of this example is the standard deck of 52 playing cards. Given any two of these cards, we can produce a third card according to this rule: "If x and y are playing cards, then the result of the operation is that card which has the suit of x and the rank of y." Thus the operation applied to the cards 2♠ and 5♢ is the card with the suit of 2♠ and the rank of 5♢; that is, the result is the card 5♠. The operation applied to 5♢ and 2♠ is the card 2♢. This process is a binary operation because it can be applied to any given pair of cards (regardless of the order in which the two cards are given) and the result of the process is always a single card.

We use the special symbol $+$ to indicate the result of the addition process upon a pair of whole numbers. Thus $3 + 5$ means the result of applying the addition process to the whole numbers 3 and 5 given in that order. If we use the special symbol $*$ to indicate the result of acting upon a pair of cards with the operation defined in Example 1, then we could write 2♠ $*$ 5♢ to mean the result of operating upon 2♠ and 5♢. Thus 2♠ $*$ 5♢ $=$ 5♠, 5♢ $*$ 2♠ $=$ 2♢, and K♣ $*$ A♡ $=$ A♣.

Example 2: On the set of all *even* whole numbers the process defined by the rule "To operate upon the even whole numbers x and y (in that order), add them" is a binary operation. This is a binary operation because any two even whole numbers can be added and the result of this process is a single even whole number.

Example 3: Is multiplication a binary operation on the set of all odd whole numbers?

SOLUTION: Yes. The reason is that the product of any two odd whole numbers (regardless of the order in which they are given) is a single odd whole number.

Example 4: Is addition a binary operation on the set of all odd whole numbers?

SOLUTION: No. Addition of odd whole numbers is not a binary operation because it is possible to find at least one pair of odd whole numbers whose sum is not an odd whole number. For example, the sum of 1 and 3 is not an odd whole number.

The idea of a binary operation has a very wide application in mathematics; there are binary operations defined on all sorts of objects besides numbers. In the next two sections we shall discuss some properties that may be possessed by binary operations.

Exercises 2.3

1. Which of the following are binary operations?
   - **(a)** Addition of odd whole numbers.
   - **(b)** Multiplication of even whole numbers.
   - **(c)** Subtraction of even whole numbers.
   - **(d)** Multiplication of whole numbers greater than ten.
   - **(e)** Addition of one-digit whole numbers.
   - **(f)** Addition of two-digit whole numbers.
   - **(g)** Addition of pairs of the numbers 0, 3, 6, 9, 12, 15, ...
2. The *average* of two whole numbers is their sum divided by 2. Is the averaging process as applied to whole numbers a binary operation on the set of all whole numbers?
3. A student missed one of the three exams in his math course and the instructor said that rather than give him a make-up he would compute the final grade on the basis of the average of the two exams the student did take. In effect the instructor has assumed that the student would have got a certain grade on this third exam if he had taken that exam. What grade is this?
4. Because addition is a binary operation, it is only possible to add two numbers at a time. In fact, using the ordinary addition methods by which we usually compute sums, we add only one-digit numbers. How many different applications of the addition operation to one-digit numbers are needed in order to find the sum of the numbers 234, 145, 37, and 97?
5. These questions apply to the playing card operation defined in Example 1.
   - **(a)** If $x * 3\diamondsuit = 3\diamondsuit$, then what can you say about the card x?
   - **(b)** If $2\heartsuit * x = y$, then how are the cards x and y related?
   - **(c)** If $x * y = z$, then how are the cards x and z related?
   - **(d)** Is it possible to find two different cards x and y such that $x * y = x$? Such that $x * y = y$?
6. Is conjunction a binary operation on the set of all true statements? That is, is the conjunction of any two true statements a true statement? Is conjunction a binary operation on the set of all false statements?
7. Repeat Exercise 6 with disjunction in place of conjunction.
8. Repeat Exercise 6 with implication in place of conjunction.

9.* Suppose that $*$ is a binary operation defined on a set S. If T is a collection of just some of the objects of S, then we say that T is *closed* with respect to the binary operation $*$ if the result of operating upon any two objects in T is again in the set T. Which of the following are sets of whole numbers that are closed with respect to addition of whole numbers?

(a) The set containing the numbers 0, 1, 2, 3, 4, and 5.
(b) The set of even whole numbers.
(c) The set of odd whole numbers.
(d) The set of numbers that are multiples of 3.
(e) The set of numbers that are greater than 10.

10.* Describe a set of whole numbers which
(a) Is closed with respect to both addition and multiplication.
(b) Is closed with respect to multiplication but not with respect to addition.
(c) Is not closed with respect to either addition or multiplication.

11.* With respect to the playing card operation discussed in Example 1, if S is a set of playing cards which is closed with respect to this operation, and if S contains 3♢, K♣, and 5♢, then what other cards must S contain?

2.4 Properties of a Binary Operation, I

We have made the point that addition of whole numbers can be applied to every pair of whole numbers regardless of the order in which the two whole numbers are given. Of course, it makes no difference in what order the numbers to be added are given—the result of the addition operation is the same in any case. Thus, for example, when addition is applied to 4 and 6, the result is the same as when addition is applied to 6 and 4. We express this by saying that addition of whole numbers has the **commutative** property. Formally, to say that addition is commutative means that $x + y = y + x$ no matter which whole numbers x and y represent.

The operation of multiplication of whole numbers also possesses the commutative property. That is to say, no matter which whole numbers x and y represent, $x \cdot y$ and $y \cdot x$ represent the same whole number: $x \cdot y = y \cdot x$.

Some operations, like addition and multiplication, possess the commutative property, but some others do not. For example, the binary operation defined on playing cards (Example 1, Section 2.3) does not possess this property. If the operation were commutative, then the 5♢ * 2♠ would have to be the same card as 2♠ * 5♢. But 5♢ * 2♠ = 2♢ while 2♠ * 5♢ = 5♠.

The second property of a binary operation is called the **associative** property. To introduce this property let us consider the following four symbols:

$$8 - 4 - 2$$

$$8 + 4 + 2$$

$$8 \cdot 4 \cdot 2$$

$$8 \div 4 \div 2$$

Now unless we use some special rules to indicate the order in which the operations are to be performed, two of these symbols are ambiguous in the sense that the number those symbols represent will depend upon the order in which the two operations are performed. Try to decide which two of these symbols are ambiguous and which two are unambiguous.

The middle two symbols are meaningful and the first and last are ambiguous. The first symbol is ambiguous because the meaning of this symbol depends upon which of the two subtractions is performed first. If the leftmost subtraction is performed first, then we get

$$8 - 4 - 2 = (8 - 4) - 2 = 4 - 2 = 2,$$

while if the rightmost subtraction is performed first we get

$$8 - 4 - 2 = 8 - (4 - 2) = 8 - 2 = 6.$$

Hence the first symbol represents either 2 or 6 depending upon which of the two subtractions is performed first. Similarly, the last symbol means either

$$(8 \div 4) \div 2 = 2 \div 2 = 1$$

or

$$8 \div (4 \div 2) = 8 \div 2 = 4$$

depending upon which division is performed first. Because of these ambiguities, we do not use such symbols without parentheses. But the middle two symbols are not ambiguous; they each present a single whole number and so no parentheses are needed. For example, consider the symbol $8 + 4 + 2$. If we first perform the leftmost addition we get

$$(8 + 4) + 2 = 12 + 2 = 14,$$

and we get the same result if we first perform the rightmost addition

$$8 + (4 + 2) = 8 + 6 = 14.$$

In a similar way you can show that the symbol $8 \cdot 4 \cdot 2$ represents the single whole number 64 regardless of which of the two multiplications is performed first.

We express the fact that symbols of the form $x + y + z$ (where x, y, and z are whole numbers) are unambiguous by saying that addition of whole numbers is associative. The associative property of addition of whole numbers is usually stated in the following way: To say that addition of whole numbers is associative means that $(x + y) + z = x + (y + z)$ no matter which whole numbers x, y, and z represent. Multiplication of whole numbers is also associative. That is, $(x \cdot y) \cdot z = x \cdot (y \cdot z)$ no matter which whole numbers x, y, and z represent.

Exercises 2.4

1. Each of the following equations is justified by using either the commutative or associative property of addition. Which is used?
   (a) $6 + (3 + 2) = 6 + (2 + 3)$.
   (b) $6 + (3 + 2) = (3 + 2) + 6$.
   (c) $6 + (3 + 2) = (6 + 3) + 2$.
2. Justify each equation using either the associative or the commutative property of multiplication.
   (a) $(6 \cdot 3) \cdot 2 = 6 \cdot (3 \cdot 2)$.
   (b) $6 \cdot (3 \cdot 2) = (3 \cdot 2) \cdot 6$.
   (c) $6 \cdot (3 \cdot 2) = 6 \cdot (2 \cdot 3)$.
3. Justify each of the following equations by using the commutative and/or associative properties of addition and/or multiplication.
   (a) $6 \cdot (3 \cdot 2) = (3 \cdot 6) \cdot 2$.
   (b) $6 + (2 + 3) = (2 + 6) + 3$.
   (c) $6 + (3 + 2) = (6 + 2) + 3$.
   (d) $6 + (3 + 2) = (2 + 6) + 3$.
4. Each of these symbols is ambiguous. What are the different possible meanings of each symbol?
   (a) $2 + 3 \cdot 4$.
   (b) $6 - 2 + 2$.
   (c) $6 \cdot 3 - 2$.
   (d) $20 - 8 - 6 - 2$. (*Hint:* There are five different ways to interpret this symbol.)

5. Is the conjunction operation commutative? That is, if p and q are statements, are the statements $p \wedge q$ and $q \wedge p$ logically equivalent? What about the disjunction operation?
6. Is the conjunction operation associative? What about the disjunction operation?
7. Give counterexamples to the commutativity and associativity of the implication operation. That is, find statements p and q such that $p \rightarrow q$ and $q \rightarrow p$ are not equivalent and such that $(p \rightarrow q) \rightarrow r$ and $p \rightarrow (q \rightarrow r)$ are not equivalent.
8. Look up the words *commutative* and *associative* in the dictionary and see if you can see why these properties were named as they were.
9. Use the cards 3♡, 6◇, and J♠ to demonstrate that the operation on playing cards (Example 1, Section 2.3) is associative. Then repeat the demonstration using three other cards of your own selection.
10.* (Before you begin this problem recall how an addition table can be used to find the sum of one digit numbers.) It is possible to define binary operations by means of tables. In the table below we have defined a binary operation (which we shall denote by $*$) on the set of letters a, b, c, and d. To find the result of applying this operation to a pair of letters x and y (that is, to find the object $x * y$) find the letter in *row* x and in *column* y. For example, $c * b = d$ and $a * d = d$. Is the operation defined by this table commutative? How can you tell the operation is commutative simply by observing the geometric properties of the four-by-four array of letters in the table?

Table 2–1

Columns

*	*a*	*b*	*c*	*d*
a	*a*	*b*	*c*	*d*
b	*b*	*c*	*d*	*a*
c	*c*	*d*	*a*	*b*
d	*d*	*a*	*b*	*c*

Rows

2.5 Properties of a Binary Operation, II

In this section we shall continue the discussion of properties of a binary operation which we began in the last section.

The whole number 0 plays a distinguished role relative to addition of whole numbers. Zero is the only number that, when added to a number, gives that number as the sum. That is, no matter which whole number x

represents, $0 + x = x$ and $x + 0 = x$. Is there a number that acts toward multiplication in the same way that 0 acts toward addition? Surely, because $1 \cdot x = x$ and $x \cdot 1 = x$, 1 is the number we want. Because of these special properties of 0 and 1, we call the whole number 0 the **additive identity** and we call 1 the **multiplicative identity**.

The number 0 acts very differently toward multiplication than it does toward addition. Indeed, the product of 0 with any whole number at all is 0: $0 \cdot x = 0$ and $x \cdot 0 = 0$ for all whole numbers x. Because of the way 0 behaves with respect to multiplication, we call 0 the **annihilator** for multiplication.

Example 1: The binary operation of addition defined on the set of even whole numbers has 0 as an identity. But multiplication defined on the set of even whole numbers has no identity since the only possible candidate for such an identity element, 1, is not an even whole number.

Example 2: With reference to the binary operation on playing cards (Example 1, Section 2.3), the card 2 ◇ is not an identity for this operation. To prove this, we need only demonstrate by means of an example that there is a card x such that $x * 2\diamondsuit \neq x$. For instance, $3\clubsuit * 2\diamondsuit \neq 3\clubsuit$. Is there any card which is an identity for this operation?

Suppose we know that

$$x + 4 = y + 4,$$

where x and y are whole numbers and + denotes addition of whole numbers. What can you say about x and y? Surely x and y are equal: $x = y$. We have been able to "erase" the 4 from both sides of the first equation to obtain the second. Because each of the equations $x + z = y + z$ and $z + x = z + y$ implies that $x = y$ we say that addition of whole numbers possesses the **cancellation** property.

Multiplication of whole numbers also possesses a cancellation property. If x, y, and z are whole numbers such that either $xz = yz$ or $zx = zy$ and if *z is not equal to* 0, then we may conclude that $x = y$. This cancellation property says that we can cancel any whole number except 0. Why can we not cancel 0? Consider the equation $3 \cdot 0 = 7 \cdot 0$. This equation is a true statement since any whole number multiplied by 0 is 0. But we cannot cancel the 0 from both sides of this equation since it is obviously untrue that $3 = 7$. Hence we cannot expect to be able to cancel zero with respect to multiplication.

Here is an example that shows how these cancellation properties may be used to help solve equations.

Example 3: Solve the equation $5x = 2x + 6$.

SOLUTION: Since $5x = 2x + 3x$, we can rewrite this equation in the form

$$2x + 3x = 2x + 6.$$

Applying the cancellation property of addition we get the equation

$$3x = 6.$$

On rewriting 6 as $3 \cdot 2$, we get the equation

$$3x = 3 \cdot 2.$$

Now applying the cancellation property of multiplication (since 3 is not zero), we finally obtain

$$x = 2.$$

Hence the solution of the given equation is 2.

The last property we shall discuss at this time is called the **distributive** property. This is not a property that is possessed by one operation alone; it is a property that is shared by two operations. For example, consider the operations of addition and multiplication of whole numbers. The symbol $3 \cdot (4 + 5)$ involves both of these operations and may be simplified in two different ways. One way is to first perform the addition and write

$$3 \cdot (4 + 5) = 3 \cdot 9 = 27.$$

The other way is to multiply 3 and 4, multiply 3 and 5, and then add these products:

$$3 \cdot (4 + 5) = (3 \cdot 4) + (3 \cdot 5) = 12 + 15 = 27.$$

This second computation involves the use of the distributive property of multiplication and addition. Formally, this property is stated as follows: To say that addition and multiplication of whole numbers share the distributive property means that $x \cdot (y + z) = (x \cdot y) + (x \cdot z)$ no matter which whole numbers x, y, and z represent. Here are some examples of how this property is used.

Example 4: The product of 34 and 57 is generally computed as follows:

$$\begin{array}{r} 57 \\ 34 \\ \hline 228 \\ 171 \\ \hline 1938 \end{array}$$

Now examine the following equation which utilizes the distributive property:

$$\begin{aligned} 57 \cdot 34 &= 57 \cdot (30 + 4) \\ &= (57 \cdot 30) + (57 \cdot 4) \\ &= 1710 + 228 \\ &= 1938 \end{aligned}$$

Comparing the "vertical" method for finding this product (this method is called the *ordinary multiplication algorithm*[1]) with the "horizontal" method, we see that the ordinary "vertical" algorithm uses the distributive property and uses this property in a very important way. Indeed, the distributive property can perhaps be regarded as the most important aspect of this "vertical" sort of algorithm.

The statement

$$a(b + c) = ab + ac,$$

[1] By an algorithm we mean a computational method by means of which we determine sums, products, square roots, and so forth.

which we have called the distributive property for addition and multiplication, is more properly called the **left distributive** property for addition and multiplication. The **right distributive** property for these two operations is

$$(b + c)a = ba + ca.$$

This right distributive property can be obtained from the left distributive property by using the commutative property of multiplication.

Addition and multiplication are not the only operations that share distributive properties of one kind or another. We shall see examples of other distributive properties in our later work.

Exercises 2.5

1. Explain why the card 5◇ is not an identity for the playing card operation defined in Example 1, Section 2.3.
2. Does the operation of conjunction have an identity? That is, is there a statement i such that $p \wedge i \leftrightarrow i \wedge p \leftrightarrow p$ no matter which statement p represents?
3. Does the operation of disjunction have an identity? That is, is there a statement i such that $p \vee i \leftrightarrow i \vee p \leftrightarrow p$ no matter which statement p represents?
4. Which of the following cancellations are correct and which are the result of a misuse of the real cancellation properties? (All letters represent whole numbers.)
   (a) $3x + 7 = 3x + 9$ implies $x + 7 = x + 9$ since we can cancel the 3's from both sides of an equation.
   (b) $7 + x = 3(a + x)$ implies that $7 = 3a$ since we can cancel the x from both sides of the equation.
   (c) $6a + b = 6x + c$ implies that $a + b = x + c$ since we can cancel the 6 from both sides of the equation.
   (d) $5x + 9 = 5y + 9$ implies $x = y$ since we can cancel first 9 then 5 from both sides of the equation.
   (e) $(a - b)(c + b) = (a - b)(2c)$ implies $c + b = 2c$.
   (f) $(a + b)(c + b) = (a + b)(2c)$ implies $c + b = 2c$.
   (g) $(a + b + 1)(c + b) = (a + b + 1)(2c)$ implies $c + b = 2c$.
5. Use the cancellation properties of addition and/or multiplication to solve the following equations.

(a) $x + 2 = 5$.
(b) $4x = 32 + 2x$.

6. Explain how the distributive property is used in multiplying 34 by 18 using the ordinary (vertical) multiplication algorithm. In using this algorithm do you ever really multiply 34 by 18? What numbers do you multiply?
7. Make truth tables and verify that conjunction and disjunction share the following distributive properties:
   (a) $p \wedge (q \vee r) \leftrightarrow (p \wedge q) \vee (p \wedge r)$.
   (b) $p \vee (q \wedge r) \leftrightarrow (p \vee q) \wedge (p \vee r)$.
8. One of the following distributive-like properties is true and the other is false. Which is true?
   (a) $p \wedge (q \rightarrow r) \leftrightarrow (p \wedge q) \rightarrow (p \wedge r)$.
   (b) $p \rightarrow (q \wedge r) \leftrightarrow (p \rightarrow q) \wedge (p \rightarrow r)$.
9. Complete the justifications for each step in this argument.

Theorem: $(a + b)(c + d) = ac + ad + bc + bd$.

PROOF:

(1) $(a + b)(c + d) = a(c + d) + b(c + d)$. (1) This is an application of the ________ distributive property for addition and multiplication.
(2) $a(c + d) + b(c + d) = [ac + ad] + b(c + d)$. (2) This is an application of the ________ distributive property.
(3) $[ac + ad] + b(c + d) = [ac + ad] + [bc + bd]$. (3) This is an application of the ________ distributive property.
(4) $[ac + ad] + [bc + bd] = ac + ad + bc + bd$. (4) We can omit the parentheses because of the ________ property of ________.
(5) $(a + b)(c + d) = ac + ad + bc + bd$. (5) This follows from equations (1) through (4) by repeated use of the ________ property of equality.

10. Use Exercise 9 to complete these equations.
    (a) $(n + m)(n + m) =$
    (b) $(x + y)(2 + ab) =$
11. We can use Exercise 9 to show that $(x + 2)^2 = x^2 + 4x + 4$. The Greeks proved this geometrically by using the figure at the left. Explain how they did this.

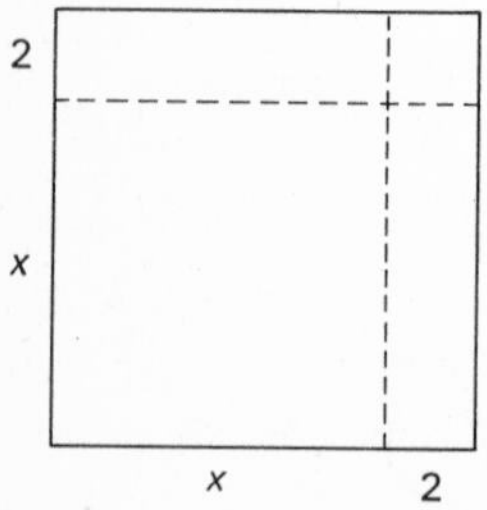

2.6

Arithmetic Modulo Six, I

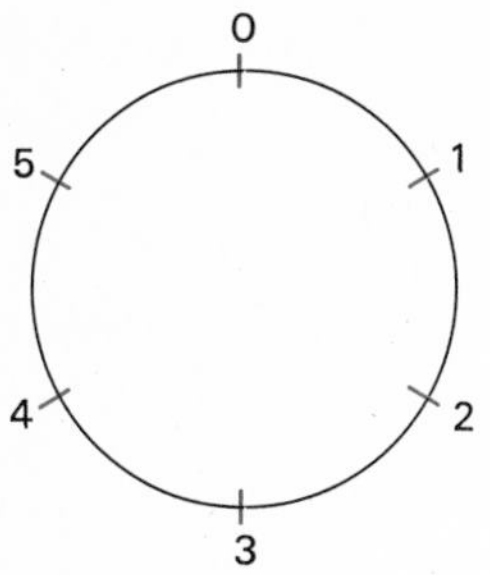

Figure 2.4

We have been discussing the idea of a mathematical system largely with reference to the mathematical system of whole numbers. To help you to see the essential aspects of a mathematical system more clearly, we shall now introduce a new and only partially familiar mathematical system called *arithmetic modulo six*.

The mathematical system called arithmetic modulo six involves only six objects, the whole numbers 0 through 5. Let us arrange these six numbers around the circumference of a circle, as shown in Figure 2.4. The only relation that we shall need is equality of objects. When we write $n = m$ (where n and m represent objects of this new system), we shall mean simply that the symbols n and m represent the same object of the system. So let us go on to the binary operations of this system. First, let us define an operation which derives from addition of whole numbers. For convenience, we shall call this operation 6-addition to remind us that it resembles addition of whole numbers but is defined only on the six objects of this new system. Here is how 6-addition is performed. Given a pair of objects, x and y, start at the number x on the circle (Figure 2.4) and move y distances in the clockwise direction. The number at which you stop is the 6-sum of x and y. We shall denote 6-addition by the symbol $\oplus$. For example (and you should verify each of these statements),

$$5 \oplus 3 = 2, \qquad 3 \oplus 3 = 0, \qquad 4 \oplus 4 = 2, \qquad \text{and} \qquad 5 \oplus 2 = 1.$$

Below is a 6-addition table for this operation. The entry in row n and column m represents the 6-sum of the objects n and m (in that order). Hence the entry in row n and column m is the object $n \oplus m$.

Table 2–2 **6-Addition Table for Arithmetic Modulo Six**

Columns (header row); *Rows* (first column)

$\oplus$	*0*	*1*	*2*	*3*	*4*	*5*
0	0	1	2	3	4	5
1	1	2	3	4	5	0
2	2	3	4	5	0	1
3	3	4	5	0	1	2
4	4	5	0	1	2	3
5	5	0	1	2	3	4

Example 1: The equation $x \oplus 4 = 2$ is solved by finding those objects that give 2 when 4 is 6-added to them. From the table we see that $4 \oplus 4$ is equal to 2 and that no other object plus 4 is equal to 2. Hence the only solution of this equation is 4.

Example 2: Solve the equation $x \oplus x = 2$.

SOLUTION: Examining the 6-addition table we see that $1 \oplus 1 = 2$ and $4 \oplus 4 = 2$. Hence 1 and 4 are solutions. There are no other solutions.

Example 3: Is there an identity for 6-addition?

SOLUTION: Yes, 0 is the identity. From the table we see that $x \oplus 0 = x$ and $0 \oplus x = x$ for all $x = 0, 1, 2, 3, 4$, and 5.

If by moving around the circle in a clockwise direction we perform 6-addition, then moving around the circle in a counterclockwise direction ought to define 6-subtraction. So let us define 6-subtraction as follows: Given two objects x and y, to 6-subtract y from x start at the point x on the circle and move y distances in the counterclockwise direction. The landing point is the result of having 6-subtracted y from x. Let us denote 6-subtraction by $\ominus$.

Example 4: $3 \ominus 5 = ?$

SOLUTION: Starting at 3 and moving 5 distances in the counterclockwise direction lands us on 4. Hence $3 \ominus 5 = 4$.

Example 5: Find the solution of the equation $4 \ominus x = 5$.

SOLUTION: Starting at 4, how many distances must we move in the counterclockwise direction in order to land on 5? The answer is 5 distances, and therefore the solution of $4 \ominus x = 5$ is 5.

Example 6: $(x \oplus y) \ominus y = ?$ $(x \ominus y) \oplus y = ?$

SOLUTION: $(x \oplus y) \ominus y = x$ since starting at x, moving y distances clockwise, and then moving y distances counterclockwise lands us back at x.

Similarly $(x \ominus y) \oplus y$ is the result of starting at x, moving y distances in the counterclockwise direction, and then moving y distances in the clockwise direction. Thus $(x \ominus y) \oplus y = x$.

Example 6 demonstrates an important connection between 6-addition and 6-subtraction. We see that 6-subtracting a number "undoes" the effect of having 6-added that number and that 6-adding a number "undoes" the effect of having 6-subtracted that same number. Because of this connection between 6-addition and 6-subtraction, we say that these two operations are **inverse operations**. More generally, when two binary operations have the effect of "undoing" each other in this way, we say that each operation is the inverse of the other.

By this time you should be wondering what is so special about the number 6. Actually there is nothing special at all about 6. There is a mathematical system similar to arithmetic modulo six built upon each of the whole numbers greater than one. For example, **arithmetic modulo four** is the mathematical system built upon the four objects 0, 1, 2, and 3. An operation called 4-addition can be defined upon these objects using a "number circle" in the same general way that 6-addition was defined here. We shall consider this mathematical system in the exercises.

In the next section we shall continue our discussion of arithmetic modulo six by introducing an operation called 6-multiplication.

Exercises 2.6

1. Find the 6-sum of the objects 3, 5, 4, 2, 1, 3, and 5.
2. Use the objects 3, 4, and 5 to demonstrate that 6-addition is associative. Is 6-addition commutative?
3. Solve the following equations in arithmetic modulo six. Remember that some of them may have more than one solution.
   (a) $x \ominus 2 = 4$. **(b)** $3 \ominus (x \oplus x) = 1$. **(c)** $5 \oplus (x \ominus 2) = 0$.
4. Is 6-subtraction a binary operation? That is, is it true that no matter which objects x and y represent, $x \ominus y$ always represents a unique object? Construct a table for 6-subtraction similar to the 6-addition table shown in Table 2–2. (The object entered in row x and column y will be $x \ominus y$.)
5. Verify by means of examples that 6-subtraction is neither commutative nor associative.

6. If x is an object in arithmetic modulo six, then by the **additive inverse** of x we mean that object y such that $x \oplus y = 0$. Find the additive inverse of each object in arithmetic modulo six. (For example, 4 is the additive inverse of 2 since $2 \oplus 4 = 0$.)
7. Does 6-addition have the cancellation property? That is, if $a \oplus b = c \oplus b$ can you always conclude that $a = c$? (You can answer this question in terms of the number circle.)
8. It would appear reasonable (on the basis of what we learned about the relation *is less than* in the system of whole numbers) to say that in arithmetic modulo six an object x is less than an object y if there is a nonzero object d such that $x \oplus d = y$. Show that, if we tried to use such a definition, we would be able to conclude both that $2 < 3$ and that $3 < 2$. We conclude therefore that it is impossible to define a "less than" relation in this number system.
9. Using the numbers 0, 1, 2, 3, and 4 and using a number circle (similar to the one in Fig. 2.4) we can build a mathematical system called **arithmetic modulo five**. In this system $2 \oplus 4 = 1$, since starting at 2 on the number circle for this system and moving four distances around the circle lands us on 1. Construct a table for 5-addition in arithmetic modulo five.
10. In arithmetic modulo five
    (a) Is 0 an identity for 5-addition?
    (b) Is 5-addition commutative and associative?
    (c) What is the 5-sum of 4, 3, 2, 4, and 1?
    (d) What is the solution of the equation $x \ominus 2 = 3$?
11. Using the numbers 0, 1, 2, and 3 placed around the circumference of a circle we can define an operation called 4-addition and a mathematical system called **arithmetic modulo four**. Construct a 4-addition table for this system. Then use this table to solve the following equations.
    (a) $x \oplus x = 3$.
    (b) $x \oplus x = 2$.
    (c) $x \oplus x = 0$.
    (d) $x \oplus 2 = 1$.
    (e) $x \ominus 3 = 2$.
    (f) $3 \ominus x = 1$.

2.7 Arithmetic Modulo Six, II

Let x and y represent two objects in arithmetic modulo six. We have seen how to define addition-like and subtraction-like operations. How can we define a multiplication-like operation? One way to define such an operation (denoted by $\otimes$) is to regard 6-multiplication as repeated 6-addition. Thus, for example, we would find $5 \otimes 3$ as follows:

$$\begin{aligned} 5 \otimes 3 &= 5 \oplus 5 \oplus 5 \\ &= 4 \oplus 5 \\ &= 3. \end{aligned}$$

Hence $5 \otimes 3 = 3$ in arithmetic modulo six.

After having performed a great many 6-multiplications, we might discover an easier way to 6-multiply. Consider the problem $5 \otimes 3 = ?$ again. If we multiply these two numbers in the mathematical system of whole numbers (using the operation of ordinary multiplication of whole numbers), we get 15 as the product. If we subtract (or "cast out") as many 6's as possible from 15, we are left with 3: $15 - 6 = 9$, $9 - 6 = 3$. Thus we see that the 6-product of 5 and 3 is obtained by casting out as many 6's as possible from the product 15. This is a general method for computing 6-products. Thus to find the 6-product of 5 and 5, multiply 5 and 5 using multiplication of whole numbers and then cast out as many 6's as possible: $25 - 6 = 19$, $19 - 6 = 13$, $13 - 6 = 7$, $7 - 6 = 1$. Hence $5 \otimes 5 = 1$. Using repeating 6-addition, we could compute this 6-product as follows:

$$\begin{aligned} 5 \otimes 5 &= 5 \oplus 5 \oplus 5 \oplus 5 \oplus 5 \\ &= 4 \oplus 5 \oplus 5 \oplus 5 \\ &= 3 \oplus 5 \oplus 5 \\ &= 2 \oplus 5 \\ &= 1 \end{aligned}$$

The same kind of casting-out procedure can be used for 6-addition.

Example 1: Find the 6-sum and 6-product of 3 and 4 by casting out 6's.

SOLUTION: $3 + 4 = 7$ in the system of whole numbers. Casting out a 6 from 7, we get 1. Hence $3 \oplus 4 = 1$. The product of 3 and 4 in the system of whole numbers is 12. We can cast out two 6's from 12, leaving 0. Hence $3 \otimes 4 = 0$ in arithmetic modulo six.

The table below is a partially filled-in 6-multiplication table. Before going further you should complete this table.

Table 2–3 **6-Multiplication Table for Arithmetic Modulo Six**

$\otimes$	*0*	*1*	*2*	*3*	*4*	*5*
0	0	0	0	0		
1	0	1	2	3		
2	0	2	4	0	2	4
3						
4				0	4	2
5			4		2	

Before we leave arithmetic modulo six, let us comment upon some of the essential differences between this arithmetic and the usual arithmetic of whole numbers. In the system of whole numbers, it is not possible to find two *nonzero* objects whose product is zero. But in arithmetic modulo six there do exist nonzero objects whose 6-product is zero. For example, $3 \otimes 4 = 0$. In the system of whole numbers, subtraction is not a binary operation (for example, $5 - 7$ has no meaning in that system). In arithmetic modulo six, 6-subtraction is a binary operation because $x \ominus y$ has a unique meaning no matter which of the six objects x and y represent. (To see why this is true, think about how subtraction is defined in terms of moving around the circle.) In the system of whole numbers, multiplication has the cancellation property (for nonzero numbers). In arithmetic modulo six, 6-multiplication does not have this property. For example, from the equation $4 \otimes 3 = 2 \otimes 3$, we cannot cancel the 3 and conclude that $4 = 2$.

Finally, let us comment on why we have not tried to define a division-like operation. Suppose we attempted to define a process called 6-division. Since (from the 6-multiplication table)

$$3 = 3 \otimes 1 \qquad \text{and} \qquad 3 = 3 \otimes 3,$$

we would have to conclude (if we tried to define 6-division) that

$$3 \oplus\!\!\!\!\div\; 3 = 1 \qquad \text{and} \qquad 3 \oplus\!\!\!\!\div\; 3 = 3.$$

That is, the result of 6-dividing 3 by 3 would be equal to two different objects—this "quotient" would not be a single number. This is sufficiently unpleasant so that we do not define 6-division at all. Generally speaking, mathematics does not deal with processes that do not yield unique results. There are exceptions to this, but they are isolated and are of no interest to us.

Exercises 2.7

1. Find the 6-product of the objects 4, 4, 5, 2, and 5.
2. Solve the following equations in arithmetic modulo six.
   (a) $x \otimes x = 1$. **(c)** $(2 \otimes x) \ominus 3 = 0$. **(e)** $x \otimes (3 \otimes 5) = 1$.
   (b) $x \otimes x = 4$. **(d)** $(2 \otimes x) \ominus 2 = 0$. **(f)** $(x \ominus 1) \otimes (x \ominus 2) = 0$.
3. Show that 6-multiplication does not possess the cancellation property by finding objects a, b, and c such that $a \otimes c = b \otimes c$ but $a \neq b$.
4. Use the objects 2, 3, and 5 to demonstrate that 6-addition and 6-multiplication share the right and left distributive properties.
5. Use the objects 3, 4, and 5 to demonstrate that 6-multiplication is associative. Is the operation commutative? Is there an identity for 6-multiplication?
6.* If x is an object in arithmetic modulo six, then we call an object y the **multiplicative inverse** of x if $x \otimes y = 1$. Does every object in arithmetic modulo possess a multiplicative inverse?
7. Write out the table for 5-multiplication in arithmetic modulo five. (You can find the entries for this table by first multiplying the objects as if they were whole numbers and by then casting out as many fives as possible from this product.)
8. We saw that in arithmetic modulo six it was possible to find nonzero objects whose 6-product is zero. Can nonzero objects be found in arithmetic modulo five whose 5-product is zero? (Refer to the table you constructed in Exercise 7.)
9. Does every nonzero object in arithmetic modulo five have a multiplicative inverse? (Refer to Exercise 6.)
10. If we try to define 5-division in arithmetic modulo five, we have better luck than we did when we tried to define 6-division in arithmetic modulo six. Show that every object can be 5-divided by every nonzero object in arithmetic modulo five. Make a 5-division table (which of course will not have any column corresponding to 0 since we cannot divide by zero).

11. A factory is working 24 hours a day to produce a certain piece of machinery. It takes 3 hours to produce one of these products and starting at 9 A.M. on a certain day they begin to fill an order for thirty-four of these pieces of machinery. At what hour of the day will they finish the order? What modular arithmetic system is involved in this problem?

3 The System of Whole Numbers

WE HAVE already discussed many of the most fundamental properties of the mathematical system of whole numbers. In this chapter we are going to pursue some of the consequences of these fundamental properties. The first half of the chapter consists of a formal study of some of these consequences, including definitions of subtraction and division. The second half of the chapter consists of a less formal introduction to some of the ideas of elementary number theory.

3.1 Review of Basic Properties

We have already discussed most of the basic properties of the system of whole numbers that are used in elementary arithmetic involving whole numbers. So let us begin by listing these properties.

Basic Properties of the System of Whole Numbers

1. The binary operation of addition of whole numbers has the following properties:

A. Addition is commutative: $a + b = b + a$ for all whole numbers a and b.

B. Addition is associative: $a + (b + c) = (a + b) + c$ for all whole numbers a, b, and c.

C. Addition has an additive identity (0): $a + 0 = a$ and $0 + a = a$ for all whole numbers a.

D. Addition has the cancellation property: $a + b = c + b$ implies that $a = c$.

2. The binary operation of multiplication of whole numbers has the following properties:
   A. Multiplication is commutative: $a \cdot b = b \cdot a$, for all whole numbers a and b.
   B. Multiplication is associative: $a \cdot (b \cdot c) = (a \cdot b) \cdot c$, for all whole numbers a, b, and c.
   C. Multiplication has an identity (1): $x \cdot 1 = x$ and $1 \cdot x = x$ for all whole numbers x.
   D. Multiplication has the cancellation property for nonzero whole numbers: $a \cdot b = c \cdot b$ implies $a = c$ if b is not zero.
3. Multiplication and addition share both right and left distributive properties: $a \cdot (b + c) = (a \cdot b) + (a \cdot c)$ and $(b + c) \cdot a = (b \cdot a) + (c \cdot a)$, for all whole numbers a, b, and c.

In the next three sections, we are going to undertake a program of development of the system of whole numbers based upon these basic properties.

3.2 Selected Consequences, I

Let us begin our development of the system of whole numbers from the basic properties of the last section by defining the inequality relations and by stating a few theorems concerning these relations. We shall begin with the relation **is less than**.

Definition of *Is Less Than*. *If x and y are whole numbers, then to say that x is less than y, in symbols $x < y$, means that there is some nonzero whole number d such that $x + d = y$.*

The definition states that x is less than y if, when x is increased by some nonzero amount d, the sum is y. For example, 5 is less than 8, $5 < 8$, because when 5 is increased by 3 the resulting sum is 8. On the other hand, $6 \nless 5$ because there is no nonzero whole number d such that $6 + d = 5$.

The most important theorems about the *is less than* relation are the following. These theorems relate this relation to the operations of addition and multiplication.

Theorem A: *If x, y, and z are whole numbers and if $x < y$, then $x + z < y + z$.*

Theorem B: *If x, y, and z are whole numbers, if $x < y$, and if $z \neq 0$, then $xz < yz$.*

Theorem A states that the same whole number can be added to both sides of an inequality involving the *is less than* relation, and Theorem B states that both sides of such an inequality can be multiplied by the same nonzero whole number. Let us prove Theorem A. This proof is typical of a *direct proof* in that the statements which comprise the argument lead directly from the hypothesis of the theorem to its conclusion. In order to make these statements and the logical connections between them abundantly obvious, we have arranged them in vertical form. Here is the proof of Theorem A:

Hypothesis: $x < y$.
Conclusion: $x + z < y + z$.

PROOF:

Statements	*Justifications*
1. $x < y$	**1.** Hypothesis.
2. There is a nonzero whole number d such that $x + d = y$.	**2.** From (1) by using the definition of *is less than*.
3. $(x + d) + z = y + z$	**3.** By adding z to both sides of the equation in (2).
4. $x + (d + z) = y + z$	**4.** From (3) by using the associativity of addition.
5. $x + (z + d) = y + z$	**5.** From (4) by using the commutativity of addition.
6. $(x + z) + d = y + z$	**6.** From (5) by using the associativity of addition.
7. $x + z < y + z$	**7.** This follows from (6) by using the fact that d is nonzero and the definition of *is less than*.

END OF PROOF

We shall supply statements leading to a proof of Theorem B in the exercises.

The second important relation is the relation **is greater than**.

Definition of *Is Greater Than*. *When we say that x is greater than y, $x > y$, we mean that y is less than x.*

According to this definition, then, $x > y$ if and only if $y < x$. There are two other inequality relations of interest, each of which is constructed using one of these two inequality relations together with the basic concept of equality. We say that x *is less than or equal to* y, $x \leq y$, if either $x < y$ or $x = y$. Hence, for example, $2 \not\leq 1$, $2 \leq 2$, and $2 \leq 3$. The relation *is greater than or equal to* is defined similarly.

Theorems A and B have analogs for these other three inequality relations. You should write out a few of these analogs.

Exercises 3.2

1. Use the definitions of *is less than* and *is greater than* to justify each of the following statements.
(a) $3 < 5$. **(b)** $5 > 3$. **(c)** $0 < 5$. **(d)** $5 > 0$.

2. State a definition for the relation *is greater than or equal to*.

3. Indicate the duplications in the list: $<$, $\leq$, $>$, $\geq$, $\nless$, $\nleq$, $\ngtr$, $\ngeq$.

4. Which of the three properties of a relation are possessed by each of the four inequality relations $<$, $>$, $\leq$, and $\geq$?

5. State the analog of Theorem A for the relation $>$. State the analog of Theorem B for the relation $\geq$.

6. Supply justifications for the statements of this proof of Theorem B.

Hypothesis: $x < y$ *and* $z \neq 0$.
Conclusion: $xz < yz$.

PROOF:

1. $x < y$.
2. $x + d = y$ for some nonzero whole number d.
3. $(x + d)z = yz$.
4. $xz + dz = yz$.
5. $dz > 0$.
6. $xz < yz$.

7. Why must we restrict z from being equal to 0 in Theorem B?

8. If you took a friend to dinner in an unfamiliar restaurant and if the bill were larger than you had anticipated and if you were not sure how much money you actually had with you, which of the two relations $<$ and $\leq$ would you be most immediately interested in?

9. Here is a proof that the relation *is less than* has the transitive property. Supply the justifications.

Theorem: *If $x < y$ and $y < z$, then $x < z$.*

Hypotheses: $x < y$ *and* $y < z$.
Conclusion: $x < z$.

PROOF:

1. $x < y$ and $y < z$.
2. $x + d = y$ and $y + e = z$, for some nonzero whole numbers d and e.
3. $(x + d) + e = z$.
4. $x + (d + e) = z$.
5. $d + e$ is nonzero.
6. $x < z$.

3.3 Selected Consequences, II

As the second step in our development of the system of whole numbers, we shall define subtraction and division of whole numbers and state a few theorems relating to these processes.

First, let us define subtraction. Observe how addition is used in this definition.

Definition of Subtraction. *If x and y are whole numbers such that $x \geq y$, then $x - y$ represents that whole number d such that $x = y + d$. If $x < y$, then the symbol $x - y$ is meaningless in the system of whole numbers.*

This definition tells us that the equations

$$x - y = d \qquad \text{and} \qquad x = y + d$$

express exactly the same relationship between the numbers x, y, and d. For example, because $6 = 4 + 2$ we know, according to this definition, that $6 - 4 = 2$. The difference $8 - 5$ is equal to 3 because $8 = 5 + 3$. But the symbol $7 - 9$ is meaningless (in this mathematical system) because there is no whole number d such that $7 = 9 + d$.

Subtraction is important in the system of whole numbers because addition and subtraction are inverse operations. By this we mean that each of these processes "undoes" the result of having performed the other. More precisely, we have the following two theorems:

Theorem C: *If x and y are whole numbers, then $(x + y) - y = x$.*

Theorem D: *If x and y are whole numbers and if $x \geq y$, then $(x - y) + y = x$.*

Here are the proofs of these two theorems.

PROOF OF THEOREM C: Let x and y be whole numbers. Then, because addition is commutative, we know that

$$x + y = y + x.$$

Now regard the left-hand member of this equation as a single entity and think of the right side as the sum of two numbers. Then, according to the definition of subtraction, this equation expresses exactly the same idea as does the equation

$$(x + y) - y = x.$$

This is just what we wanted to prove.

PROOF OF THEOREM D: Let x and y be whole numbers such that $x \geq y$. Since $x \geq y$, the symbol $x - y$ is meaningful in this system and so we can write

$$x - y = x - y.$$

Regard the right-hand side of this equation as a single number and the left-hand side as being the difference of two numbers. Then the definition of subtraction tells us that

$$x = y + (x - y).$$

Using commutativity of addition, we can rewrite this equation in the form

$$x = (x - y) + x,$$

and this can be rewritten as

$$(x - y) + x = x,$$

which is exactly what we wanted to prove.

There are many theorems having to do with subtraction that we could prove now, but let us go on and define division of whole numbers.

Definition of Division. *If x and y are whole numbers and if y is not equal to zero, then $x \div y$ (the result of dividing x by y) is that number q such that $x = y \cdot q$,* if there is such a number. *If no such number q exists, then the symbol $x \div y$ is meaningless and x cannot be divided by y.*

The definition of division tells us that the equations

$$x \div y = q \qquad \text{and} \qquad x = y \cdot q$$

express precisely the same relationship between the numbers x, y, and q. Observe how the definition of division in terms of multiplication resembles the definition of subtraction in terms of addition.

Example 1: The symbol $8 \div 4$ represents the whole number 2 because it is true that $8 = 4 \cdot 2$. Because $15 = 5 \cdot 3$, we may conclude that $15 \div 5 = 3$. The symbol $15 \div 7$ has no meaning in the system of whole numbers because there is no whole number q such that $15 = 7 \cdot q$.

In this definition of division of whole numbers, we specifically restricted y from being 0. That is, according to our definition, it is not permissible to divide by 0. Why did we say this? There are two cases to consider: first, why we cannot divide a nonzero whole number by 0, and second, why we cannot divide 0 by 0. The reasons are different in each case.

To see why we cannot divide a nonzero whole number by 0, let us consider the illustration of 5 divided by 0. If it were possible to divide 5 by 0 (that is, if the symbol $5 \div 0$ had any meaning), then we could write $5 \div 0 = q$, where q is some definite whole number. Then according to our definition, because $5 \div 0 = q$, it would be true that $5 = 0 \cdot q$. But $0 \cdot q = 0$, and so we would have $5 = 0$, which is absurd. Hence $5 \div 0$ cannot have any meaning at all.

To explain why $0 \div 0$ has no meaning requires different reasoning. First, we note that each of the following equations is true: $0 = 0 \cdot 0$, $0 = 0 \cdot 1$, $0 = 0 \cdot 2$, and so on. According to our definition, because $0 = 0 \cdot 0$, it would have to be true that $0 \div 0 = 0$. Also, since $0 = 0 \cdot 1$, it would have to be true that $0 \div 0 = 1$. Since $0 = 0 \cdot 2$, it would have to be true that $0 \div 0 = 2$, and so on. Thus we see that $0 \div 0$ would have to be equal to 0, to 1, to 2, and to 3, and in fact to every whole number. This is entirely undesirable because we want the answer to a division problem to be unique. Hence we do not assign any meaning to $0 \div 0$.

Division and multiplication are inverses of each other in the same general way that subtraction and addition are inverses. More precisely, we have the following two theorems.

Theorem E: *If x and y are whole numbers and $y \neq 0$, then $(x \cdot y) \div y = x$.*

Theorem F: *If x and y are whole numbers such that $x \div y$ is also a whole number, then $(x \div y) \cdot y = x$.*

The proofs of these theorems are included in the exercises. The following examples illustrate how Theorems A through F are used in solving even the simplest equations and inequalities.

Example 2: Solve the equation $x - 3 = 5$.

SOLUTION: The usual way to solve this equation is to begin by adding 3 to both sides:

$$(x - 3) + 3 = 5 + 3$$

Then, according to Theorem D, we can simplify the left-hand side of this equation and write $x = 5 + 3$ or $x = 8$.

Example 3: Solve the equation $2x + 4 = 6$.

SOLUTION: We would begin by subtracting 4 from both sides and obtaining the equation $(2x + 4) - 4 = 6 - 4$. Then using Theorem C we would rewrite this equation as $2x = 6 - 4$ so that $2x = 2$. Now $2x = x \cdot 2$, so we can write $x \cdot 2 = 2$. Dividing both sides by 2, we obtain the equation $(x \cdot 2) \div 2 = 2 \div 2$. According to Theorem E, then, we can write $x = 2 \div 2$, so that $x = 1$.

Each of the equations in these two examples can be solved easily by inspection. Nevertheless, these theorems are involved in determining these solutions. The fact is that we generally ignore this and, for example, go directly from the equation $x - 3 = 5$ to the equation $x = 5 + 3$ by ignoring the intermediate step $(x - 3) + 3 = 5 + 3$.

Example 4: Solve the inequality $x - 5 < 8$. That is, find all whole number values of x for which this inequality is a true statement.

SOLUTION: Applying Theorem A to add 5 to both sides of the given inequality, we get the inequality

$$(x - 5) + 5 < 8 + 5.$$

Now use Theorem D to reduce the left side of this inequality to x and addition to reduce the right side to 13. We then have

$$x < 13.$$

Clearly, then, the solutions of the given inequality are the whole numbers 0, 1, 2, 3, 4, 5, 6, 7, 8, 9, 10, 11, and 12. This set of whole numbers is called the **solution set** of the given inequality.

Exercises 3.3

1. Explain why the symbols $3 \div 0$, $3 \div 2$, $2 - 3$, and $0 \div 0$ are all meaningless in the system of whole numbers. Explain why the symbol $0 \div 3$ has meaning and state its meaning.
2. Subtraction and multiplication share a (right) distributive property: $(x - y)z = xz - yz$. Use this distributive property to explain why $14x - 3x = 11x$. Do these operations share a left distributive property?
3. Which of the following statements do you think are true? (Assume that all the quotients are meaningful in the system of whole numbers.)
   (a) $a \div (b + c) = (a \div b) + (a \div c)$.
   (b) $(a + b) \div c = (a \div c) + (b \div c)$.
   (c) $a \div (b - c) = (a \div b) - (a \div c)$.
   (d) $(a - b) \div c = (a \div c) - (b \div c)$.
   (e) $a \div (b \cdot c) = (a \div b) \cdot (a \div c)$.
   (f) $a - (b \div c) = (a - b) \div (a - c)$.
   Each of these statements resembles a distributive property but only some of them are true. Does it make any sense at all to say that multiplication is ambidextrous but that division is only right-handed?

4. Solve the following equations and indicate where and how in each solution you use any of Theorems C through F.

(a) $x + 6 = 13$. **(c)** $3x - 5 = 10$.

(b) $x - 4 = 7$. **(d)** $5x + 6 = 41$.

5. Theorem A has an analog for subtraction: *If x, y, and z are whole numbers, if $x < y$, and if $z \leq x$, then $x - z < y - z$.* Theorem B has this analog for division: *If x, y, and z are whole numbers, if $x < y$, and both $x \div z$ and $y \div z$ are meaningful, then $x \div z < y \div z$.* Show how these theorems can be used to solve the following inequalities.

(a) $x + 2 < 7$. **(b)** $2x + 2 < 6$.

6. To prove Theorem E we can begin by writing down the equation

$$x \cdot y = y \cdot x,$$

which we know is true because of the ________________ property of ________________. Since $y \neq 0$ (by hypothesis), we can use the ________________ to rewrite this equation in the form

$$(x \cdot y) \div y = x,$$

which is exactly what we wanted to prove and so the proof is complete. (Fill in the blanks.)

7. To prove Theorem F we can begin by observing that according to hypothesis $x \div y$ is meaningful and so we can write

$$x \div y = x \div y$$

because of the ________________ property of ________________. Next, applying ________________ we see that this equation can be rewritten in the form

$$x = y \cdot (x \div y).$$

Then, using the ________________ property of ________________, we may write

$$x = (x \div y) \cdot y.$$

Lastly we use the ________________ property of ________________ which tells us that

$$(x \div y) \cdot y = x,$$

which is exactly what we wanted. Thus the proof is complete. (Fill in the blanks.)

3.4 Selected Consequences, III

The number zero has a murky history and we know very little about the development of this important number idea. We do know that zero was regarded as a definite number by certain Hindu mathematicians as early as 900, but this may have been an isolated awareness. The idea that zero is as definite a number as the other whole numbers appears and disappears over the centuries. We read from a Hindu manuscript dated about 850 that a number "remains unchanged when divided by zero. . . ." This is obvious nonsense. As late as 1150 we read (again in a Hindu manuscript) that $3 \div 0$ represents an "infinite quantity"—more nonsense. And of course we read nothing much at all about zero in European works until even later. In this section we shall discuss one of the important features of this number in the system of whole numbers.

We know already that zero is an annihilator for multiplication—that zero times any number is zero. Let us phrase this statement in the form of a theorem.

Theorem G: *If one (or possibly both) of x and y is zero, then $xy = 0$.*

It is a very important property of the system of whole numbers that the converse of Theorem G is also true. That is, we have a companion theorem to Theorem G.

Theorem H: *If x and y are whole numbers and if $xy = 0$, then at least one (and possibly both) of x and y is zero.*

Proof of Theorem H: Suppose that x and y are whole numbers and that $xy = 0$. Keep in mind that we are trying to prove that at least one of the numbers x and y is zero. Obviously x, being a whole number, is either zero or it is not. We can therefore separate the proof into two cases.

Case 1: x is equal to zero.

Case 2: x is not equal to zero.

In Case 1 the theorem is obviously true, because if x is zero, then surely at least one of x and y is zero. Hence we only need to establish the truth of the theorem in Case 2, where x is not zero. So let us suppose that

$$xy = 0 \qquad \text{and} \qquad x \neq 0. \tag{1}$$

We already know (Theorem G) that

$$0 = x0. \tag{2}$$

We next combine equations (1) and (2) and get the equation

$$xy = x0. \tag{3}$$

Finally, we apply the cancellation property of multiplication to equation (3) and cancel the x. (Recall that $x \neq 0$ and we can cancel any nonzero number with respect to multiplication.) Hence we get

$$y = 0.$$

We have proved that if x is not equal to zero, then y is equal to zero. This means that *at least* one of x and y is zero. Thus we have proven the theorem.

In the system of whole numbers, if the product of two numbers is zero, then one or the other of the two numbers must equal zero. Contrast this with the situation in the arithmetic modulo six discussed in the preceding chapter. In that mathematical system it is possible to find two nonzero numbers whose product is 0.

Theorem H has applications to solving equations, as the following example shows.

Example 1: Solve the equation $(x - 1)(x - 2) = 0$.

SOLUTION: The given equation tells us that the product of $x - 1$ and $x - 2$ is 0. Therefore by Theorem H either $x - 1$ must equal 0 or $x - 2$ must equal 0. If $x - 1 = 0$, then $x = 1$. If $x - 2 = 0$, then $x = 2$. Each of the numbers 1 and 2 is a solution.

In the rest of this chapter, we shall be dealing with ideas that come under the heading of *elementary number theory.* Our treatment of elementary number theory will be considerably more informal than our treatment in this and the two preceding sections of the elementary consequences of the basic properties.

Exercises 3.4

1. Use Theorem H to solve the following equations.
(a) $(x + 2)(x - 2) = 0$. **(b)** $(x - 1)(x - 2)(x - 3) = 0$.

2. Examine the argument based upon this sequence of statements.
(1) Let $a = b \neq 0$.
(2) Then $aa = bb$.
(3) So $aa = ab$ (since $a = b$).
(4) So $aa - bb = ab - bb$.
(5) So $(a + b)(a - b) = (a - b)(b)$. (You can verify for yourself that $(a + b)(a - b) = aa - bb$.)
(6) So $a + b = b$.
(7) So $b + b = b$. (Since $a = b$).
(8) So $2b = b$ or $2b = 1b$.
(9) So $2 = 1$.
What is wrong?

3. In Exercise 7, Section 2.7, we asked you to construct the 5-multiplication table for arithmetic modulo five. Examine this table and see if it is possible to find nonzero objects x and y in that system such that $x \otimes y = 0$. Is it possible to find such nonzero objects in arithmetic modulo four?

4. In a hopeless but well-meant attempt to save the children of the Okefenokee the tribulations of the new math, Howland Owl invented the *aftermath.* The aftermath is a mathematical system containing as its only object the number 0. In this system subtraction and even division are binary operations. Also, it is impossible to find nonzero objects whose product is equal to 0. Explain all this.

3.5 Exponents

Before we continue with our discussion of the system of whole numbers, we must digress for a moment to discuss an important method of symbol abbreviation. Very often in the study of whole numbers we must deal with products like $2 \cdot 2 \cdot 2 \cdot 2$ and $3 \cdot 3 \cdot 3 \cdot 3 \cdot 3$. Since such products are somewhat awkward to write down, we abbreviate them by writing 2^4 in place of $2 \cdot 2 \cdot 2 \cdot 2$ and 3^5 in place of $3 \cdot 3 \cdot 3 \cdot 3 \cdot 3$. In the symbol 2^4, the number 4 is called the **exponent** or power and is said to occupy the superscript position. The number 2 in the symbol 2^4 is called the **base**.

The important thing to remember is that the exponential symbol n^m is nothing more than an abbreviation for a product, and when this symbol is seen it is the product itself that one should think of. For example, when you see the symbol "$," you think of the word this symbol abbreviates. The symbol is simply the key that brings the word "dollars" to your mind. In exactly the same way the symbol 4^3 should bring the product $4 \cdot 4 \cdot 4$ to mind. We rarely think in terms of the abbreviations themselves. We only use the abbreviations to tell us what to think about. Students who have difficulty with exponents are most often trying to think in terms of the abbreviations themselves instead of in terms of what the abreviations abbreviate.

It should be clear now what the symbol x^y means when both x and y are nonzero whole numbers. If x is zero and y is nonzero, then x^y represents the product $0 \cdot 0 \cdot 0 \cdot 0 \cdots 0$ (y factors) and so represents 0. But if y is zero and x is nonzero, then x^y cannot properly be thought of as an abbreviation of a product. By common agreement (that is, by definition) we assign the meaning 1 to all symbols of the form x^0 where x is nonzero. (We shall explain why we do this in a moment.) Finally, we shall give the symbol 0^0 no meaning at all. For us, 0^0 will be a nonsense symbol.

The exponential symbols (except for x^0) are nothing more than abbreviations for longer products, but there are many different ways that such products could be abbreviated. Why was this particular method chosen over all alternatives? The answer to this lies in the fact that these exponential symbols lend themselves to symbol manipulation. For example, consider the product of 2^3 and 2^4. We write

$$\begin{aligned} 2^3 \cdot 2^4 &= (2 \cdot 2 \cdot 2)(2 \cdot 2 \cdot 2 \cdot 2) \\ &= 2 \cdot 2 \cdot 2 \cdot 2 \cdot 2 \cdot 2 \cdot 2 \\ &= 2^7 \\ &= 2^{3+4}. \end{aligned}$$

This example illustrates the general fact that

$$x^p \cdot x^q = x^{p+q}.$$

Thus, to multiply powers of the same base, all you have to do is add the exponents.

Next, suppose the bases are different but the powers are the same. For example, $3^2 \cdot 7^2 = ?$ If we replace the exponential symbols by the products they abbreviate, then we can rearrange the factors and simplify the product:

$$\begin{aligned} 3^2 \cdot 7^2 &= (3 \cdot 3)(7 \cdot 7) \\ &= (3 \cdot 7)(3 \cdot 7) \\ &= (3 \cdot 7)^2. \end{aligned}$$

This example suggests that to multiply the same powers of different bases, multiply the bases and raise this product to the common power:

$$x^p \cdot y^p = (x \cdot y)^p.$$

The last theorem concerning these exponential symbols that we shall need has to do with division. Suppose that we want to divide different powers of like bases. For example, consider $3^5 \div 3^2 = ?$ Again, replace the exponential symbols by the products they abbreviate and rearrange:

$$\begin{aligned} 3^5 \div 3^2 &= (3 \cdot 3 \cdot 3 \cdot 3 \cdot 3) \div (3 \cdot 3) \\ &= 3 \cdot 3 \cdot 3 \\ &= 3^3 \\ &= 3^{5-2}. \end{aligned}$$

This example illustrates the fact that to divide different powers of the same base, simply subtract exponents—if it is possible to do so. That is,

$$x^p \div x^q = x^{p-q}, \qquad \text{if } p \geq q.$$

Suppose $x \neq 0$ and look again at the equation

$$x^p \cdot x^q = x^{p+q}.$$

We can see from this equation why we were induced to define x^0 to mean 1. Suppose that in this equation q is 0. Then we would have

$$x^p \cdot x^0 = x^{p+0}.$$

But x^{p+0} is equal to x^p. So what we have is

$$x^p \cdot x^0 = x^p.$$

Since the only way this equation can be true is for x^0 to be 1, we define it to be 1.

Exercises 3.5

1. Rewrite each of these products using exponential notation.
   (a) $3 \cdot 3 \cdot 2 \cdot 3 \cdot 2$.
   (b) $2 \cdot 3 \cdot 5 \cdot 2 \cdot 3 \cdot 5 \cdot 2$.
   (c) $2 \cdot 3 \cdot 5^2 \cdot 7^2 \cdot 2 \cdot 3 \cdot 5 \cdot 7$.
2. Use the theorems to rewrite each of these products in a simpler exponential form. For example, $2^2 \cdot 3^2 \cdot 2^4 = 2^6 \cdot 3^2$.
   (a) $2^4 \cdot 2^0 \cdot 3^2 \cdot 2^2 \cdot 5^4 \cdot 3^3$.
   (b) $2^0 \cdot (313^2 \cdot 55^5)^0$.
   (c) $(2^2 \cdot 2^4) \div 2^3$.
3. You have seen the famous equation $E = mc^2$ many times before. Does this equation say that $E = mcc$ or that $E = mcmc$? How should you insert parentheses if you wanted to make this equation mean what it does not mean?
4. Suppose x, p, and q are all nonzero whole numbers. If necessary experiment with a few specific numbers in order to complete the statement: $(x^p)^q = x^?$.
5. How many parents does a person have? How many grandparents? How many great-grandparents? How many great-great-grandparents? How many great-great-great-grandparents? Assuming three generations every 100 years, how many ancestors do you have going back 200 years?
6. Each number of the form 1 followed by 0's can be written as a product of ten's and can then be abbreviated using exponential notation. Write each of the numbers 10, 100, 1000, 10000, and 100000 as a power of ten. 10^{56} is a number of the form 1 followed by 0's; how many 0's? The number 1 has the form 1 followed by a certain number of 0's. How is 1 written as a power of 10?
7. A *googol* is defined to be 1 followed by 100 zeros. Express a googol as a power of ten. A *googolplex* is 1 followed by a googol of zeros. Express a

googolplex as a power of ten. A googol is a very large number, for it has been estimated that the total number of electrons in the universe is only about 10^{79}.

3.6 Prime Numbers

There are a great many ways of classifying whole numbers. You know, for example, of the classification of all whole numbers into even and odd numbers. Another classification is into prime and composite numbers. The study of prime numbers is ancient and still occupies a central part of number theory. In this section we shall discuss these numbers.

One of the most important relations on whole numbers is the one called *is a divisor of*. When we say that x is a divisor of y, we mean that

$$y = x \cdot \text{(some other whole number)}.$$

Thus 4 is a divisor of 20 since $20 = 4 \cdot 5$. But 4 is not a divisor of 21 since there is no whole number x such that $21 = 4 \cdot x$.

There are other ways to express the fact that a number x is a divisor of a number y. We can say that *y is a multiple of x*. For example, 20 is a multiple of 4 and 18 is a multiple of 9. We can also say that *y is divisible by x*. Thus 20 is divisible by 4 and 18 is divisible by 9. The statements "x is a divisor of y," "y is a multiple of x," and "y is divisible by x" all mean exactly the same thing.

One of the useful things to know about a whole number is the divisors of that number. For example, the divisors of 20 are 20 itself, 1 (which is a divisor of every number), 2, 4, 5, and 10. In fact, there are methods of classification of whole numbers on the basis of the divisors of the numbers. Of these the most important is the classification of whole numbers with regard to whether or not they are **prime numbers**. A prime number is a number that has no divisors other than the number itself and the omnipresent divisor 1. In Table 3–1 we have listed all the prime numbers less than 1000. Incidentally, while it might seem reasonable to call 1 a prime, if we were to do so there would be many times when we would have to make statements like, "For all prime numbers except 1, it is true that . . . ." To avoid having to make this exception, we do not call 1 a prime.

A whole number greater than 1 that is not a prime number is called a **composite** number. Every number greater than 1 is either composite or prime, and 0 and 1 are neither composite nor prime.

Table 3–1 **Table of Primes Less Than One Thousand**

2	101	211	307	401	503	601	701	809	907
3	103	223	311	409	509	607	709	811	911
5	107	227	313	419	521	613	719	821	919
7	109	229	317	421	523	617	727	823	929
11	113	233	331	431	541	619	733	827	937
13	127	239	337	433	547	631	739	829	941
17	131	241	347	439	557	641	743	839	947
19	137	251	349	443	563	643	751	853	953
23	139	257	353	449	569	647	757	857	967
29	149	263	359	457	571	653	761	859	971
31	151	269	367	461	577	659	769	863	977
37	157	271	373	463	587	661	773	877	983
41	163	277	379	467	593	673	787	881	991
43	167	281	383	479	599	677	797	883	997
47	173	283	389	487		683		887	
53	179	293	397	491		691			
59	181			499					
61	191								
67	193								
71	197								
73	199								
79									
83									
89									
97									

There are many interesting questions concerning prime numbers. For example, Euclid proved that there are infinitely many prime numbers, but it has not been possible to actually determine more than a finite number of primes. The problem is that it is extremely difficult to determine divisors of very large numbers. Generally speaking, this requires prodigious amounts of computation. Computers have been applied to this task and have met with some success. For example, the largest known prime number is the number $2^{11213} - 1$ which was proven to be a prime in 1962 at the University of Illinois using the computer called ILLIAC II. This number has about 3400 digits.

Another question about prime numbers that has enjoyed continued attention over the years is the famous **Goldbach Conjecture.**[1] Goldbach's conjecture was that every even whole number greater than two can be

[1] In 1742, C. Goldbach (1690–1764) posed this conjecture to the great eighteenth century mathematician, Leonhard Euler. This conjecture is Goldbach's only claim to fame.

written as the sum of two primes.[2] For instance,

$4 = 2 + 2$	$12 = 7 + 5$	$20 = 13 + 7$
$6 = 3 + 3$	$14 = 7 + 7$	$22 = 11 + 11$
$8 = 5 + 3$	$16 = 11 + 5$	$24 = 11 + 13$
$10 = 5 + 5$	$18 = 11 + 7$	$26 = 13 + 13$

This conjecture has been shown to be true for all even numbers small enough to be amenable to computational techniques, and thus one might guess that it is true in general. The conjecture is very famous and mathematicians have tried without success to prove that it is true. It is interesting that in trying to prove that every even number greater than two could be written as the sum of two primes, a Russian mathematician named Schnirelmann (1905–1938) proved in 1931 that every even whole number greater than two can be written as the sum of not more than 300,000 primes! A contemporary Russian, Vinogradoff, made another advance by proving that there is a whole number N (the value of N is not known, it is only known that such a number exists) such that every even whole number greater than N can be written as the sum of at most four primes. This is the present state of the problem.

Another famous and long unsolved conjecture has to do with what are called *twin primes.* Two whole numbers x and y are called **twin primes** if they are consecutive odd primes. For example, the pairs listed below are twin primes.

3 and 5

5 and 7

11 and 13

17 and 19

29 and 31

The conjecture is that there are infinitely many pairs of twin primes. Whether there exist infinitely many such pairs of primes is unknown and the question has not been resolved, even though it has received a great deal of attention over the years.

[2] The conjecture is obviously false for odd numbers. Consider 11 or 17.

These examples illustrate that one need not delve very deeply into the theory of numbers in order to come up with a question that cannot, at present, be answered. Many unanswered questions lie very near to the surface.

Exercises 3.6

1. By inspection find all the divisors of the numbers 12, 145, and 144.
2. To say that x is an even prime says what about x?
3. Using the table of primes find all pairs of twin primes between 1 and 1,000.
4. Verify Goldbach's Conjecture for the even whole numbers 38, 40, 42, 68, 70, 72, 146, 148, 150, 638, 640, and 642.
5. It can be proved that every odd whole number greater than 5 can be written as the sum of three primes. Verify this for the odd whole numbers from 7 to 25. Also verify that 143 and 301 are sums of three primes.
6. Consider the relation defined on the set of whole numbers and which is called *is a divisor of*.
   (a) Find all whole numbers that are related to 16 by this relation.
   (b) Find all whole numbers to which 16 is related by the relation.
   (c) Are any whole numbers related to themselves by this relation?
   (d) Is the relation transitive?
   (e) Show that the relation is not symmetric by giving an example.
7. Consider the relation *is a multiple of* defined on the set of whole numbers.
   (a) To which whole numbers is 16 related?
   (b) Which whole numbers are related to 16?
   (c) Is this an equivalence relation?

8.* As you move out in the list of whole numbers the primes get rarer and rarer in the sense that given any whole number n by going out far enough in the list you can find a succession of n composite numbers. For example, there is a place in the list where there are fifty composite number numbers in a row. Explain why each of the following numbers is composite:

$$51! + 2,\ 51! + 3,\ 51! + 4, \ldots,\ 51! + 51$$

and explain why there are fifty successive numbers in this list. (The symbol 51! is an abbreviation for the product of all the whole numbers from 1 to 51. For example, $4! = 4 \cdot 3 \cdot 2 \cdot 1$.) How would you find 100 successive composite numbers?

9. Prove that after you pass by 2 and 3 in the list of whole numbers you can never find two successive prime numbers.

3.7 Prime Factorizations

The prime numbers are the basic building blocks from which all whole numbers (greater than one) are built. In this section we shall discuss this idea.

The prime numbers are basic in the sense that each whole number greater than 1 can be expressed as a product of prime numbers. For example,

$$20 = 2 \cdot 5 \cdot 5 \qquad 198 = 2 \cdot 3 \cdot 3 \cdot 11$$

$$45 = 3 \cdot 5 \cdot 5 \qquad 144 = 2 \cdot 2 \cdot 2 \cdot 2 \cdot 3 \cdot 3$$

The prime numbers can be regarded as the building blocks from which other whole numbers greater than 1 can be obtained by using multiplication. This intuitively obvious fact is a part of the statement of an important theorem called the "Fundamental Theorem of Arithmetic."

The Fundamental Theorem of Arithmetic. *Every whole number greater than 1 can be written as a product of prime numbers. Apart from the order in which these prime number factors are written down, there is only one such way to write each whole number as a product of prime numbers.*

Example 1: 30 can be expressed as $2 \cdot 3 \cdot 5$ and as $3 \cdot 2 \cdot 5$, but these are really the same way of writing 30 as a product of primes, only the order of writing down the prime factors is different.

When we write a whole number as a product of primes, we call this product the **prime factorization** of the whole number. Thus $2 \cdot 3 \cdot 5$ is the prime factorization of 30 and $2 \cdot 2 \cdot 5$ or $2^2 \cdot 5$ is the prime factorization of 20.

The Fundamental Theorem implies that every whole number greater than 1 is divisible by at least one prime. If such a number is a prime, then it is divisible by itself. If the number is composite, then according to the Fundamental Theorem that number can be written as a product of primes and so is divisible by each of its prime factors. We shall use this simple fact to prove a theorem mentioned in the last section.

Theorem: *There are infinitely many prime numbers.*

PROOF: We shall use the *indirect method* to prove this theorem. The proof we shall use is a classical example of the elegant simplicity of many indirect proofs, and is attributed to Euclid. We shall begin by making the tentative assumption that there are only a finite number of primes. Then, on the basis of this tentative assumption, we shall draw logically valid conclusions, one of which will be a contradiction to something we already know. This contradiction will mean that the tentative assumption must have been false, and this will mean that there are infinitely many prime numbers. We shall present this proof as a sequence of numbered statements.

1. There are only finitely many primes. (This is the tentative assumption on the basis of which we shall reach a contradiction.)
2. There is a largest prime, say, p. (Every finite set of whole numbers contains a largest number.)
3. Let n be the product of the finitely many primes: $n = 2 \cdot 3 \cdot 5 \cdot 7 \cdot 11 \cdots p$. (This is simply the definition of the symbol n and does not require justification.)
4. Let $m = n + 1$. (This is simply the definition of the symbol m and does not require justification.)
5. m is divisible by some prime, say q. (By the remark preceding this theorem, every whole number greater than 1—and m is greater than 1—is divisible by some prime number.)
6. $m = qx$, where x is some whole number. (This is simply another way of expressing the fact that m is divisible by q.)
7. $n = qy$, where y is some whole number. (The number n is defined to be the product of all primes. q is a prime and so is a divisor of n.)
8. $qx = qy + 1$. (From statements (4), (6), and (7).)
9. $qx - qy = 1$. (This follows from statement (8) by using the definition of subtraction.)
10. $q(x - y) = 1$. (This follows from statement (9) since subtraction and multiplication share a distributive property.)

But now we have reached a contradiction. Statement (10) states that the prime number q divides 1, and this is false. As the argument that leads from tentative assumption to this contraction is valid, it can only be that the tentative assumption is incorrect. Thus it is incorrect that there are only finitely many primes and so what must be true is that there are infinitely many primes. This is precisely the statement that we were to prove and the proof is complete.

Exercises 3.7

1. Write out the prime factorization of each whole number from 50 to 65.
2. Why does the fact that we can write 24 as $2^3 \cdot 3$ and as $2^3 \cdot 3 \cdot 5^0$ not contradict the Fundamental Theorem?
3. How many divisors does 5^{57} have?
4. Duplicate the proof in the text to show that it is false that the only primes are the numbers 2, 3, 5, 7, 11, and 13.
5. How can you tell whether or not a whole number is a perfect square simply by looking at its prime factorization?
6.* A whole number greater than one is called *square-free* if it has no divisors that are perfect squares. How can you tell whether or not a number is square-free simply by looking at its prime factorization? Write out all the square-free whole numbers between 1 and 30.
7.* There are some divisibility tests that can be used to help locate small divisors of numbers. Among these are the following:

   A number is divisible by 2 (or by 5) if its last digit is divisible by 2 (or by 5).
   A number is divisible by 4 (or by 10) if the number formed from its last two digits is divisible by 4 (or by 10).
   A number is divisible by 8 if the number formed by its last three digits is divisible by 8.
   A number is divisible by 3 (or by 9) if the sum of its digits is divisible by 3 (or by 9).

   Use these tests to determine divisors of the following numbers.
   (a) 73,624. **(c)** 2,468. **(e)** 354,629,805,041,020.
   (b) 123,456,789. **(d)** 12,618. **(f)** 983.
8.* Use the divisibility tests of the preceding exercise to find the prime factorizations of the following numbers:
   (a) 1,080. **(b)** 1,620. **(c)** 2,754. **(d)** 2,244.

3.8 Greatest Common Divisor and Least Common Multiple

In this section we shall use prime factorizations to introduce some number-theoretic ideas that will be useful in our study of rational numbers in Chapter 6.

Suppose that x and y are two whole numbers, neither of which is zero. The greatest number that is a divisor of both x and y is called the **greatest common divisor** of x and y. For instance, the greatest number that divides both 20 and 45 is 5. We can see why 5 is the greatest common divisor of these numbers by writing 20 and 45 in their prime factorizations and then comparing these prime factorizations:

$$20 = 2^2 \cdot 5 \qquad \text{and} \qquad 45 = 3^2 \cdot 5.$$

We see that the only prime numbers that divide 20 are 2 and 5, while the only prime numbers that divide 45 are 3 and 5. Hence the only prime number that will divide *both* 20 and 45 is 5. Then we observe that the highest power of 5 that will divide both numbers is the first power. We conclude, therefore, that 5^1 or 5 is the greatest common divisor of 20 and 45. Here are some more examples of finding greatest common divisors using prime factorizations. From now on we shall abbreviate greatest common divisor by GCD.

Example 1: Find the GCD of 45 and 81.

SOLUTION: We write $45 = 3^2 \cdot 5$ and $81 = 3^4$. Then we observe that the only prime that divides both numbers is 3. Then we observe that the largest power of 3 which divides both numbers is 3^2. Hence 3^2 or 9 is the GCD of these numbers.

Example 2: Find the GCD of $2 \cdot 3^2 \cdot 5$ and $2^3 \cdot 3^3 \cdot 7$.

SOLUTION: The only primes that divide both numbers are 2 and 3. The greatest power of 2 that divides both numbers is the first power. The greatest power of 3 that divides both numbers is the second power. Hence the GCD is the product of 2^1 and 3^2: 18.

The concept of greatest common divisor has a spin-off concept of importance. If x and y are whole numbers whose greatest common divisor is 1, then we say that x and y are **relatively prime**. Thus 15 and 14 are relatively prime whole numbers since their GCD is 1.

If x and y are whole numbers then the smallest whole number that is divisible by both x and y is called the **least common multiple** of x and y. The least common multiple of 4 and 6 is 12 since 12 is divisible by both 4 and 6 and is the least number with this property. The least common multiple of 12 and 18 is 36 since 36 is divisible by both 12 and 18 and no number less than 36 is divisible by both 12 and 18.

Prime factorizations can also be used to find least common multiples. (We shall henceforth abbreviate least common multiple by LCM.) For example, consider the numbers 12 and 15. Since

$$12 = 2^2 \cdot 3 \qquad \text{and} \qquad 15 = 3 \cdot 5,$$

we see that any number which is divisible by *both* 12 and 15 must involve all of the primes 2, 3, and 5 in its prime factorization. Hence the LCM of 12 and 15 has the general form $2^a \cdot 3^b \cdot 5^c$. Moreover, the least number of this form which is divisible by both $2^2 \cdot 3$ and $3 \cdot 5$ is $2^2 \cdot 3^1 \cdot 5^1$ and so the LCM of 12 and 15 is 60.

Example 3: The LCM of 45 and 81 is found by first writing these numbers in their prime factorizations: $45 = 3^2 \cdot 5$ and $81 = 3^4$. Any number that is a multiple of both 45 and 81 must therefore have the general form $3^a \cdot 5^b$. Of all such numbers the LCM is the one with the smallest possible exponents. The least a can be is 4 (or else this number would not be divisible by 3^4) and the least b can be is 1. Hence the LCM of 45 and 81 is $3^4 \cdot 5^1$ or 405.

Example 4: Find the LCM of $2 \cdot 3^2 \cdot 5^3$ and $2^3 \cdot 3^3 \cdot 7$.

SOLUTION: The LCM must involve the primes 2, 3, 5, and 7 in order to be divisible by both of the given numbers. So the LCM has the form $2^a \cdot 3^b \cdot 5^c \cdot 7^d$. Now select a, b, c, and d to be as small as possible so that the LCM will be divisible by both of the given numbers. The exponents desired are $a = 3$, $b = 3$, $c = 3$, and $d = 1$. The LCM is $2^3 \cdot 3^3 \cdot 5^3 \cdot 7^1$.

Exercises 3.8

1. Compute the GCD and LCM of each pair of numbers by using prime factorizations.
   - **(a)** 12 and 30.
   - **(b)** 70 and 462.
   - **(c)** 198 and 144.
   - **(d)** 1350 and 120.
2. Use your answers to Exercise 1 to demonstrate the truth of the following theorem.

Theorem: *If x and y are whole numbers greater than zero, then* (GCD)(LCM) $= x \cdot y$.

3. If x and y are relatively prime, then what is their LCM?
4. Find three numbers between 100 and 200 that are relatively prime to 144.
5. Suppose a and b are relatively prime and that c and d are relatively prime.
   (a) Are ac and bd relatively prime?
   (b) Are $a + c$ and $b + d$ relatively prime?
   (c) Are a^2 and b^2 relatively prime?
   (d) Are a and $a + b$ relatively prime?
   (It is anticipated that you will answer these questions experimentally rather than by proving them to be true or false.)
6. Let $*$ denote the operation defined on the nonzero whole numbers according to the rule

$$x * y = \text{GCD}(x, y)$$

   Answer the following questions about this operation.
   (a) Does this process always result in exactly one number no matter which nonzero whole numbers x and y represent? That is, is $*$ really a binary operation?
   (b) Is $*$ commutative? Is it associative?
   (c) Is there an identity for this operation? That is, is there a whole number i such that $x * i = i * x = x$ no matter which whole number x represents?
   (d) Does the cancellation property hold for this operation? That is, if $x * z = y * z$, can you conclude that $x = y$?
7. Replace the "GCD operation" in Exercise 6 by the operation $*$ defined by the rule:

$$x * y = \text{LCM}(x, y)$$

   and answer the same questions for this operation.
8. Suppose n, x, and y are whole numbers such that x divides n and y divides n. Then does it necessarily follow that the product of x and y divides n? Find some examples to substantiate your answer. Using the ideas of this section it is possible to impose a condition involving x and y so that it will necessarily follow that n will be divisible by xy. Can you find such a condition?

3.9

Fermat's Last Problem

No study of number theory would be complete without mention of the father of modern number theory and one of his most famous problems. Pierre de Fermat (French, 1601?–1665) did work on many parts of mathematics and we shall run across his name again, but he is most famous for his work in number theory. He is responsible for the most famous unresolved problem in all of mathematics. In this section we shall discuss this problem, which is called "Fermat's Last Problem."

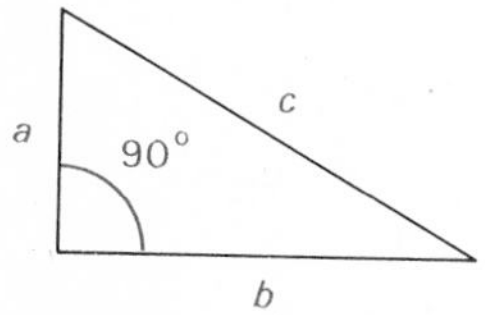

Figure 3.1

Consider the right triangle shown in Figure 3.1. The famous theorem from geometry called the Pythagorean theorem states that the lengths of the sides of such a right triangle are related by the equation

$$a^2 + b^2 = c^2,$$

where c denotes the length of the side of the triangle opposite the right angle and a and b represent the lengths of the sides adjacent to the right angle. A triple of numbers (a,b,c) is called a **Pythagorean triple** if the numbers a, b, and c satisfy such an equation.

Example 1: The triple (3,4,5) is a Pythagorean triple since $3^2 + 4^2 = 5^2$. Other Pythagorean triples are (5,12,13), (7,24,25), and (51,140,149).

If we now generalize the problem of finding Pythagorean triples, we can ask the following question: If n is a whole number greater than 2, is it possible to find nonzero integers[3] x, y, and z such that $x^n + y^n = z^n$? Fermat (so the story goes) wrote in the margin of one of his mathematics books that he had found an elegant proof of the fact that it is impossible to find such numbers x, y, and z if n is greater than 2. Unfortunately, there was not enough room in the margin to contain the proof itself. Fermat died before he could write out his proof—hence the name, Fermat's Last Problem.

The important thing here is that no one has ever been able to prove that there are integers x, y, and z such that $x^n + y^n = z^n$ when $n > 2$ or that there are not any such triples of integers. It is most probable that Fermat was mistaken and that his "elegant proof" was somehow in error. This problem has received an incredible amount of attention and very little real progress has been made toward answering it. It has been shown, however, that there

[3] An integer is a number that is either a whole number or the negative of a whole number: $-1, -2, -3, -4, \ldots$. We shall discuss integers in Chapter 6.

Pierre de Fermat (1601 ?–1665)

do not exist integers x, y, and z such that $x^n + y^n = z^n$ if n is between 2 and 250,000. This result was achieved by using a computer.

Exercises 3.9

1. Prove that if (a,b,c) is a Pythagorean triple then so is $(2a,2b,2c)$. Prove in general that if (a,b,c) is a Pythagorean triple, then so is (na, nb, nc) where n is a nonzero whole number. This proves that there are infinitely many Pythagorean triples.
2. Let x and y be nonzero whole numbers with $x > y$. Prove that the triple $(x^2 - y^2, 2xy, x^2 + y^2)$ is a Pythagorean triple. Use this fact to find three Pythagorean triples.

3.* Another famous unresolved problem has to do with what are called "perfect numbers." A whole number is said to be **perfect** if it is equal to the sum of its proper divisors. For example, 6 is perfect since the proper divisors of 6 are 1, 2, and 3 and $6 = 1 + 2 + 3$. Show that 28 and 496 are perfect numbers. Euclid proved that if $2^{n+1} - 1$ is a prime number, then $(2^{n+1} - 1)(2^n)$ is a perfect number. Use this theorem to prove that 8128 is a perfect number. That is, show that 8128 has this particular form. Whether or not there are any odd perfect numbers is unknown. It is not even known whether there are infinitely many even perfect numbers.

4 The Theory of Sets

② History of set

FROM THE TIME of the ancient Greeks the notion of infinity has posed the most serious kinds of difficulties to mathematicians and scientists. There appeared to be no logical way to handle the idea of an infinite set and perhaps the principal reason for this was due to the fact that the notion of an infinite set is entirely foreign to our experience and environment. Trying to gain understanding of infinite sets by approaching them on the basis of the understanding we have for finite sets is impossible. The best mathematicians recognized this and, not knowing what to do, declared that mathematicians should not be allowed to become involved with infinite sets at all. The trouble with this is that most of the important parts of modern mathematics would be impossible without infinite sets. By the beginning of the nineteenth century mathematics was approaching a crisis point due, in large part, to the misuse and mistrust of infinite sets. Consequently, when in 1874 Cantor presented his ingenious and original method of dealing with infinite sets in a mathematically rigorous way, the effect upon mathematics was staggering. After some initial resistance, his ideas were accepted readily and work was immediately begun to reestablish the notoriously weak foundations of mathematics upon this new and precise theory of sets.

However, it was not long before weak spots began to show up in this theory and, in fact, work is still going on to shore up these logical weaknesses. But set theory is firmly established in mathematics now and will remain so. It is an indispensable part of modern mathematics. In this chapter we shall discuss some of the more elementary aspects of Cantor's theory of sets.

4.1 The Concept of Set

When Georg Cantor (1845–1918) presented his theory of sets, he wrote that a set was "a bringing together into a whole of definite well-established objects of our perception or thought . . . ." Now this can in no sense be taken as a careful definition of what we mean by a set of objects. This partial description does, however, hint at two important aspects of this concept. First, a set is a "bringing together into a whole." That is, a set is an entity in itself. While a set may contain many different and very diverse objects, when we think of the set of those objects we are thinking of a single entity. Second, a set is a bringing together of "well-established objects" and this means that when we want to talk about a specific set, we must have some way of determining which objects belong to the set and which objects do not belong to the set. For example, we may talk about the set of all digits because this verbal description of this set enables us to determine which numbers are in the set and which are not.

If we do not use the set concept except in natural and ordinary situations, then we may as well take the concept of set to be undefined; in such cases there is nothing to be gained by attempting to give a carefully drawn mathematical definition for the concept. In all of our work in this book, the concept will apply to very ordinary sets and so we need not be too concerned over the exact meaning of the term *set*. However, if we try to use the concept in less trivial and natural instances, then we can easily run into logical complications if we do not somehow restrict the meaning of the concept. In the next section we shall demonstrate the necessity for sometimes being very careful about how we use the term. Except for Section 4.2, however, we may use the term *set* freely without worrying about becoming enmeshed in logical contradictions.

We most often symbolize sets by capital Latin letters. Thus we may talk about the set W of all whole numbers, the set E of all even whole numbers, and the set D of digits. Objects belonging to sets are symbolized by small Latin letters. Thus we might talk about an object s belonging to a set S. To symbolize the fact that the object s belongs to the set S we write

$$s \in S.$$

The symbol $\in$ is read "is an object of" or "belongs to." This is an invented symbol, but it derives from the Greek letter ε (epsilon) which is the first letter of the Greek word for "is."

Example 1: If D represents the set of digits, then $0 \in D$, $1 \in D, \ldots, 8 \in D$, and $9 \in D$. But $10 \notin D$ and $11 \notin D$.

We can describe sets using the brackets { and } as illustrated in these examples.

Example 2: The set of all digits can be written as $\{0,1,2,3,4,5,6,7,8,9\}$.

Example 3: The set of all whole numbers can be written as $\{0,1,2,3,4,5,\ldots\}$. In this case we cannot hope to list all of the objects of this set, so the best we can do is to actually list enough of these objects so that the reader can get the idea of which objects the set contains, and then use the ellipsis symbol $(\cdots)$ to indicate that the listing is to continue in the manner indicated by the objects which were actually listed. The set of all even whole numbers would be described as $\{0,2,4,6,8,\ldots\}$.

Example 4: The set of all whole numbers less than 100 contains too many objects to be listed conveniently, so we write $\{0,1,2,3,4,\ldots,99\}$ instead. The ellipsis symbol indicates that some of the objects have not been written down.

There is one set that is unusual enough to deserve special attention. This is the set that we call the **empty set** and that, as its name implies, does not contain any objects at all. For example, the empty set is the set of all whole numbers less than 0. It is the set of all people in the United States who are more than 250 years old. This set is usually denoted by the special symbol $\varnothing$.

Exercises 4.1

1. Think of some words that are commonly used as synonyms for the term *set*. For example, a set of people who are related is sometimes called a *clan*.
2. Let A denote the set of cloth objects and B denote the set of white objects. Name an object x such that
   (a) $x \in A$ but $x \notin B$. **(c)** $x \notin A$ and $x \notin B$.
   (b) $x \in A$ and $x \in B$. **(d)** $x \notin A$ but $x \in B$.
3. Describe a set S that contains exactly four people. Then find two objects x and y such that $x \in S$ and $y \notin S$.
4. Use the bracket notation to describe the following sets.
   (a) The set of last words on pages 10, 11, and 12 of this text.

(b) The set of all whole numbers less than your age.

(c) The set of all whole numbers greater than your age and less than 10,000,000.

5. Let S denote the set of whole numbers for which the inequality $x - 3 < 10$ is a true statement. Insert $\in$ or $\notin$ in the spaces as appropriate:

(a) 3 [ ] S. **(c)** 5 [ ] S. **(e)** 13 [ ] S.
(b) 4 [ ] S. **(d)** 12 [ ] S. **(f)** 14 [ ] S.

6. The empty set may be described as the set of all unicorns in the Foosland Zoo. Describe the empty set using the concept of

(a) Whole number. **(b)** Disjunction. **(c)** Addition.

7. What is the difference between the sets $\varnothing$ and $\{\varnothing\}$?

8. Use the bracket notation to describe the set of whole numbers that are solutions of the inequality

(a) $x - 3 > 10$. **(b)** $2 - x < 5$. **(c)** $2x - 1 \leq 15$.

It is most often the case that all of the sets under discussion at any one time will consist of objects drawn from some all-encompassing set called the **universal set**. For example, throughout Chapter 3 the universal set was the set of all whole numbers. List the objects of the set S of all numbers that are less than 10 if the universal set is

(a) The set of all even whole numbers.

(b) The set of all whole numbers.

(c) The set of all odd whole numbers.

(d) The set of all whole numbers that are less than 5.

This exercise demonstrates the necessity for always making it clear just what the universal set is during any particular discussion involving sets.

10.* List the whole numbers for which the statement is true.

(a) x is less than 5 and x is greater than 2.

(b) If x is less than 5, then x^2 is also less than 5.

(c) Either x is less than 5 or x is greater than 5.

(d) It is false that x is less than 5.

Statements such as these are called **open statements** because they cannot be regarded as being true or false until x is specified to represent a specific number. The letter x is called the **variable** of each statement.

4.2 Some Paradoxes

In the last section we said that we were going to take the notion of a set as an undefined concept. We know that every deductive system must contain such undefined concepts, and since it is quite difficult to find a good definition of set in terms of more primitive ideas, we may as well start with set as being undefined. For most elementary purposes in mathematics, and for everything we have to do with sets in this book, this is a perfectly acceptable thing to do. But in the larger context of set theory generally, this does not present serious logical complications. If we do not somehow place a restriction upon what can be called a set and what cannot be called a set, then we run into logical paradoxes. In this section, then, we shall introduce the notion of a paradox and then show how an immoderate application of the term *set* results in a paradox.

A paradox is a seemingly self-contradictory statement. The logic used in mathematics is a consistent logic in the sense that this logic does not permit the existence of a statement that is self-contradictory. Hence whenever a paradox is found, it is necessary to explain how the paradoxical statement is only *seemingly* self-contradictory. In this section we are going to present a short list of famous paradoxes. However, we shall not explain them, because this involves a more sophisticated study of mathematical logic and we are not prepared to enter into these studies. We can only state that all known paradoxes have been explained to the satisfaction of most mathematical logicians.

Our first example of a paradox is perhaps the oldest and most well-known of all paradoxes. It is called the "liar's paradox." Consider the statement

THIS STATEMENT IS FALSE.

If this statement is in fact false, then it is false that this statement is false and so this statement is true. Hence if the statement is false, then it is true. On the other hand, if the statement is true, then it is true that the statement is false and so the statement is false. We see that if the statement is false, then it is true, and if it is true, then it is false.

Another ancient paradox involves a shifty crocodile and a clever father. The crocodile has stolen a child and has been hunted down by the child's father. The crocodile agrees to return the child to his father if the father can correctly guess whether or not the crocodile really will return the child. What should the crocodile do if the father guesses that the crocodile will not return the child?

Next let us consider the situation in the Foosland, Illinois, Public Library. This library, like all libraries, contains many catalogs of books. There is the card catalog itself and there are various bibliographies that are really nothing more than catalogs of books. For example, there is a catalog of the complete works of Alfred Lord Tennyson. Now this catalog obviously was not written by Lord Tennyson himself and so the catalog would not be listed in itself. But the catalog of books published in 1960, publication date December 31, 1960, obviously would list itself. That is, this catalog of books was itself published in 1960 and so it would list itself. Certainly most catalogs would not list themselves and these are by far the most common kinds of catalog. For identification purposes, let us agree to call such a catalog an *ordinary* catalog. An ordinary catalog, then, is one that does not list itself. The other catalogs, like the catalog of books for 1960, shall be called *special* catalogs. A special catalog is one that lists itself. It should be clear that every catalog is either ordinary or special, but not both.

As the librarian at the Foosland Public Library likes to catalog things, he undertakes to compile a catalog of all the ordinary catalogs in his library. We shall refer to this catalog as the Foosland Catalog. It lists all catalogs in the library that do not list themselves. But now the existence of this Foosland Catalog raises the question: Is the Foosland Catalog an ordinary catalog or a special catalog? It must be one or the other. You should try to decide which it is before reading further.

If the Foosland Catalog is an ordinary catalog, then according to what we mean by ordinary, the Foosland Catalog does not list itself. Now remember that the Foosland Catalog lists exactly those catalogs that are ordinary. Since the Foosland Catalog is not listed in the Foosland Catalog, the Foosland Catalog is not ordinary—it is special. What we have just proved is that if the Foosland Catalog is ordinary, then it is special!

On the other hand, if the Foosland Catalog is special, then it does list itself (this is what we mean by a special catalog). So the Foosland Catalog is listed in the Foosland Catalog. But every catalog listed in the Foosland Catalog is an ordinary catalog. Hence the Foosland Catalog must be ordinary too. This proves that if the Foosland Catalog is special, then it is ordinary!

We have shown that if the Foosland Catalog is ordinary then it is special and if it is special then it is ordinary. Something, clearly, is wrong here. This paradox is sometimes called the "librarian's paradox."

When we strip this paradox of its linguistic trappings, we see that it is not really a paradox in the field of librarianship, it is really a paradox in the theory of sets. The catalogs are really nothing more than sets of objects, the ordinary catalogs are sets that do not contain themselves as one of their own objects, and the special catalogs are sets that do contain themselves as one of their own objects. The Foosland Catalog is simply the collection (synonym for set) of all sets that do not contain themselves as one of their own objects. What the paradox shows, in set-theoretic language, is that there is no such thing as the collection of all sets that do not contain themselves as one of their own objects. It is not that this collection is the empty set or any other such thing—to speak of this collection is simply and purely nonsense. In the language of the paradox itself, it is completely meaningless to talk about the catalog of all ordinary catalogs. But, you say, how can it be meaningless to talk about this catalog—didn't you just do it? No. The phrase

The catalog of all ordinary catalogs

is just as meaningless a sequence of words as is the phrase

Cow hypotenuse girl swatch spigot horseshoe.

Bertrand Russell (English, contemporary) communicated a paradox like this one to the German mathematician Gottlob Frege (1848–1925) in 1902. Frege had just completed a huge work on arithmetic, his purpose being to

Bertrand Russell (1872–)

restructure all of arithmetic upon the "firm logical basis" of Cantor's set theory. The Russell paradox came as a real blow to Frege because it effectively negated his just-finished work. The paradox, in effect, asserted that Cantor's set theory was capable of giving rise to contradictions, and mathematicians abhor contradictions as nature used to abhor a vacuum. The subsequent revision of Cantor's set theory so that such paradoxes would be avoided is only now being completed.

Exercises 4.2

1. Referring to the example of the Foosland Library, can you think of any other catalogs besides the catalog of books published in 1960 that would list themselves? (You can make them up—they do not really have to exist.)
2. The expression, "The least whole number not nameable in fewer than twenty-two syllables" names a certain whole number. Since this whole number cannot be named in fewer than twenty-two syllables, the expression above, which names this whole number, must contain not fewer than twenty-two syllables. How about that?
3. There once was a town with a law that every male inhabitant of the town had to be freshly shaved each Sunday morning. But the town had only one barber who was hard pressed to shave all the men in just one morning. So another law was passed to the effect that the men who shaved themselves regularly had to shave themselves on Sunday morning too. The barber could shave those and only those men who never shaved themselves. This law worked and presented no problems and all of the people in the town were happy. What was the sex of the barber?
4. Call an adjective *autological* if it describes itself. For example, the adjective "short" is autological because it describes itself. So are "polysyllabic" and "English." Call an adjective *heterological* if it does not describe itself. Examples are "long," "monosyllabic," and "French." Is the adjective "heterological" heterological or autological?
5. Let $x = 1$. Then since $1^2 = 1$ it is true that $x^2 = x$. Then $x^2 - 1 = x - 1$. Now since $x^2 - 1 = (x - 1)(x + 1)$ we have $(x - 1)(x + 1) = (x - 1)(1)$ from which it follows that $x + 1 = 1$ by the cancellation property. So $x = 0$. That is, $1 = 0$. This paradox can be explained easily. Can you do it?
6. The tortoise was given a headstart in his race with Achilles. Poor Achilles—he never could catch that tortoise after that. For each time Achilles reached

a spot where the tortoise had been, the tortoise had moved on a certain distance. Thus Achilles was continually reaching places where the tortoise had already been and so he could never get ahead of the tortoise. Moral: The pursuer can never catch the pursued. [This paradox was given by Zeno (Greek, *c.* 450 B.C.).] Study this paradox.

4.3 Relations on Sets

Now that we have identified and discussed the objects of the mathematical system of sets, we may define some relations. One of the relations on sets is the relation of **equality of sets**. We say that two sets A and B are equal if they contain exactly the same objects. For example, the set of all whole numbers less than 10 is equal to the set of all whole numbers whose squares are less than 82. When two sets A and B are equal, we write $A = B$.

Example 1: The set $\{2,3\}$ has exactly the same objects as the set $\{3,2\}$—each set contains the numbers 2 and 3 and no other objects. Hence $\{2,3\} = \{3,2\}$. This example illustrates that the order in which the objects of a set are listed is irrelevant.

Example 2: The sets $\{2,3\}$ and $\{3,2,2,3\}$ are equal since they each contain the whole numbers 2 and 3 and no other objects. This example illustrates that in listing the objects of a set, it makes no difference whether an object is listed more than once. However, it is convenient to adopt the convention that we shall not repeat the listing of an object.

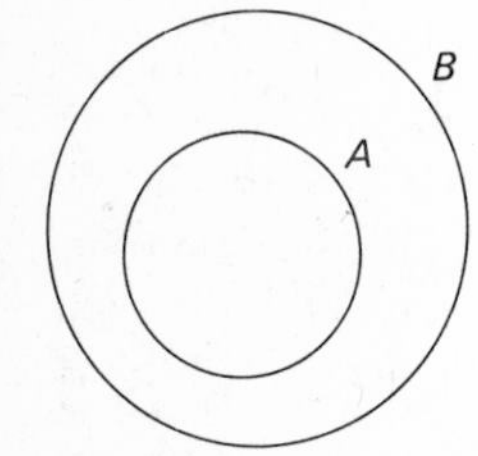

Figure 4.1

Another relation on sets is the **proper subset** relation. The sets $\{2,3\}$ and $\{1,2,3\}$ are related by this relation. That is, the set $\{2,3\}$ is a proper subset of the set $\{1,2,3\}$. More generally, to say that set A is a proper subset of set B means that every object of A is also an object of B and B contains at least one object not contained in A. The set $\{a,b,c\}$ is a proper subset of the set $\{z,a,b,d,c\}$ since each object of $\{a,b,c\}$ is also an object of $\{z,a,b,d,c\}$ and $\{z,a,b,d,c\}$ contains at least one object that $\{a,b,c\}$ does not. When A is a proper subset of B, we write $A \subset B$.

The relation of proper subset lends itself to illustration by pictures. In Figure 4.1 we have illustrated two sets A and B such that $A \subset B$.

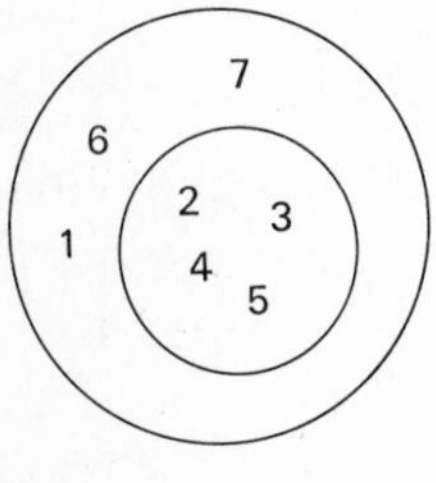

Figure 4.2

Example 3: The sets $\{2,3,4,5\}$ and $\{1,2,3,4,5,6,7\}$ are illustrated using the picture in Figure 4.2.

A third relation on sets is the **subset** relation. When we say that a set A is a subset of a set B, we mean that either A is equal to B or that A is a proper subset of B. The symbol for the subset relation is $\subseteq$.

Example 4:

$\{1,2,3\} \subseteq \{1,2,3,4\}$

$\{1,2,3\} \subset \{1,2,3,4\}$

$\{1,2,3\} \subseteq \{1,2,3\}$

$\{1,2,3\} \not\subset \{1,2,3\}$

The *subset* relation is a combination of the *equality* and *proper subset* relations in the same way that the *is less than or equal to* relation for whole numbers is a combination of the *is equal to* and *is less than* relations.

A fourth relation on sets is the **disjointness** relation. The sets A and B are called disjoint if they contain no objects in common. There is no special symbol to denote this relation.

Example 5: The set E of all even whole numbers and the set O of all odd whole numbers are disjoint sets. The set of all one-digit numbers is disjoint from the set of all two-digit numbers.

The illustration in Figure 4.3 illustrates a pair of disjoint sets A and B.

There is a fifth relation on sets called the "relation of being in one-to-one correspondence with" that we shall consider in Section 4.5.

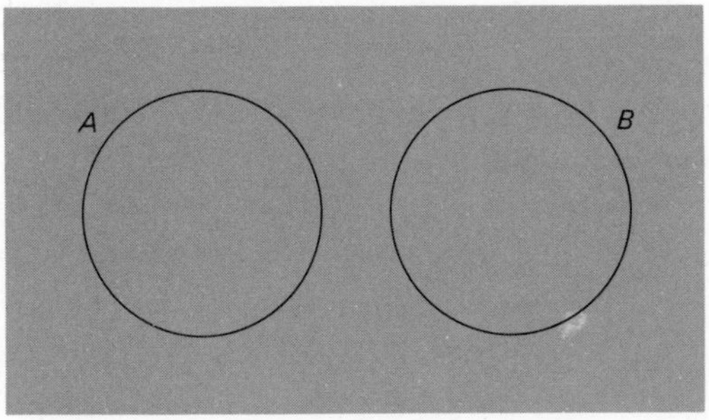

Exercises 4.3

1. Which of the following are proper subsets of $\{1,2,3\}$? Which are disjoint from $\{1,2,3\}$? Which are equal to $\{1,2,3\}$? Which are subsets of $\{1,2,3\}$?
   (a) $\{1\}$ **(e)** $\{3,1,2\}$.
   (b) $\{1,3\}$. **(f)** $\{2,6\}$.
   (c) $\varnothing$. **(g)** $\{5,6\}$.
   (d) $\{1,3,4\}$. **(h)** $\{3,1,5\}$.
2. List all the subsets of the set $\{1\}$. Of $\{1,2\}$. Of $\{1,2,3\}$. Can you make a conjecture as the the number of subsets of a set with n objects?
3. A subset of a set S that is not a proper subset is called an *improper* subset. If S is a set, how many improper subsets does S possess?
4. As in Figure 4.1, illustrate sets A, B, and C such that
   (a) $A \subset B$ and $B \subset C$. **(b)** $A \subset C$, $A \subset B$, but $B \not\subset C$.
5. As in Figure 4.2, illustrate the following sets.
   (a) $\{1,2,3,4,5,6,7\}$, $\{3,5,6\}$, and $\{1,2,3\}$.
   (b) $\{1,2,3\}$, $\{1,2\}$, $\{1\}$, $\{2\}$, $\{2,3\}$, $\{3\}$, and $\{1,3\}$.
6. Find a subset of all digits (the whole numbers 0 through 9) that is disjoint from the set $\{1,2,3,4,5,6,7\}$. How many subsets are there?
7. Is it possible to find a set that is disjoint from one of its subsets? (Careful!)
8. Fill in the table with *Yes* and *No*.

	Reflexive	*Symmetric*	*Transitive*
Equality of Sets			
Subset			
Proper Subset			
Disjointness			

9.* If we have a collection of two or more sets $S, T, U, V, \ldots$, then we say that these sets are **pairwise disjoint** if every two of these sets are disjoint. Are the sets $\{1\}$, $\{1,2\}$, $\{3\}$, and $\{4,5,6\}$ pairwise disjoint? Find a collection of six sets of whole numbers that are pairwise disjoint.

10.* Let us use the (nonstandard) term *overlaps* to describe the relationship between a set A and a set B when neither set is a subset of the other but the sets are not disjoint. For example, $\{1,2,3\}$ overlaps $\{2,3,4\}$. Draw a picture to illustrate the general relationship between sets A and B such that A overlaps B. Is this relation reflexive? Symmetric? Transitive?

11. Which of the following are logically equivalent?
(a) A is either equal to B or A is a proper subset of B.
(b) A is disjoint from B.
(c) A is a subset of B.
(d) A and B have no objects in common.
(e) A is not equal to B.
(f) A is not a subset of B or B is not a subset of A.
(g) A contains no object of B and B contains no object of A.

4.4 Operations on Sets

Having defined some relations on sets, we are now in a position to define some binary operations on sets. The operations that we shall discuss here are familiar to the reader already, although he may not have used these ideas in quite the same way that we shall use them.

The first operation on sets is related to the familiar operation of addition of whole numbers. The operation is called **union** and is performed on two sets A and B by combining the objects of the two given sets to form a new third set. For example, the result of the union operation applied to the sets $\{1,2\}$ and $\{3,4,5\}$ is the set $\{1,2,3,4,5\}$. The symbol that denotes this operation is the symbol $\cup$. So we would write $\{1,2\} \cup \{3,4,5\} = \{1,2,3,4,5\}$. Here are more examples.

Example 1: The union of the sets $\{1,2,3\}$ and $\{2,3,4\}$ is the set $\{1,2,3,4\}$. We could have written $\{1,2,3\} \cup \{2,3,4\} = \{1,2,3,2,3,4\}$, but we have agreed not to repeat any object in the listing of the objects of a set.

Example 2: $\{1,2,3\} \cup \{0,1,2,3,4,5,6\} = \{0,1,2,3,4,5,6\}$. This example illustrates that if A is a proper subset of B, then the union of A and B is B.

Example 3: $\{a,b,c\} \cup \varnothing = ?$

SOLUTION: Since the empty set contains no objects at all, this union is simply the set $\{a,b,c\}$.

We may use pictures to illustrate the union of two sets. The picture in Figure 4.4 is intended to show the union of two arbitrary sets A and B. The shaded region represents $A \cup B$.

Figure 4.4

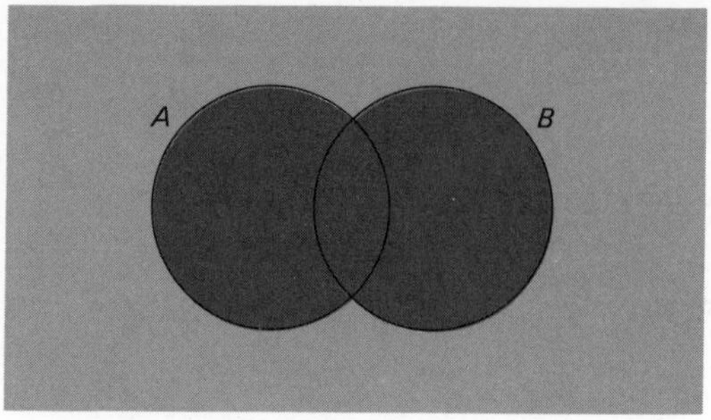

The second binary operation on sets that we shall need is called the **intersection** operation. The intersection of two streets can be thought of as that portion of the earth which lies in both streets at the same time—that portion of the earth common to both streets. If A and B are sets, then we say that their intersection is the set consisting of all objects common to both sets. For example, the intersection of $\{2,3,4\}$ and $\{3,4,5\}$ is the set $\{3,4\}$. We use the special symbol $\cap$ to denote this operation, and so we can write $\{2,3,4\} \cap \{3,4,5\} = \{3,4\}$. Here are more examples.

Example 4: $\{a,b,c\} \cap \{a,b,c,d,e\} = \{a,b,c\}$. This example illustrates that if A is a proper subset of B, then the intersection of A and B is the set A.

Example 5: If A and B are disjoint sets, then what is $A \cap B$?

SOLUTION: Since disjoint sets have no objects in common, $A \cap B = \varnothing$. The intersection of two arbitrary sets A and B is pictured in Figure 4.5 as the shaded portion of that illustration.

Figure 4.5

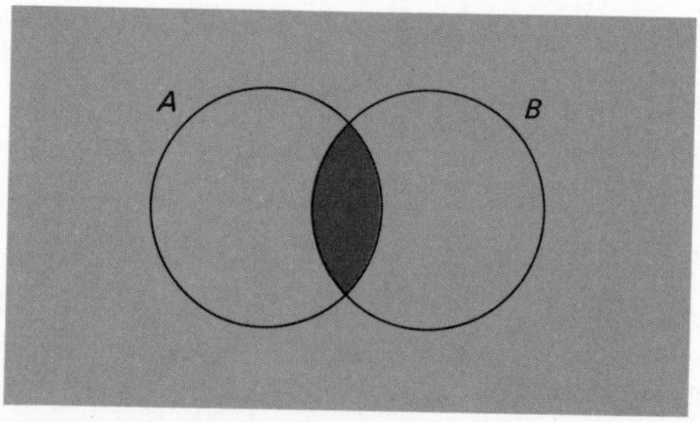

Exercises 4.4

1. Using the sets $A = \{1,2,3\}$, $B = \{2,3,4\}$, and $C = \{0,5,6\}$ describe the following sets by listing their objects.
   (a) $A \cap (B \cup C)$. **(c)** $A \cup (B \cup C)$.
   (b) $A \cap (B \cap C)$. **(d)** $(A \cap B) \cup (A \cap C)$.
2. If $A \subset B$ and $B \subset C$, then $A \cap B = ?$ $A \cap C = ?$ $B \cap C = ?$
3. If $A \subset B$ and $B \subset C$, then $A \cup B = ?$ $A \cup C = ?$ $B \cup C = ?$
4. If $A \cup B = B$ and $A \cap B = \varnothing$, what can you say say about A?
5. Which of these statements are logically equivalent?
   (a) $A \subseteq B$. **(b)** $B \subseteq A$. **(c)** $A \cup B = A$. **(d)** $A \cap B = A$.
6. Are the operations of union and intersection commutative? Are they associative? Give some examples.
7. Can you find three sets A, B, and C such that $A \cup C = B \cup C$ and $A \neq B$? What does your answer tell you about the union operation? Can you find three sets such that $A \cap C = B \cap C$ and $A \neq B$? What does this tell you about the intersection operation?
8. Using the sets $A = \{1,2,3,4\}$, $B = \{2,3,6,7\}$, and $C = \{2,4,6,8\}$ verify that the operations of union and intersection share the following two distributive properties:
   (i) $A \cap (B \cup C) = (A \cap B) \cup (A \cap C)$.
   (ii) $A \cup (B \cap C) = (A \cup B) \cap (A \cup C)$.
   These two properties show that each of union and intersection distributes over the other (on the left).
9. The kingdoms of Klutz and Smorg both claim sovereignty over the Duchy of Muck. The population of Muck is 13. Klutz has a population of 7,891 and Smorg has a population of 9,047. What is the combined population of Klutz and Smorg?

10.* Is there an identity object for the operation of union? That is, is there a set I such that $A \cup I = I \cup A = A$ for all sets A? Does the operation of intersection have an identity? (You should assume that we are asking these questions relative to some universal set U. See Exercise 9, Section 4.1, for a discussion of universal sets.)

11.* If A and B are sets then the set of all objects in A which are not in B is denoted by $A - B$ and is called the **set difference** of A and B (in that order).
   (a) Find $A - B$ if $A = \{1,2,3\}$ and $B = \{2,3\}$. If $A = \{1,2,3\}$ and $B = \varnothing$. If $A = \{1,2,3\}$ and $B = \{5,6,7\}$.
   (b) If $A - B = A$, how are A and B related?
   (c) If $A - B = \varnothing$, how are A and B related?

(d) Is the operation of set difference commutative?
(e) Using circles, illustrate the set $A - B$.

12.* Using the array of circles shown below, shade in the region which represents each of the following sets. These diagrams are called *Venn diagrams.*

(a) $(A \cap B) \cap C$.

(b) $(A \cup B) \cap C$.

(c) $B \cup C$.

(d) $(A \cap C) \cup (B \cap C)$.

(e) $A \cap (B \cap C)$.

(f) $B \cup (C \cap A) \cup C$.

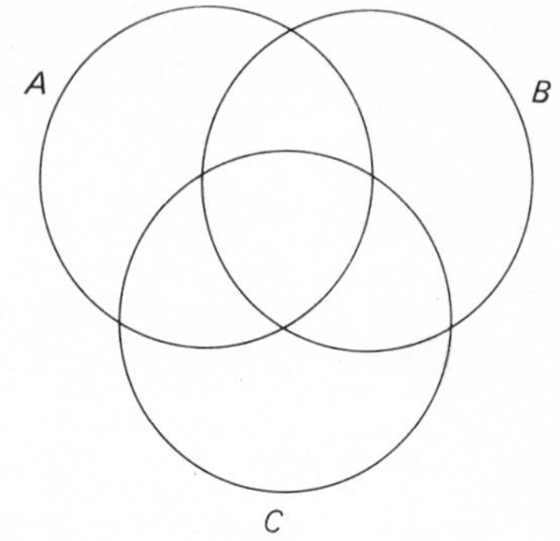

By comparing the shaded regions can you find any equalities between sets in this list?

13.* Zero is called an **annihilator** for multiplication in the system of whole numbers because $x \cdot 0 = 0 \cdot x = 0$ for all whole numbers x. Is there an annihilator for the operation of intersection in the theory of sets? That is, is there a set A such that $X \cap A = A \cap X = A$ for all sets X? Is there an annihilator for union?

4.5

One-to-One Correspondence

We have discussed the objects, some of the relations, and some of the operations of the mathematical system of set theory. In this section we shall discuss one more relation, a relation that is prerequisite to the study of "infinite numbers."

The objects of the sets $\{a,b,c\}$ and $\{1,2,3\}$ can be paired as shown in Figure 4.6. This pairing is one that pairs each object of each set with exactly one object of the other set. Such a pairing between the objects of the two sets is called a **one-to-one correspondence.** More generally, two sets A and B are said to be in one-to-one correspondence if the objects of the two sets are paired in such a way that each object of A is paired with exactly one object of B and each object of B is paired with exactly one object of A.

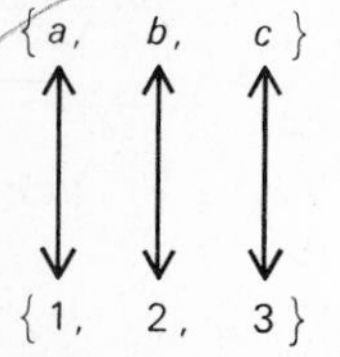

Figure 4.6

Here are some more examples of pairs of sets that have been placed in one-to-one correspondence.

Example 1: The set of letters of the alphabet and the set of nonzero whole numbers less than 27 can be placed in a one-to-one correspondence, as shown in Figure 4.7. The two sets are related to each other by the relation *is in one-to-one correspondence with.*

Figure 4.7

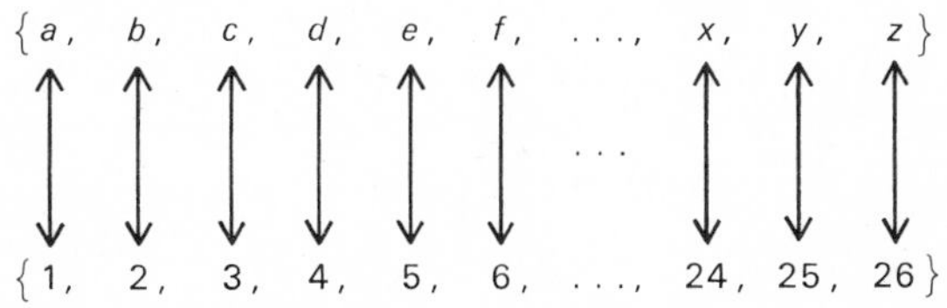

Example 2: There are six different ways to construct a one-to-one correspondence between the sets $\{1,2,3\}$ and $\{a,b,c\}$. These six different pairings are shown in Figure 4.8.

Figure 4.8

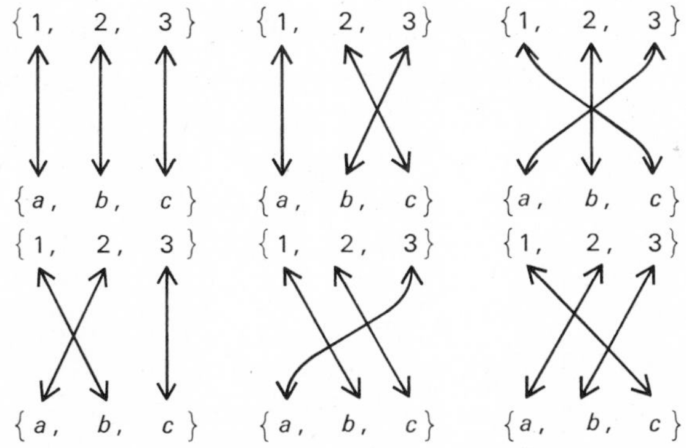

Examples 1 and 2 dealt with finite sets. More interesting things happen when we put infinite sets in one-to-one correspondence.

Example 3: The set of all whole numbers can be put into one-to-one correspondence with the set of all even whole numbers, as shown in Figure 4.9.

Example 3 demonstrates that an infinite set may be put into one-to-one correspondence with a proper subset of itself. This cannot happen with

Figure 4.9

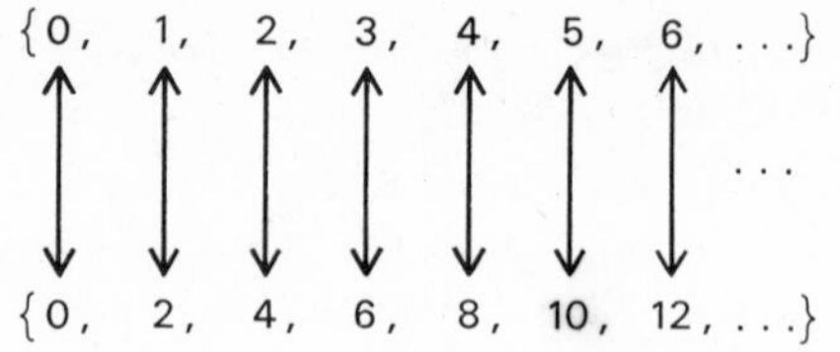

finite sets. That is, a finite set cannot be put into one-to-one correspondence with a proper subset of itself. (Try to construct a one-to-one correspondence between the set {1,2,3} and its proper subset {1,2}.) This idea was taken by Cantor to be the defining characteristic of an infinite set. That is, we define an **infinite set** to be one that can be put in one-to-one correspondence with a proper subset of itself, and we define a **finite set** to be one that cannot be put into one-to-one correspondence with any of its proper subsets.

Prior to 1872 it had been thought that the fact that some sets could be put into one-to-one correspondence with proper subsets of themselves was paradoxical. Indeed, if you insist that all sets have the same properties and obey the same laws as do finite sets, then the fact that some sets (the infinite ones) can be put into one-to-one correspondence with proper subsets of themselves is indeed paradoxical. But Cantor (and others as well) saw that this was not paradoxical at all—it was simply the characteristic of infinite sets which differentiates them from finite sets and hence could be taken as the definition of an infinite set. This was the first breakthrough towards a theory of infinite sets.

Example 4: Explain why the set of whole numbers greater than 5 is an infinite set.

SOLUTION: By definition of infinite set, the set of whole numbers greater than 5 is infinite because it can be put into one-to-one correspondence with one of its proper subsets. It can, for instance, be put into one-to-one correspondence with its proper subset {7,8,9,10,11, . . .} as shown in Figure 4.10.

Figure 4.10

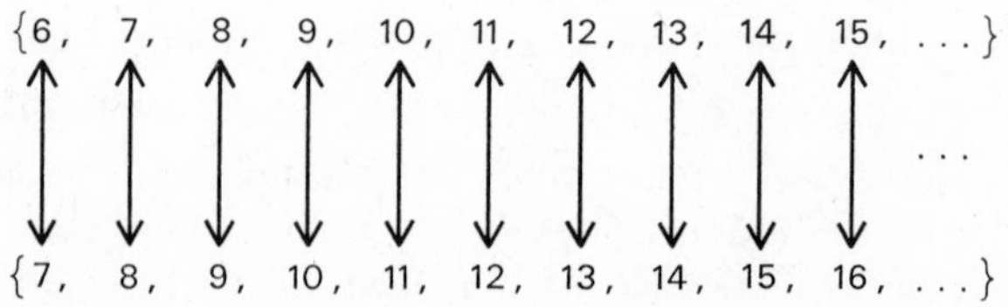

{6, 7, 8, 9, 10, 11, 12, 13, 14, 15, ...}
{7, 8, 9, 10, 11, 12, 13, 14, 15, 16, ...}

Example 5: Consider the parallel line segments $\overline{AB}$ and $\overline{CD}$ shown in Figure 4.11. Each of these line segments is a set of points and as sets these two segments can be placed in one-to-one correspondence in the following manner. Construct the lines $\overleftrightarrow{CA}$ and $\overleftrightarrow{DB}$ in order to determine the point P. Then pair points X on line segment $\overline{AB}$ and Y on line segment $\overline{CD}$ by drawing lines through P as shown. In this way each point of $\overline{AB}$ can be paired with exactly one point of $\overline{CD}$ and, conversely, each point of $\overline{CD}$ can be paired with exactly one point of $\overline{AB}$.

Figure 4.11

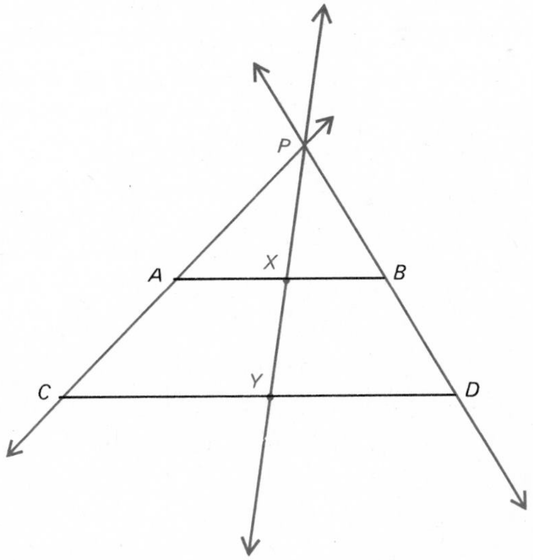

In the next section we are going to use the relation of *is in one-to-one correspondence with* to define finite and infinite cardinal numbers.

Exercises 4.5

1. Illustrate all possible one-to-one correspondences between the sets
   (a) $\{a,b\}$ and $\{1,2\}$. **(c)** $\{a,b,c\}$ and $\{1,2\}$.
   (b) $\{a,b,c,d\}$ and $\{1,2,3,4\}$.
2. Set up a one-to-one correspondence between the set of all whole numbers and the set $\{0,3,6,9,12,15,18,21,\ldots\}$. Under your correspondence which multiple of 3 would correspond to the whole number 145? To which whole number would the multiple 333 correspond?
3. Explain why the set of all whole numbers that are multiples of 3 is an infinite set.

4. Discuss the bigamy laws in terms of one-to-one correspondence.
5. What does the fact that your college has chosen to use a "number-name" of one kind or another to name you rather than to use your given name have to do with the idea of one-to-one correspondence?
6.* We call two sets A and B that can be placed in one-to-one correspondence **equivalent** sets. For example, $\{a,b,c\}$ and $\{1,2,3\}$ are equivalent sets.
   (a) Are equivalent sets necessarily equal sets? Are equal sets necessarily equivalent sets?
   (b) Which of the properties of reflexivity, symmetry, and transitivity are possessed by the relation *is equivalent to*?
7. Let $\mathscr{C}_1$ and $\mathscr{C}_2$ be circles of radius 1 inch and 2 inches, respectively. These circles may be regarded as being sets of points in the plane. Show that these sets of points can be put into one-to-one correspondence with each other. (Hint: Situate the circles so that their centers coincide. Then draw a half-line issuing from this center. The intersection points can be paired. Explain why this method gives a one-to-one correspondence.)

4.6 Cardinal Numbers

In this section we are going to introduce some of Cantor's "infinite numbers." These numbers are obtained from infinite sets in the same way that the whole numbers are obtained from finite sets. We shall begin, therefore, by considering finite sets.

Every finite set contains a certain definite number of objects. The set $\{a,b,c\}$ contains 3 objects. We call the number of objects in a finite set the **cardinal number** of that finite set. Clearly, the cardinal number of a finite set is a whole number. When a whole number is being used to indicate the number of objects in a finite set, we say that the whole number is being used as a cardinal number. When we say that there are 26 letters in the English alphabet, we are using the whole number 26 as a cardinal number.

There is another way to use whole numbers. For example, when we say that z is the 26th letter of the alphabet, we are using 26 to indicate the position of the letter z in an ordering of the letters of the alphabet. In this case, we say that we are using the whole number 26 as an **ordinal number**.

Example 1: The page number of this page refers to the position of this page in an ordering of pages. Hence the number of this page is an ordinal number. It is a whole number being used in the ordinal sense.

It is at this point that the concept of one-to-one correspondence becomes important. For what does it mean to say that two finite sets A and B have the *same cardinal number*? It means that the finite sets A and B can be placed into one-to-one correspondence with each other. That is, *the cardinal number of set A is equal to the cardinal number of set B if and only if A can be placed into one-to-one correspondence with B.*

We often talk of "counting" the number of objects of a finite set. What exactly do we do when we "count" a finite set? Suppose we look at the set $\{a,b,c\}$ and "count" its objects. We "count" this set by looking at a and thinking 1:

$$a \leftrightarrow 1$$

Then we look at b and think 2:

$$b \leftrightarrow 2$$

Finally, we look at c and think 3:

$$c \leftrightarrow 3$$

What we have done is to construct a one-to-one correspondence between the given set and the set $\{1,2,3\}$ and so we say that the given set contains 3 objects—has cardinal number 3. The counting process is therefore seen to be nothing more than a process that sets up a one-to-one correspondence between a given finite set and a set of the special form $\{1,2,3,4,5,\ldots,n\}$. After this correspondence has been constructed, we conclude that the given set has cardinal number n.

We have seen that every finite set has a cardinal number and that two finite sets have the same cardinal number if and only if they are in one-to-one correspondence with each other. Does this mean that only finite sets have cardinal numbers? Not at all. Cantor's primary contribution was to understand that every set, finite *or* infinite, could have a cardinal number and that the cardinal numbers of two sets, finite *or* infinite, were equal if and only if the two sets were in one-to-one correspondence with each other. Of course the cardinal number of an infinite set could not be a whole number; it would have to be some new kind of number— a new kind of number which we call an **infinite cardinal number**. For example, the set W of all whole numbers is an infinite set and so has a cardinal number which is an infinite cardinal number. We denote the cardinal number of this set by the symbol $\aleph_0$ (read "aleph-sub-nought"). The cardinal number $\aleph_0$ is an infinite cardinal number.

We have one example of a set of cardinality $\aleph_0$. Can you think of any others? Remember that two sets have the same cardinal number if and only if they can be placed into one-to-one correspondence with each other. So any set that can be put into one-to-one correspondence with the set W of whole numbers will also have cardinal number $\aleph_0$. Well, we have seen that the set E of even whole numbers can be put into one-to-one correspondence with W and so E also has the cardinal number $\aleph_0$. This situation is one that bothers many students at first and so perhaps we should discuss it more fully. We have here two sets W and E, one of which is a proper subset of the other, and yet they have the same cardinal number. This sort of thing cannot happen with finite sets. That is, if A and B are finite sets and if $A \subset B$, then the cardinal number of A must be less than the cardinal number of B. But if A and B are infinite sets, then simply because B has objects not contained in A does not necessarily mean that A and B have different cardinal numbers. The reason for this is that infinite sets can be placed into one-to-one correspondence with proper subsets of themselves.

Cantor was not the first to see clearly what an infinite set was, but he was the first to see that there were infinite sets having different cardinal numbers. In other words, $\aleph_0$ is not the only infinite cardinal number, it is only the smallest of infinitely many different infinite cardinal numbers. A larger infinite cardinal number is $\aleph$, which is the cardinal number of the set of all points on a line. Hence $\aleph > \aleph_0$. Still larger cardinal numbers can be obtained by using the following scheme: If S is a set, then we call the collection of all subsets of S the **power set** of S and denote it by $P(S)$. Cantor proved that the cardinal number of the set $P(S)$ is always greater than the cardinal number of S. Hence W, $P(W)$, $P(P(W))$, $P(P(P(W)))$, $P(P(P(P(W))))$, $P(P(P(P(P(W)))))$, ..., are infinite sets, each of which has cardinal number greater than the one that came before it. Hence there are infinitely many infinite cardinal numbers. We shall not prove this theorem, but let us consider an example of it when S is a finite set.

Example 2: What is the cardinal number of the power set of a set that has cardinal number 3?

SOLUTION: Consider the set $\{a,b,c\}$. Then the power set contains as its objects the following sets: $\varnothing$, $\{a\}$, $\{b\}$, $\{c\}$, $\{a,b\}$, $\{a,c\}$, $\{b,c\}$, and $\{a,b,c\}$. Hence the power set has cardinal number 8.

Example 2 illustrates the theorem that if S is a finite set of cardinal number n, then the power set of S is a finite set whose cardinal number is 2^n.

If you are left up in the air with this discussion of infinite cardinal numbers, you might better be able to appreciate the situation that a member of one of the primitive tribes who count "One—Two—Many" found himself in when first confronted with a missionary who talked to him about 300 years before the birth of Christ and 1,500 years after the birth of Christ. His experience had not prepared him to accept the idea of a negative number as an intuitively reasonable idea. Your experience has not prepared you to discuss infinite sets and their cardinal numbers because you have never seen an infinite set in your life. Your total experience in the real world lies with finite sets. For this reason, the study of such numbers (and we shall work with them only a little in this book) must necessarily be conducted on an abstract level. Only after extensive association with infinite sets can one claim any intuition concerning them. In fact, there is a kind of mathematician-logician-philosopher who claims that it is impossible to regard the notion of an infinite set as a legitimate concept in mathematics—or in anything else for that matter. Such logicians are called **intuitionists** and they reject the use of the infinite altogether. The reason that they are in a minority is that, generally speaking, mathematicians want to get results with their mathematics; they feel that certain results must be obtainable and that these results are not obtainable if one restricts himself by denying the use of infinite sets. Doing modern mathematics without infinite sets is like trying to swim in a lead life jacket.

Exercises 4.6

1. What is the cardinal number of the set $\{1,10,100,1000,10000,\ldots\}$? Show that your answer is correct by using the notion of one-to-one correspondence.
2. How many different ways are there to count the number of objects in the set $\{a,b,c\}$? In the set $\{a,b,c,d\}$? In a set of n objects?
3. In each sentence identify whether the whole number is being used as a cardinal number or as an ordinal number.

   (a) Ugh; I gained another pound.

   (b) I'll meet you at 6 sharp.

(c) You owe me $6.00.

(d) There sure are a lot of rooms in this building—there is Room 24516798013.

(e) I shot three on the third hole, four on the fourth hole, five on the fifth hole, six on the sixth hole, threw my eight clubs in the water hazard on the seventh hole, and was first into the clubhouse after 10 A.M.

4. Find three sets of numbers A, B, and C such that $A \subset B \subset C$ and all of these sets have the same cardinal number. Can you find such an example where any one of the sets is finite?

5. Let A and B be two sets each of which has cardinal number $\aleph_0$. Write $A = \{a_0, a_1, a_2, a_3, \ldots\}$ and $B = \{b_0, b_1, b_2, b_3, \ldots\}$, where the subscripts are used to indicate to which whole number the object corresponds. Set up a one-to-one correspondence between $A \cup B$ and the set of whole numbers in order to show that $A \cup B$ also has cardinal number $\aleph_0$.

6. Consider a square of side 1 inch and the circle of radius $\frac{1}{2}$ inch inscribed inside it. Show that these two geometric figures, when regarded as sets of points, have the same cardinal number. (*Hint*: You might reconsider Exercise 7, Section 4.5.)

7. Let S be a set containing 2 objects. Determine the cardinal numbers of the power sets $P(S)$, $P(P(S))$, and $P(P(P(S)))$.

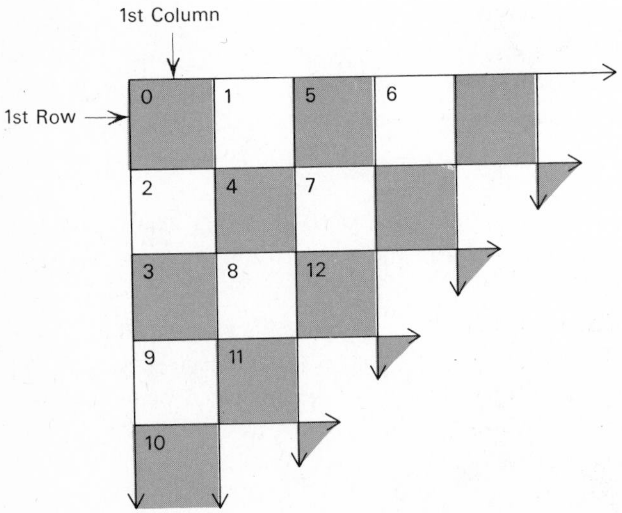

8.* The usual checkerboard consists of eight rows and eight columns comprising a total of $8 \cdot 8 = 64$ squares. Imagine a checkerboard consisting of $\aleph_0$ rows and $\aleph_0$ columns like that suggested in the drawing above. Using the concept of one-to-one correspondence explain why there are $\aleph_0$ squares in the first row of this checkerboard. How many squares in the first column? How many squares are there altogether? (To answer this question using one-to-one correspondences use the hint suggested by the whole numbers that have been put into some of the squares.) How many green squares are there? How many white squares?

4.7 Addition of Countable Cardinal Numbers

The cardinal numbers $\aleph_0$, 0, 1, 2, 3, 4, 5, ... are called **countable** cardinal numbers. All other cardinal numbers (for example $\aleph$ and all larger infinite cardinal numbers) are called **uncountable**. In this section we want to extend the idea of addition of whole numbers (that is, finite cardinal numbers) to include the infinite cardinal number $\aleph_0$. To do this we must first reexamine addition of whole numbers in a set-theoretic context.

Suppose that we want to add the whole numbers 3 and 4. How would we accomplish this using the ideas of set theory? In fact, how do we teach very young children to add these numbers? We might ask them to think of two sets, one set containing 3 triangles and the other containing 4 squares. We then ask them to form the union of these two sets and then to count the number of objects in the union. The cardinal number of the union will be the sum of the given cardinal numbers. Thus to add 3 and 4 we must find two disjoint sets A and B such that the cardinal number of A is 3 and the cardinal number of B is 4. The sum of 3 and 4 is then the cardinal number of $A \cup B$. (Note that A and B must be disjoint or else the union will contain fewer than $3 + 4$ elements. For example, if $A = \{a,b,c\}$ and $B = \{a,b,c,d\}$, then $A \cup B$ contains only 4 elements.)

Using this same idea, how might we add the countable cardinal numbers 1 and $\aleph_0$? We would first find two disjoint sets A and B such that A has cardinal number 1 and B has cardinal number $\aleph_0$. The sets $A = \{0\}$ and $B = \{1,2,3,4,5,\ldots\}$ will do. Then we form $A \cup B$ and get the set $\{0,1,2,3,4,5,\ldots\}$ of all whole numbers. This union obviously has cardinal number $\aleph_0$. Hence the sum of $\aleph_0$ and 1 is $\aleph_0$:

$$\aleph_0 + 1 = \aleph_0.$$

There is a story about a hotel with $\aleph_0$ rooms which illustrates the above addition fact. The rooms are numbered using the positive whole numbers (room 1, room 2, room 3, and so on). During the tourist season this hotel is almost always full, and in particular it is full on a certain day when Mr. Beaumont walks into the hotel and demands a room. The management would like very much to provide him with a room. Can they do it? Yes. How? The management calls each of their $\aleph_0$ guests and requests that each guest should move into the room whose room number is one greater than the number of the room in which they presently are staying. Hence the man in room 456 should move into room 457, and so on. After all this moving has been accomplished what is the state of the hotel? Every one of the old guests still has a room, but also Room 1 is now vacant. Mr. Beaumont can then be put into this room. We have added one more guest to the original $\aleph_0$ guests and we still have just $\aleph_0$ guests. That is, $\aleph_0 + 1 = \aleph_0$.

With reference to this same hotel, there was once a baseball game between two teams, each of which had $\aleph_0$ players. The first team arrived at the hotel and each player was given a room. Thus the hotel was filled up. Then the second team arrived and asked for rooms. The management was able to find rooms for these additional $\aleph_0$ players. How did they do this? The management simply had each player on the first team move to the room which had a number twice the number of his original room. Thus the player in room 415 would move to room 830, and so on. After the move had taken place each player of the first team to arrive still had a room and all of the rooms with odd numbers were now vacant. The players on the second team to arrive were then put into these odd-numbered rooms. This story demonstrates the addition fact

$$\aleph_0 + \aleph_0 = \aleph_0.$$

This introduction to cardinal arithmetic is the end of the trail for us. We shall want to refer to the cardinal number of certain infinite sets in later chapters, but we shall not become involved with cardinal arithmetic. The point that we have tried to make here is that such a thing as cardinal arithmetic (with infinite cardinal numbers) exists, is meaningful, and is important in mathematics.

Exercises 4.7

1. A hotel has exactly 1,000 rooms. On a night when all these rooms are occupied Mr. Beaumont arrives at the hotel and requests a room. What

does the manager tell him? How does this situation differ from the one described in the text?

2. Show how to use sets to find the sum of 2 and 5. To find the sum of 5 and $\aleph_0$. To find the sum of $\aleph_0$ and $\aleph_0$.

3. Using the interpretation of multiplication by a whole number as repeated addition, it is possible to give meaning to the symbol $n \times \aleph_0$ (where n is a whole number). What meaning can be given to this product?

4.* Use the checkerboard exercise (Exercise 8, Section 4.6) to explain why $\aleph_0 + \aleph_0 = \aleph_0$. (*Hint*: Consider the set of green squares and the set of white squares.) Explain how the standard checkerboard can be used to explain why $8 \times 8 = 64$. Draw an analogy from this, and using the checkerboard with $\aleph_0$ rows and $\aleph_0$ columns, could you say what $\aleph_0 \times \aleph_0$ should be equal to?

5 Two Geometries

THE TERM *geometry* is so general as to be almost meaningless. The fact is that there are many different kinds of geometry and in this chapter we shall look at two of these. We shall begin by considering the old and familiar geometry of Euclid and shall direct our attention toward the relations of congruence and similarity. These relations will be defined in terms of motions through space. Then we shall use these relations to introduce the notion of a geometric invariant. The notion of a geometric invariant will be used to define Euclidian geometry and to demonstrate how other geometries can be defined. Finally, we shall introduce (still using the notion of a geometric invariant) the most important of the geometries different from Euclidian geometry, the geometry called topology.

Throughout this chapter our approach will be entirely intuitive and informal. We shall base our arguments upon pictures and upon facts that we believe you will accept as being intuitively obvious or nearly so. This is in contrast to our study of the system of whole numbers in Chapter 3, where we based our arguments upon a predetermined list of properties possessed by that system.

5.1 Dictionary of Geometric Figures

Before we begin our study of geometry, let us introduce the geometric figures that we shall be working with. The definitions given in this section are for the most part informal and, hence, imprecise. This, however, should cause no difficulty in our application of these ideas. To supply carefully drawn definitions for these terms would in some cases be extremely difficult to do.

In our informal treatment we shall take the notions of **point**, **line**, **plane**, and **space** as undefined terms. We shall assume, then, that we know what these terms mean without defining them. Using these basic ideas (and others as well), we can go on and define other less basic concepts.

By a **geometric figure** we mean nothing more or less than a set of points in space. You are probably more inclined (by reason of experience) to think of geometric figures as having some definite and recognizable shape or configuration, but they may consist of any scattering of points either in the plane (planar figures) or in space (spatial figures). This emphasis on the set nature of geometric figures obviously stems from the relatively recent introduction of set theory into geometry. Euclid, for example, tended to think of geometric figures as entities in their own right rather than as particular sets of points.

Let ℓ be a line and let A and B be distinct points on the line. Then by the **segment** (or line segment) with endpoints A and B, we mean the set of all points of the line lying between A and B including the points A and B (see Figure 5.1). The line ℓ is denoted by the symbol $\overleftrightarrow{AB}$ and the segment by the symbol $\overline{AB}$.

Figure 5.1

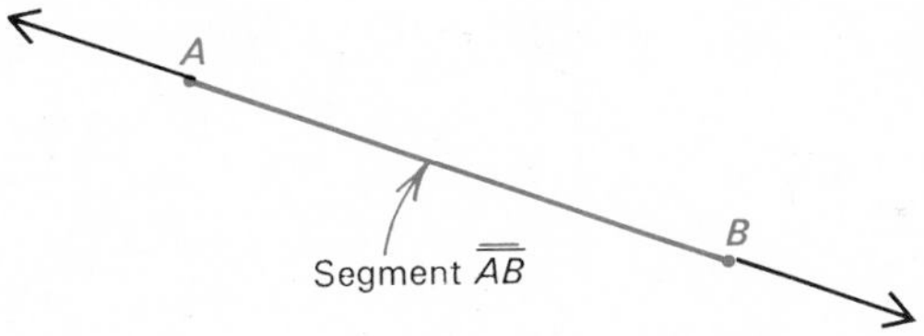

A concept more general than *line* is *curve*. By a **curve** (either in the plane or in space), we shall mean the trace of a moving point that moves in such a way that it does not skip any points. Examples are shown in Figure 5.2.

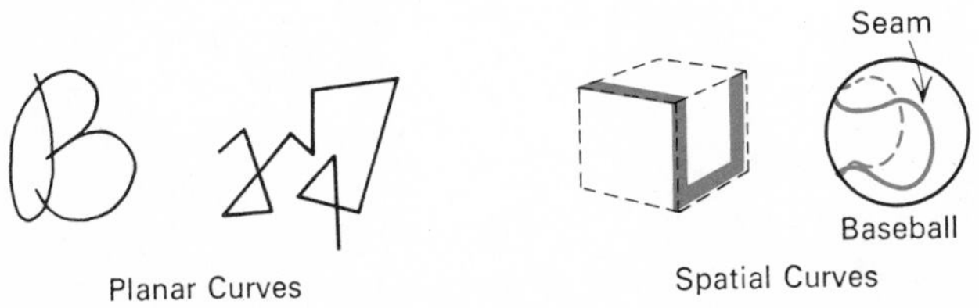

Figure 5.2

A curve is called **closed** if it is the trace of a moving point that stops at the same point at which it started. A curve is called **simple** if it is the trace of a moving point that, between starting and stopping, does not pass through the same point twice (see Figure 5.3).

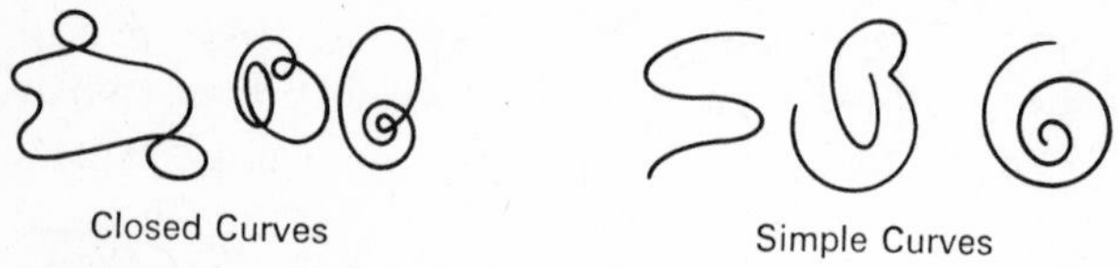

Figure 5.3

The most important kind of curve is a **simple closed curve**. A simple closed curve is both simple and closed and so it is the trace of a moving point that stops at the same point at which it started and which does not pass through the same point twice (see Figure 5.4).

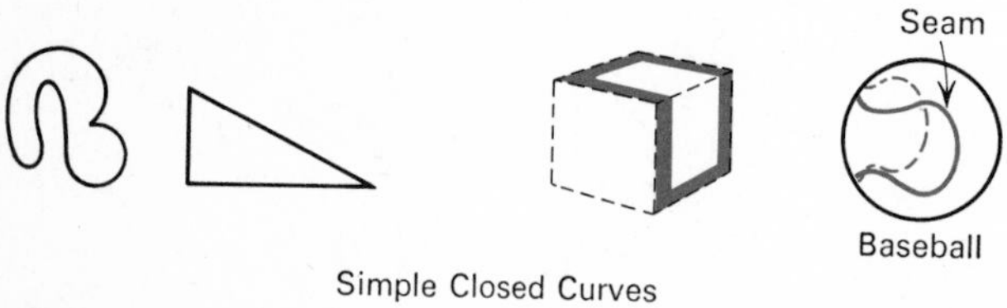

Figure 5.4

The property of simple closed curves that makes them important is exceedingly intuitive and is displayed in the following important theorem first discussed by Camille Jordan (French, 1838–1922).

The Jordan Curve Theorem. *Every simple closed curve in the plane separates the plane into three pairwise disjoint sets of points called the* **interior** *of the curve, the curve itself, and the* **exterior** *of the curve* (see Figure 5.5).

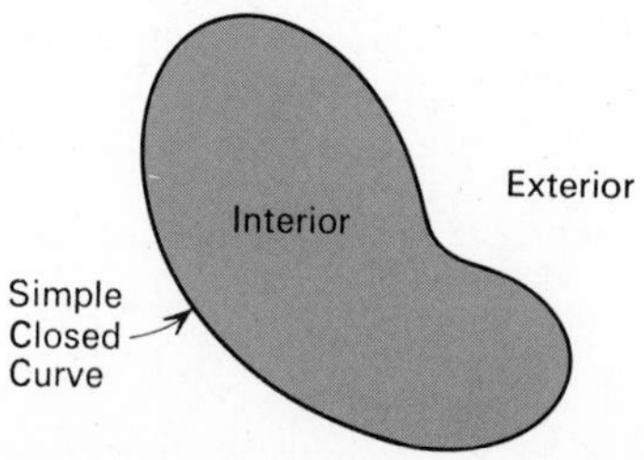

Figure 5.5

By a **planar region** we shall mean a portion of the plane that is bounded by simple closed curves. The curves that are the boundaries of these regions are not themselves a part of the regions. The regions we shall be working with most either consist of the interiors of simple closed curves or will be annular. Refer to Figure 5.6.

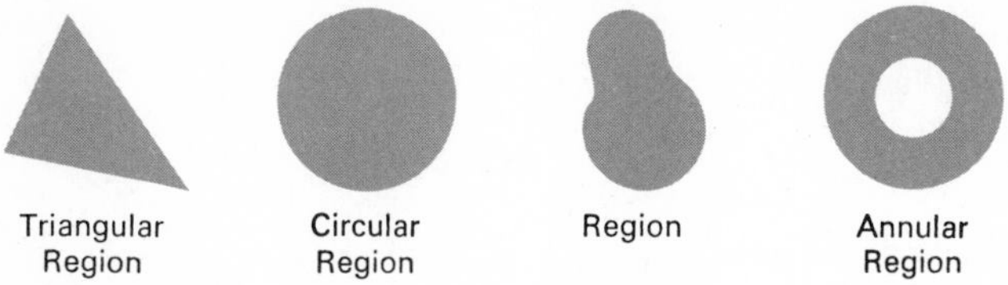

Figure 5.6

It is difficult to give a careful definition of a **surface** in space, but examples of the more common surfaces are easy to find. Spheres, cubes, and cylinders are surfaces. The surface that corresponds to the annulus in the plane is called the **torus**. These and some other surfaces are shown in Figure 5.7.

Figure 5.7

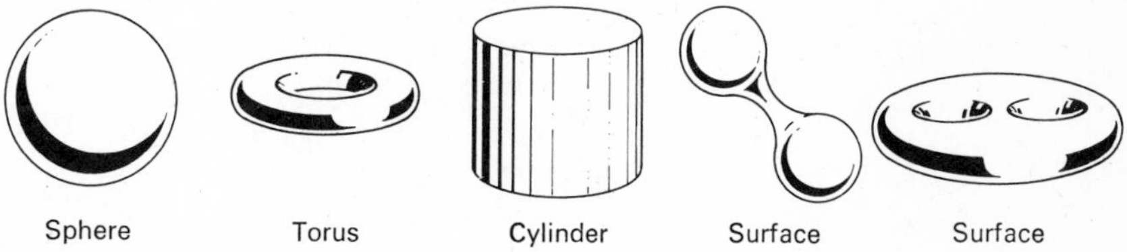

Each planar region is a surface when regarded as a spatial figure. The main thing to keep in mind is that surfaces are only "one point thick."

Exercises 5.1

1. Find examples in your environment of each of the following kinds of curves both in the plane and in space.
(a) Curves that are neither simple nor closed.
(b) Curves that are simple but not closed.
(c) Curves that are closed but not simple.
(d) Simple closed curves.

2. Identify to which of the four classes mentioned in Exercise 1 each of these letters belongs: A, B, C, D, E, F, G, H, I, J, K, L, M, N, O, P, Q, R, S, T, U, V, W, X, Y, Z.

3. Two lines in the plane must either intersect or be parallel. In space there is a third possibility. What is it?
4. Which of the following are true in space? If a statement is false give an example of its falsity.
   (a) Every two distinct lines are either parallel or intersect.
   (b) Every two distinct planes that intersect, intersect in exactly one line.
   (c) A line is uniquely determined by two distinct points.
   (d) A plane is uniquely determined by two distinct points.
   (e) Given a line and a point not on that line, there is exactly one plane containing both the line and the point.
   (f) Given two distinct lines, they determine exactly one plane.
5. Imagine a point situated at the end of your nose. From the time you got up this morning until the time you go back to bed this evening that point will trace out a curve through space. Will this curve be simple? Will it be closed?
6. A bus running on its route might under the right circumstances trace out a simple closed curve. Can you think of any other simple closed curves traced out by the motion of familiar objects?
7. Give a number of examples of different kinds of surfaces found in your everyday environment.
8. Let $\mathscr{R}$ be a region in the plane bounded by a simple closed curve and let ℓ be a line. Is it possible that
   (a) $\mathscr{R} \cap \ell$ might consist of a single point? (*Hint*: The curve that bounds the region is *not* a part of the region.)
   (b) $\mathscr{R} \cap \ell$ might consist of a segment?
   (c) $\mathscr{R} \cap \ell$ might consist of exactly two points?
   (d) $\mathscr{R} \cap \ell$ might contain (as a subset) a segment?
   (e) $\mathscr{R} \cap \ell$ might be the union of two disjoint sets?
9. Can you find examples of simple closed curves $\mathscr{C}_1$ and $\mathscr{C}_2$ in the plane such that
   (a) $\mathscr{C}_1 \cap \mathscr{C}_2$ consists of just one point?
   (b) $\mathscr{C}_1 \cup \mathscr{C}_2$ is a simple closed curve?
   (c) $\mathscr{C}_1 \cup \mathscr{C}_2$ is a closed curve?
10. Let $\mathscr{C}$ be some simple closed curve in the plane and let Y be a point lying in the exterior of this curve. Let X be point of the plane not belonging to the curve $\mathscr{C}$ itself. Draw the segment $\overline{XY}$. By counting the number of intersections this segment makes with the curve $\mathscr{C}$ you can determine whether X lies in the interior or in the exterior of the curve. How?

11.* We call a region in the plane **convex** if given any two points of the region the segment determined by them is contained entirely within the region. That is, $\mathscr{R}$ is convex if $\overline{XY} \subseteq \mathscr{R}$ for all points X and Y belonging to $\mathscr{R}$. Which of the regions in Figure 5.6 are convex? Which of the surfaces in Figure 5.7 enclose convex regions in space?

12.* Give an example of a convex region in the plane whose boundary is cut by every line in no more than two points. Can you find an example of a nonconvex region with the same property?

5.2 Congruence of Plane Figures

The objects of study in Euclidian geometry are geometric figures and, while we have identified only a few of these, we have enough to begin our study. There are two relations defined on geometric figures that are of particular importance in Euclidian geometry. We shall study the first of these in this section and the second in the next section.

The first relation defined on geometric figures that we shall discuss is the **congruence** relation. Loosely speaking, when we say that two figures are congruent we mean that it is possible to move one of the figures through space in such a way as to superimpose it upon the second figure. The pairs of figures in Figure 5.8 are congruent.

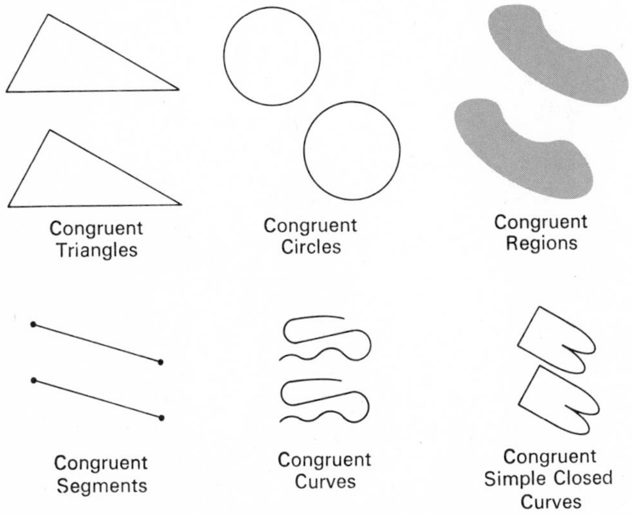

Figure 5.8

In the above rough description of what it means to say that two figures are congruent, we spoke of moving one figure through space in such a way as to superimpose it upon the second figure. We did not specifically say it, but you surely took it for granted that as the first figure is moved it should not be bent, stretched, shrunk, torn, or otherwise deformed in any way. In other words, as we move the first figure we must keep it rigid. Hence the kind of motion we are talking about here is called **rigid motion**. A rigid motion is described by saying that such a motion of a geometric figure preserves distances between all pairs of points of that figure. Thus if points A and B are points of a certain geometric figure and are a certain distance apart, then after that figure has been moved by a rigid motion, the points A and B are still that same distance apart. Here are some examples of rigid motions.

Example 1: The motion that moves a train along a straight track is a rigid motion. This particular kind of rigid motion is called a **translation**. When a sash window is opened or closed the window is moved by means of a translation. The motion the carriage of a typewriter goes through as it moves along is also a translation.

Example 2: Imagine a ring binder lying flat open. When a page in the binder (see Figure 5.9) is turned, the page is moved through space with a rigid motion.

Figure 5.9

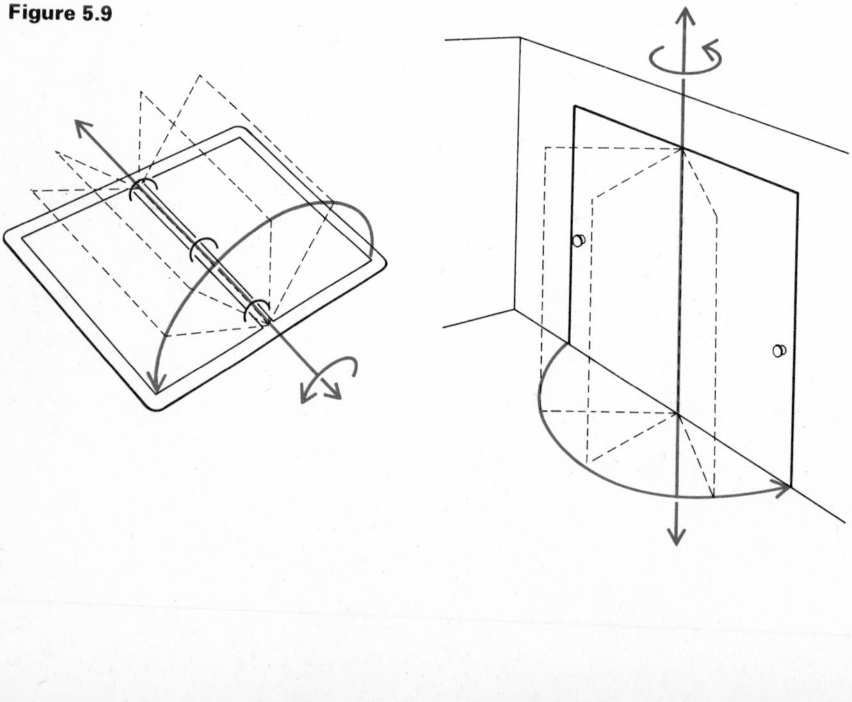

This particular kind of rigid motion is called a **reflection**. The page is reflected about a line running down the spine of the binder. When a door is opened all the way (180 degrees), the door undergoes a rigid motion that is a reflection about a line running down the door jamb.

Example 3: When a roulette wheel is spun, the wheel undergoes a rigid motion called a **rotation**. When a phonograph turntable is moved through a certain angle, the surface of the table is moved with a rotation. The motion here takes place in the plane of the table and the rotation is about the center of the turntable. The motion that moves the knob on a radio when stations are changed is a rotation.

In these examples we have described three distinct kinds of rigid motions: translations, reflections, and rotations. Translations and rotations do not take a planar figure out of the plane that contains it, but a reflection takes a figure out of its plane through space and then back into its plane again when the motion is completed. These three special rigid motions are important because of the following theorem.

Theorem: *Every rigid motion of a plane figure is a combination of one or more translations, reflections, or rotations.*

These three special kinds of rigid motions are therefore the basic building blocks from which all rigid motions are constructed. Here are some examples.

Example 4: Consider the two triangles shown in Figure 5.10. These two triangles are congruent because the left-hand triangle can be moved so as to coincide exactly with the right-hand triangle by means of rigid motions. In this case a translation alone will serve.

Figure 5.10

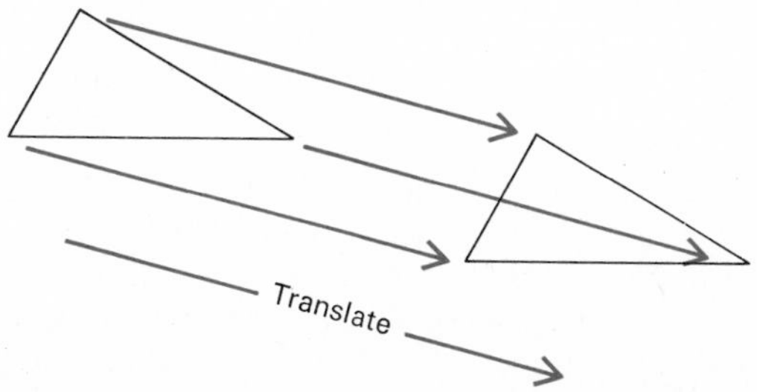

Example 5: The triangles in Figure 5.11 are congruent; thus it should be possible to make the left-hand triangle coincide with the right-hand one. This can be accomplished by a combination of a translation and rotation as shown in the illustration. First the left-hand triangle is rotated through a certain angle around the point X. Then the rotated triangle is translated until it coincides with the right-hand triangle.

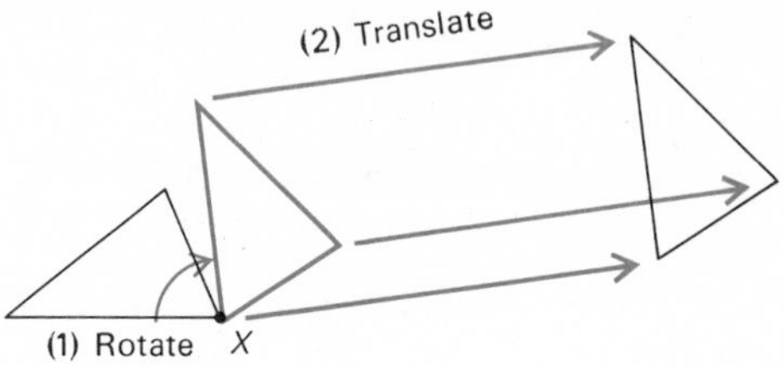

Figure 5.11

Example 6: The two triangles shown in Figure 5.12 are congruent, and it is therefore possible to move the left-hand triangle using a rigid motion so that it will coincide with the right-hand triangle. We leave it to you to convince yourself that this cannot be accomplished without using at least one reflection. One way to accomplish this (there are many ways) is to first reflect the left-hand triangle about the line ℓ and then to translate the reflected triangle in the indicated direction until it coincides with the right-hand triangle.

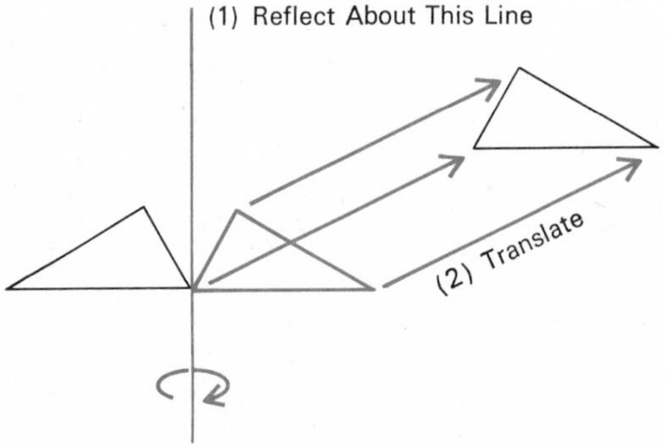

Figure 5.12

The notion of congruence in space is very similar to that of congruence in the plane and can be discussed equally well in terms of translations, reflections, and rotations. However, we shall restrict our attention to the plane.

We shall return to the congruence relation in Section 5.4 after pausing to discuss a second relation on geometric figures.

Exercises 5.2

1. Give some everyday examples of motions that are translations, reflections, or rotations.
2. The following pairs of figures are congruent. Describe a rigid motion that will make the left-hand figure coincide with the right-hand figure.

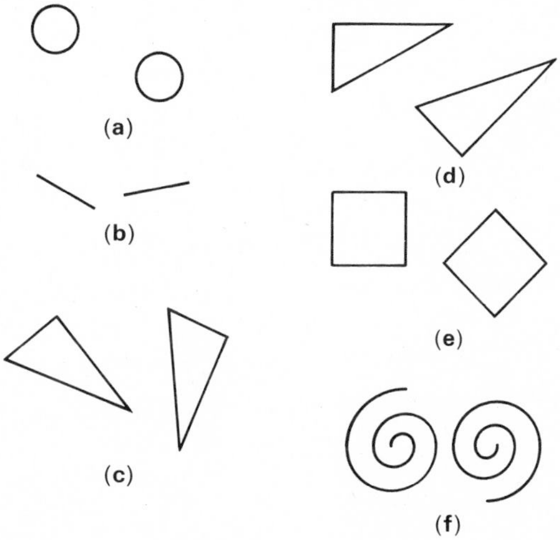

3. Draw two congruent triangles that can be brought into coincidence without using a reflection. Draw two that cannot be brought into coincidence without using a reflection.
4. Find some examples of rigid motions that you use in everyday life to make congruent figures coincide. (For example, stacking plates.)
5. Explain using rigid motions why the relation "is congruent to" is an equivalence relation on plane figures.
6. A triangle was moved by a rigid motion in such a way that exactly one point of the triangle was left unmoved—that is, was left fixed by the motion. What kind of a motion was this?
7. A triangle was moved by a rigid motion. In the process at least one point of the triangle was moved to a different position in the plane but two (or possibly more than two) points of the triangle were not moved. What can you say about the motion?

8. A triangle was moved by a rigid motion in such a way that three non-collinear points were left fixed by the motion. What can you say about the motion?
9. The result of performing two translations in succession is not necessarily a translation. Under what circumstances will it be a translation?
10. What kinds of rigid motions are needed to make two congruent circles coincide? To make two congruent squares coincide? To make two congruent rectangles coincide? To make two congruent isosceles triangles coincide?

5.3 Similarity of Plane Figures

The second relation on geometric figures that is important in Euclidian geometry is the similarity relation. This relation is a generalization of the congruence relation in the sense that any two congruent figures are also similar.

An imprecise but partially meaningful description of congruence is: Two geometric figures are congruent if and only if they have the same shape and the same size. (The trouble with this statement is that the concepts of "size" and "shape" have not been carefully defined.) In this same vein, we might say that two geometric figures are similar if they have the same shape but not necessarily the same size. The pairs of figures in Figure 5.13 are similar but not congruent. Our purpose in this section will be to formulate a more precise definition of similarity in terms of motions.

Figure 5.13

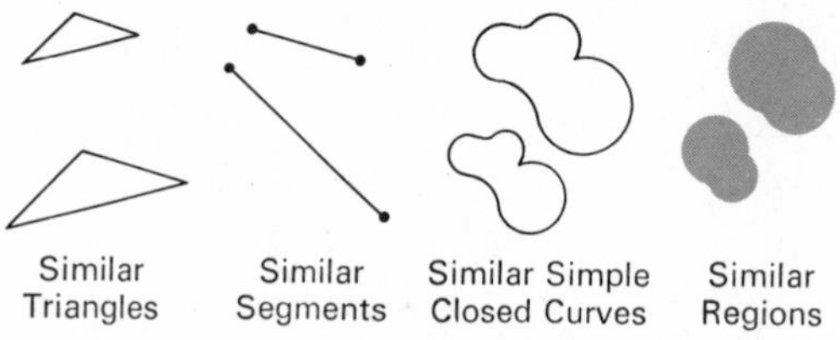

It is obvious that similar figures cannot be made to coincide using just the rigid motions. What is needed is a new kind of motion which, together with the rigid motions, can be used to make similar figures coincide, and clearly this new motion must be one that stretches or shrinks figures. This new kind of motion is called a "homothety."

A **homothety** is a motion that has the effect of moving the individual points of a geometric figure inwards toward, or outwards from, a fixed point called the **center** of the homothety. The motion of the points with respect to this center is *uniform* in the following sense. Suppose (Figure 5.14) that X and Y are points of a certain geometric figure and that this figure is to be moved by a homothety whose center is at the point C. If, before the homothety is

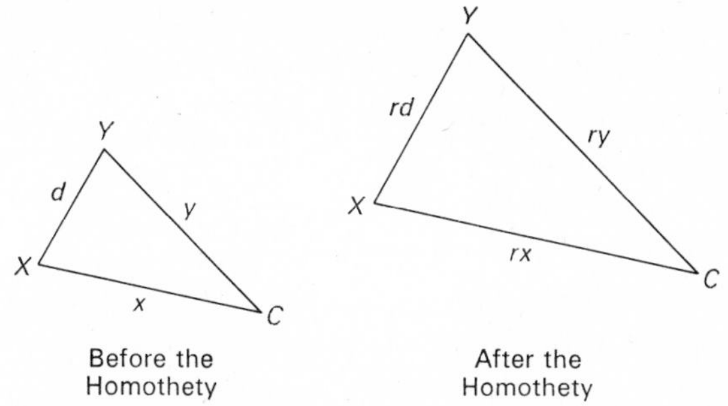

Figure 5.14

applied to the figure, the distances of X and Y from the center C are x and y, respectively, and if the distance between X and Y is d, then after the homothety has been applied, the distances of X and Y from C are rx and ry, respectively, and the distance between X and Y is rd, where r is some number. This number r is called the **ratio** of the homothety.

A magnifying glass accomplishes a homothety that enlarges figures. It moves points outward away from the central point P, which lies directly under the center of the glass (refer to Figure 5.15). The ratio of the distances

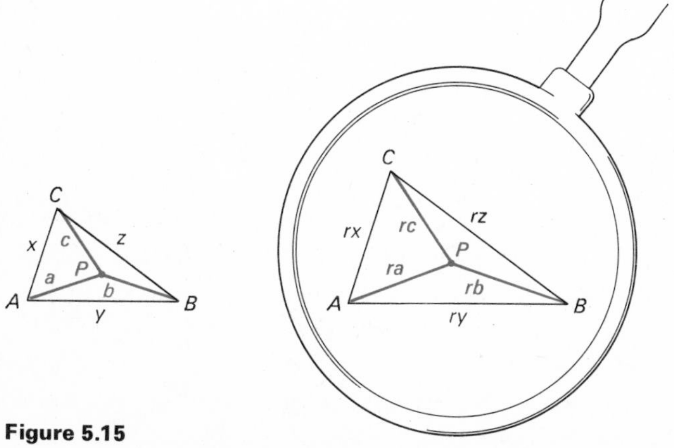

Figure 5.15

of the points from this central point when viewed through the glass to their distances from this central point when viewed without the glass is a measure of the magnifying power of the glass. The ratio of the homothety displayed in Figure 5.15 is r.

Now we can say what it means for two geometric figures to be similar. Two figures are **similar** if it is possible to make one of the figures coincide exactly with the other figure by moving it by means of a homothety and one or more of the rigid motions discussed in the preceding section. Here are some examples of similar figures and the motions that can be used to make one of the figures coincide with the other.

Example 1: The circle $\mathscr{C}_1$ shown in Figure 5.16 can be moved so that it will coincide with the circle $\mathscr{C}_2$ as follows. First, apply a homothety whose center is at the center, X, of circle $\mathscr{C}_1$ and whose ratio is 5:3. This homothety will produce an enlarged circle of radius 5 and center at X. Then a translation will move this enlarged circle to coincide with circle $\mathscr{C}_2$. Hence the circles $\mathscr{C}_1$ and $\mathscr{C}_2$ are similar.

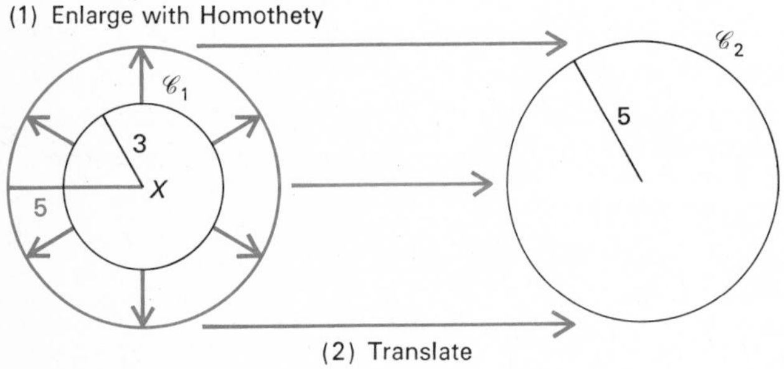

Figure 5.16

Example 2: The two triangles shown in Figure 5.17 are similar. It is therefore possible to make the left-hand triangle coincide with the right-hand triangle by applying an appropriate combination of a homothety and some rigid motions. We have first applied a homothety with ratio 1:2 and center at the point P. The resulting triangle is congruent to the right-hand triangle and so all that we need to do is to rotate and translate the shrunken triangle to make it coincide with the right-hand triangle.

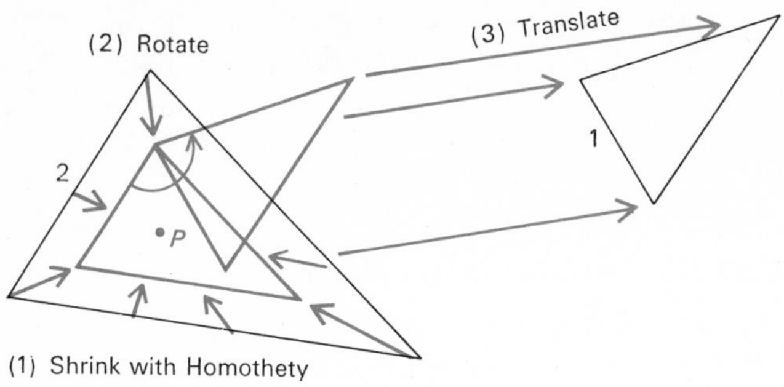

Figure 5.17

Applications of similarity are easy to find. We have already mentioned the magnifying glass. Scale drawings of all kinds, model airplanes and trains, dolls and toy soldiers, all utilize this relation.

The notion of similarity applies equally well for spatial figures as for planar figures. However, we shall deal only with similarity in the plane.

Exercises 5.3

1. Find some examples of motions experienced in everyday life which at least resemble homotheties.
2. The following pairs of figures are similar. Describe rigid motions and homotheties that can be used to make the left-hand figure coincide with the right-hand figure.

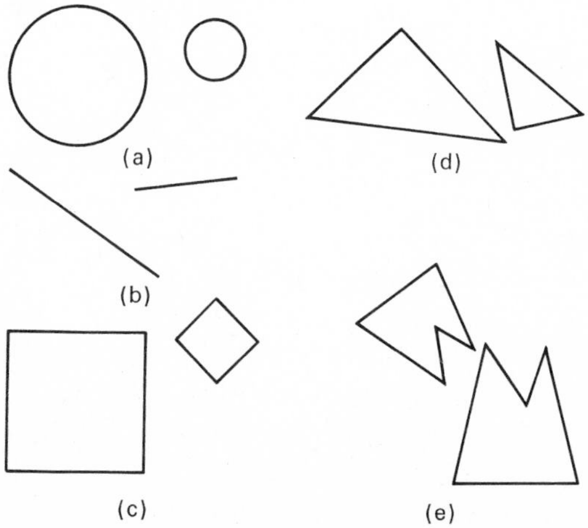

3. If the ratio of a homothety is greater than 1, then in what way does the homothety change the figure? What happens to the figure if the ratio is less than 1? What happens if the ratio is equal to 1?
4. Suppose that ℓ and ℓ' are lines such that ℓ can be moved onto ℓ' by a homothety. What can you say about the lines ℓ and ℓ'? That is, how are they related?
5. How is the idea of a homothety involved in maps? How is it involved in model airplanes?
6. Construct a square of side 1 inch. Now move that square by applying a homothety of ratio 2 and center at one of the vertices of the square. Now move the square again, this time with a homothety of ratio 2 and center at the center of the square. How do the two new squares obtained by moving the given square with these two homotheties compare with each other? Can you draw a generalization from this experiment?
7. When moved by a certain homothety two points of a figure were left unmoved. What is the ratio of the homothety? What was the effect of the homothety upon the other points of the figure?
8. Explain in terms of rigid motions and homotheties why the relation *is similar to* defined on the set of all plane figures is an equivalence relation.
9.* If $\mathscr{R}$ is a convex region and if $\mathscr{R}$ is moved by a homothety, is the resulting region also convex?
10. If a square is moved by a homothety of ratio r, then how does the area of the original square compare with the area of the square which results from the homothety motion?
11. Explain why, if two triangles ABC and $A'B'C'$ are similar, then their sides are proportional. That is, explain why there is a real number r such that $(r)(\overline{AB}) = \overline{A'B'}$, $(r)(\overline{BC}) = \overline{A'B'}$, and $(r)(\overline{AC}) = \overline{A'C'}$.

5.4 What Is a Geometry?

As we observed in Chapter 1, by the middle of the nineteenth century there were a number of different geometries being studied, among which were Euclidian geometry and the non-Euclidian geometries of Lobachevsky and Riemann. Each of these geometries was defined in terms of the axiom system upon which it was built. Then, in 1872 Felix Klein introduced a method for classifying geometries not according to their axiom systems, but instead in terms of what are called "invariant properties." In this section we shall describe Klein's codification of geometries and use this method to define

Euclidian geometry. In the next section we shall use Klein's method to introduce another geometry called "topology."

Suppose that $\mathscr{F}$ is a geometric figure and that we move $\mathscr{F}$ by using one or more of the rigid motions so as to obtain a second figure $\mathscr{F}'$. If $\mathscr{F}$ has the property of being a circle, then what can you say about $\mathscr{F}'$? Surely, $\mathscr{F}'$ is also a circle. We say that the property of being a circle is preserved by rigid motions and call this property a congruence invariant. A **congruence invariant** is a property of geometric figures which is preserved when those figures are moved by rigid motions. Some other congruence invariants are:

1. The property of being a triangle, square, circle, and so forth.
2. If two lines make a certain angle with each other, then when this configuration of lines is moved by a rigid motion, the angle between the lines is unchanged. Hence angles are preserved by rigid motions and so *angle* is a congruence invariant.
3. If a region has a certain area and is moved by a rigid motion, then the resulting region has the same area. Hence *area* is a congruence invariant.
4. If two points are situated a certain distance apart, then after these points are moved by using a rigid motion, they remain the same distance apart. Hence *distance* is a congruence invariant.

A **similarity invariant** is a property preserved by the motions that define the relation of similarity—homotheties and rigid motions. The properties of being a triangle, square, circle, and so on are similarity invariants. *Angle* is also a similarity invariant. However, *area* and *distance* are not similarity invariants since neither the area of regions nor the lengths of segments are preserved by homotheties. Every similarity invariant is also a congruence invariant (since properties preserved by homotheties and rigid motions are preserved by rigid motions alone), but not every congruence invariant is a similarity invariant.

The importance of these invariants was first discussed by Felix Klein (German, 1849–1929) in 1872. Klein defined Euclidian geometry to be the mathematical study of congruence and similarity invariants. That is to say, Euclidian geometry is the study of geometric properties that are preserved by rigid motions or by homotheties and rigid motions. Actually Klein was considerably more general than this. There are a wide variety of different geometries, Euclidian geometry being only one of them. Klein's codification of geometries according to their invariants goes something like this: Suppose that $\mathscr{R}$ is a relation on geometric figures.[1] Then it is possible to define this relation in terms of certain kinds of motions. (For example, the relation of congruence is defined in terms of rigid motions.) The properties of figures which are preserved by these motions are called the invariants for the relation $\mathscr{R}$. The study of these invariants is called $\mathscr{R}$-geometry.

As an example of how Klein's method of describing a geometry works, consider the (equivalence) relation of congruence. This relation can be defined in terms of the rigid motions alone. The invariants of these rigid motions are the congruence invariants. The study of these congruence invariants is called **congruence geometry**. Congruence geometry is different from Euclidian geometry because Euclidian geometry utilizes the similarity relation as well as the congruence relation.

As another example of a geometry, we may consider **similarity geometry**. We begin with the relation of similarity and then define this relation in terms of motions. The properties left unchanged by these motions are the similarity invariants; similarity geometry is the study of these invariants.

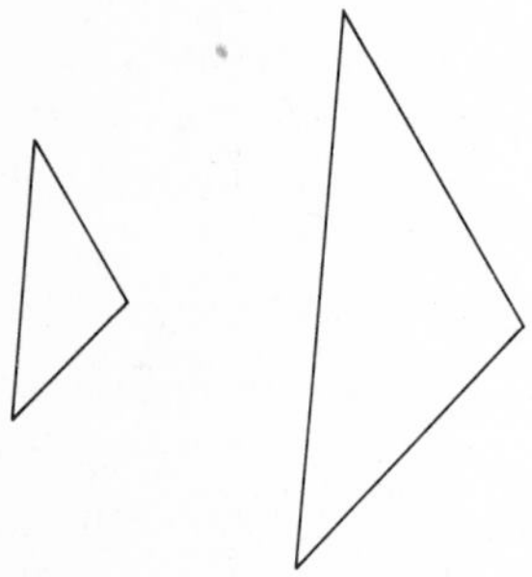

Figure 5.18

To illustrate the differences between congruence geometry, similarity geometry, and Euclidian geometry, consider the two figures in Figure 5.18. The congruence geometer would look at this illustration and see two completely different figures. This is all he could say about these figures—they are different because they are not congruent. The similarity geometer would look at these figures and tell you that they are the same. He could not distinguish between them because they are similar. The Euclidian geometer would look at these (just as you do) and say that while they are in one sense different figures, in another sense they are the same too. That is, the Euclidian geometer could see differences and similarities between these figures.

In the presence of Euclidian geometry, congruence geometry and similarity geometry are pretty much ignored. We have discussed them only because we wanted to show by means of very simple examples how Klein's codification of geometries works. There are a number of other geometries, however, that are very unlike Euclidian geometry and that have been very important in the historical development of mathematics. Of these we wish to discuss only the one that is far and away the most important, the geometry called *topology*.[2] We shall do this in the next two sections.

[1] For technical reasons the relation $\mathscr{R}$ must be an equivalence relation, but since we are not going to get technical we may ignore this.

[2] *Topology* comes from the Greek words *topo* (space) and *logia* (study).

Exercises 5.4

1. Which of the following properties are congruence invariants? Which are similarity invariants?
   (a) The property of being two parallel lines.
   (b) The property (of simple closed curves) of containing an area of 10 square inches.
   (c) The property of being an equilateral triangle.
   (d) The property of being a simple closed curve.
   (e) The property of being a closed curve that is not simple.
   (f) The property of being two perpendicular lines.
   (g) The property of being contained in the interior of a certain fixed circle.
   (h) The property (of rectangles) of having a length to width ratio of 2 to 1.
   (i) The property of being intersecting lines.
   (j) The property of being a segment.
   (k) The property of being a segment 2 inches long.
2.* Is the property of being a convex region a congruence invariant? Is it a similarity invariant?
3. The formula $A = lw$, which gives the area of a rectangle in terms of its length and width, is a statement from which kind of geometry: congruence, similarity, or Euclidian?
4. Is every congruence invariant a Euclidian invariant? Is every congruence invariant a similarity invariant? Is every similarity invariant a Euclidian invariant? Is every similarity invariant a congruence invariant?

5.5 Topological Equivalence

Of the geometries that are substantially different from classical Euclidian geometry, topology is by any measure the most important. Topology arrived on the scene about twenty years after Cantor's set theory and evolved from the work of a number of different mathematicians working in different parts of mathematics. Henri Poincaré (French, 1854–1912) is regarded as the principal developer of modern topology. Along with set theory, to which it is closely allied, topology has invaded all parts of mathematics and is one of the basic subjects upon which modern mathematics depends.

We are going to arrange our introduction to topology along the lines of Klein's definition of a geometry. We begin by introducing a new (equivalence) relation and the motions that define it. Then we shall look at a few of the simpler invariants for that relation. Topology is the study of these invariants.

Place a rubber band on a table and using your fingers move the rubber band around so as to deform it in various ways. For example, the rubber band can be moved into the shapes shown in Figure 5.19. Such deforming motions are

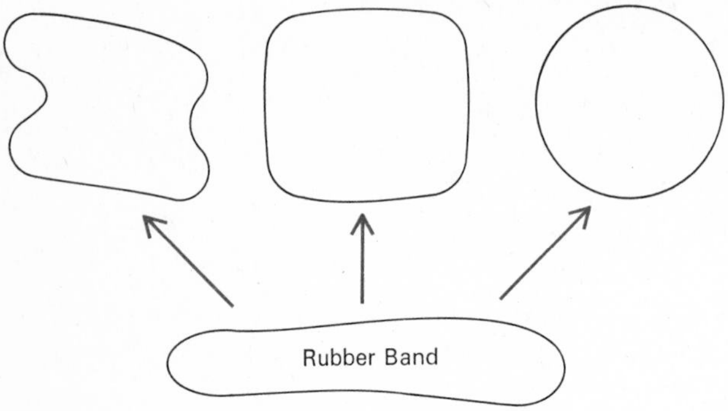

Figure 5.19

called **deformations**. Roughly speaking, a deformation of a figure is a motion that changes the shape and the size of a figure in ways subject only to the following three restrictions: (1) A deformation cannot puncture a figure. That is, it cannot remove a point from a figure. (2) A deformation cannot tear a figure.[3] For example, it cannot deform a circle into two separate circles. (3) A deformation cannot amalgamate points. That is, it cannot bring distinct points together into one point. For example, it cannot deform a line segment in such a way that it becomes a single point.

Here are some examples of deformations of planar figures.

Example 1: The left-hand region in Figure 5.20 can be deformed in such a way that, after it has been deformed, it will be congruent to the right-hand region. The deformation that is required is one that will shrink the "ends" of the region and stretch its "middle."

Figure 5.20

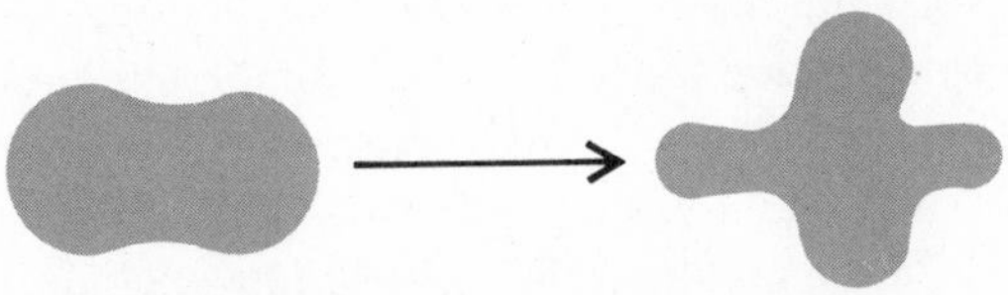

[3] It is permissible to tear a figure, deform it, and then repair the tear so that the edges fit together exactly as they did before the tear was made. We shall, however, not become involved with such deformations in our work.

Example 2: By appropriately deforming the figure on the left in Figure 5.21, it can be made congruent to the figure on the right. This is accomplished by deforming the circle into a triangle, stretching and bending the short vertical segment, and shrinking the longer horizontal segment.

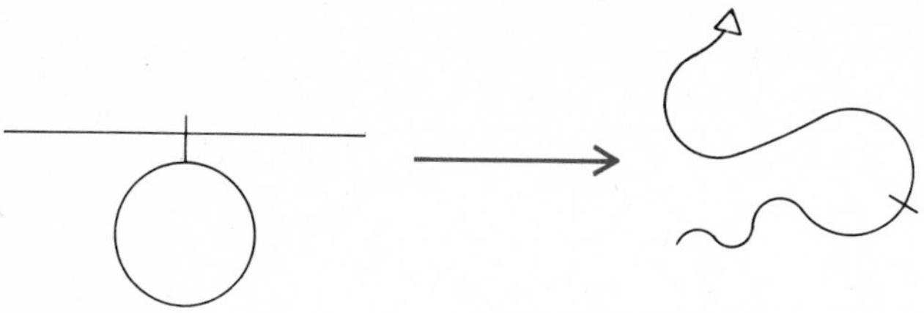

Figure 5.21

Example 3: In Figure 5.22, figure $\mathscr{A}$ can be deformed so as to be congruent to figure $\mathscr{B}$, but cannot be deformed (without amalgamating points) so as to be congruent to figure $\mathscr{C}$.

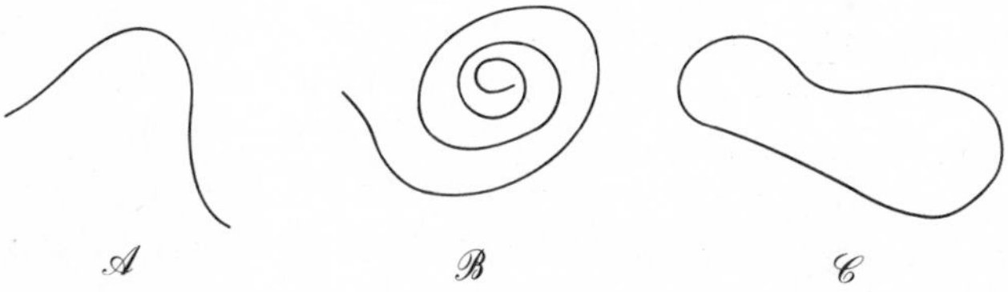

Figure 5.22

When two figures can be made to coincide using rigid motions, they are called congruent. When they can be made to coincide using homotheties and rigid motions, they are called similar. When they can be made to coincide using deformations and rigid motions, they are called **topologically equivalent.** Here are more examples of topologically equivalent figures.

Example 4: The pairs of figures in Figure 5.23 are topologically equivalent.

Figure 5.23

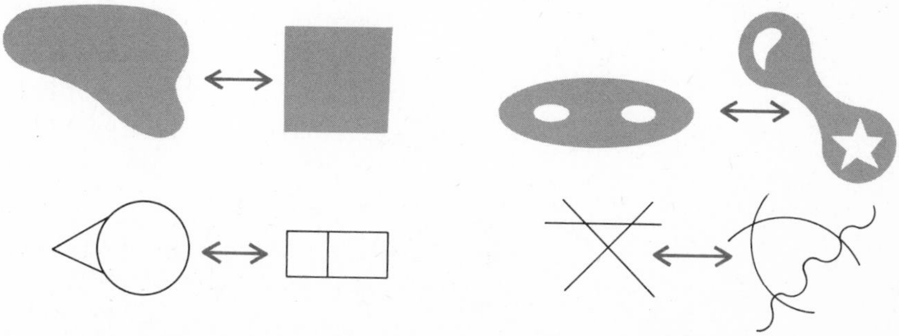

Example 5: The pairs of figures in Figure 5.24 are not topologically equivalent. In each case the left-hand figure could be deformed into the right-hand figure only by either puncturing the figure, tearing the figure, or amalgamating some points of the figure.

Figure 5.24

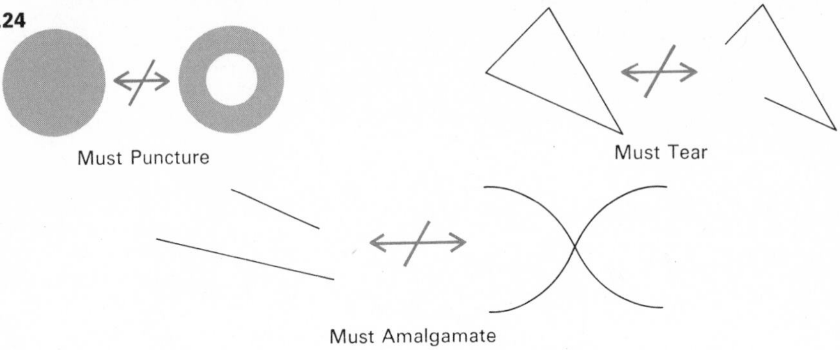

If a congruence geometer is a person who cannot tell the difference between two circles of radius one inch, and if a similarity geometer is a person who cannot tell the difference between a circle of radius one inch and a circle of radius two inches, then a topologist is a person who cannot tell the difference between a circle and a square. This is because a circle and a square are topologically equivalent. A topologist can tell the difference between two geometric figures only if those figures are not topologically equivalent. Thus a topologist should not even be able to read because he cannot tell the difference between the letters C, L, M, N, S, U, V, W, and Z. These letters are all topologically equivalent and so look the same to the topologist.

Now we can list some of the invariants of the relation of topological equivalence. Here is a partial list of such invariant properties.

1. *The property of being a simple closed curve.* (A curve is a simple closed curve if and only if it is topologically equivalent to the circle.)
2. *The property of being* **simply connected**. A region (in the plane) is called simply connected if every simple closed curve contained within the region can be shrunk to a point without leaving the region. In Figure 5.25 the region $\mathscr{A}$ is simply connected whereas region $\mathscr{B}$ is not.
3. *The property of containing a circular region.* In Figure 5.26 region $\mathscr{A}$ contains a circular region while curve $\mathscr{B}$ does not. Hence region $\mathscr{A}$ is not topologically equivalent to curve $\mathscr{B}$.

Figure 5.25

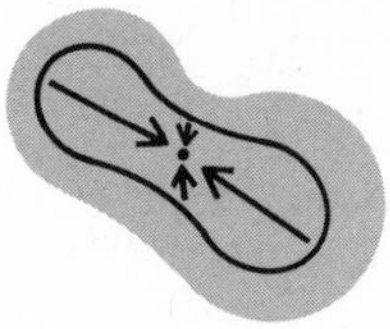

Region $\mathscr{A}$

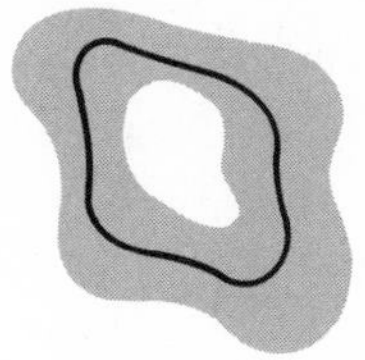

Region $\mathscr{B}$

Figure 5.26

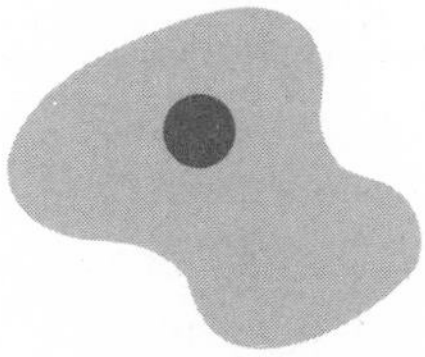

Region $\mathscr{A}$

Curve $\mathscr{B}$

4. *The property of consisting of a finite set of points.* Since a deformation cannot amalgamate points, if two figures are topologically equivalent, then each figure must contain the same (cardinal) number of points. Hence, if one figure is finite, then so is the other.
5. *The property of being* **arcwise connected**. A planar region is called arcwise connected if it is possible to join every point of the region to every other point of the region by an arc (that is, a curve) that is contained entirely inside the region. The interior of a circle is arcwise connected, but the interior of a figure eight curve is not.

Topology deals with only the most general properties of geometric figures in contrast to Euclidean geometry, which becomes deeply enmeshed with rather precise properties of figures. For example, in Euclidean geometry we differentiate between equilateral triangles, isosceles triangles, right triangles, acute triangles, obtuse triangles, and so on. But in topology these triangles are indistinguishable from one another. More than this, in topology we do not even distinguish between triangles and circles. Hence a standard theorem from Euclidean geometry such as, "the diagonals of a rectangle bisect each other" or "the sum of the angles of a triangle is 180°" is meaningless in topology. In the study of topology, there is no such figure as a rectangle or a triangle; the nearest we can get to these figures is a simple closed curve. But a theorem from topology, on the other hand, will also make sense in Euclidean geometry. An example is the Jordan curve theorem mentioned in Section 5.1. This theorem is really a topological theorem, because it deals only with ideas that are meaningful in topology: simple closed curves, interiors, and exteriors.

In the next section we shall discuss two of the more interesting surfaces that are important in topology.

Exercises 5.5

1. Give some examples of deformations that are used in everyday life. (For example, crumpling up a piece of paper.)
2. Is a rigid motion a topological deformation? Is a homothety a topological deformation?
3. Find topologically equivalent figures.
4. Explain why the relation *is topologically equivalent to* is an equivalence relation on the collection of all figures.

(a)

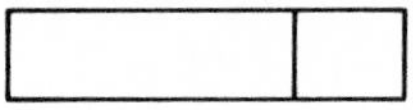

(e)

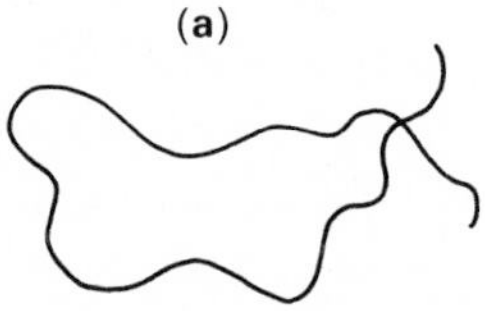

(b)

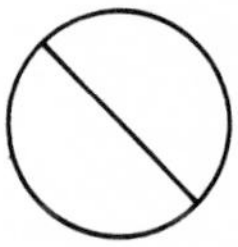

(f)

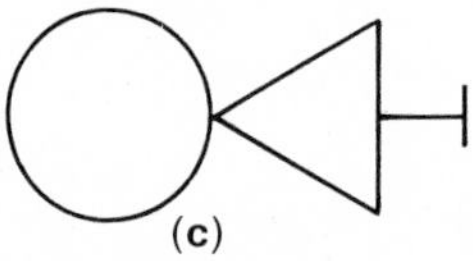

(c)

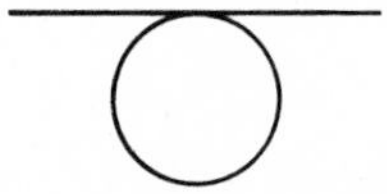

(g)

(d)

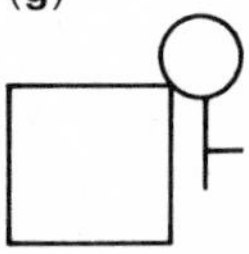

(h)

5. Draw pictures of three curves topologically equivalent to a figure eight. To a circle. To the block letter A. Describe a surface that is topologically equivalent to the surface of a donut.

6. Separate the letters of the alphabet (when written as simple block letters) into pairwise disjoint sets such that no letter from one set is topologically equivalent to any letter of any different set, but any two letters in the same set are topologically equivalent. Use the letters in Exercise 2, Section 5.1.
7. Which of the properties listed in Exercise 1, Section 5.4, are topological invariants?
8.* Is the property of being a convex region a topological invariant? Is a convex region always simply connected? Is a simply connected region necessarily convex? Is a convex region necessarily arcwise connected? Is every arcwise connected region convex?
9. Is every arcwise connected region simply connected? Give an example.
10. If a topologist is a person who can't tell the difference between two equivalent figures, then why is a topologist a person who can't tell the difference between a donut and a coffee cup?
11. Is the interior of a simple closed curve simply connected? Is it arcwise connected? Is the exterior simply connected? Is it arcwise connected?
12. A problem of great historical interest to topology is the problem of the **Konigsberg bridges**. (Konigsberg is now called Kaliningrad and lies in East Germany.) Through the city ran two branches of a river at whose confluence there was an island. (See the drawing below.) Seven bridges connected the island to the banks. The problem was to try to find a path that would cross each bridge once and only once. Is there such a path?

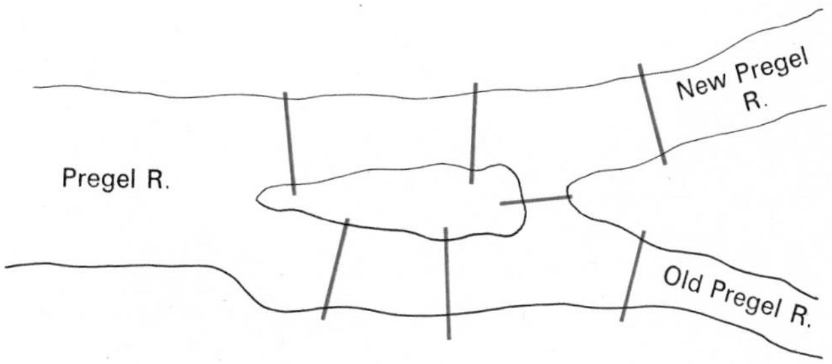

13.* Imagine that each country is a connected land area (not like Michigan or Hawaii) and that we are to make a map using the least possible number of colors. If two countries share a border consisting of a curve then they must be colored differently. However, if they only share a border consisting of a point (like Arizona and Colorado), then they may be colored the same. The **Four-Color Problem** asks whether every map can be made with at most four colors. (This can be any imaginary map—it does not have to be a map of the real world.) There are maps that require four colors and no one has ever found a map that required five colors, but neither has anyone been able to prove that only four colors would ever be needed. This is one of the famous unsolved problems of topology and has been under study since about 1840. Show that any map of the United States would require four colors. (*Hint:* Daniel Boone or slot machines.)

14.* Some states like Nevada and Colorado are arcwise connected. Some are convex. Some are not convex.

(a) Name some states that are convex and some that are not.

(b) Name some states that are arcwise connected and some that are not.

(c) Are there any states that are not simply connected?

(d) Can you think of any countries in the world that are not simply connected? That are not arcwise connected?

5.6 One-Sided Surfaces

Compared with the kinds of geometric figures dealt with in topology, most of the figures of importance in Euclidean geometry are prosaic indeed. In this section we shall discuss two "topological" surfaces, each of which has only one side. These one-sided surfaces were not even invented until mathematicians began to study topology, there being no motivation to study such exotic figures in Euclidean geometry. Euclidean geometry, after all, derives from the need to find a mathematical representation for the useful physical objects we experience in our real world. Topology is not restricted to this "practical" sort of figure but may deal with any sort of figures, whether they have a practical existence in our experience or not.

Make two pieces of paper about 2 inches wide and 24 inches long and label the vertices as shown in Figure 5.27(a). If these vertices are joined as shown in Figure 5.27(b) and then taped together, the surface that results is called a **right circular cylinder.** This is a very familiar surface, which is of considerable importance in Euclidean geometry. This surface has two sides and two edges, as shown in the illustration. In order to move from one side to the other, it is necessary to cross over one of the edges.

Figure 5.27

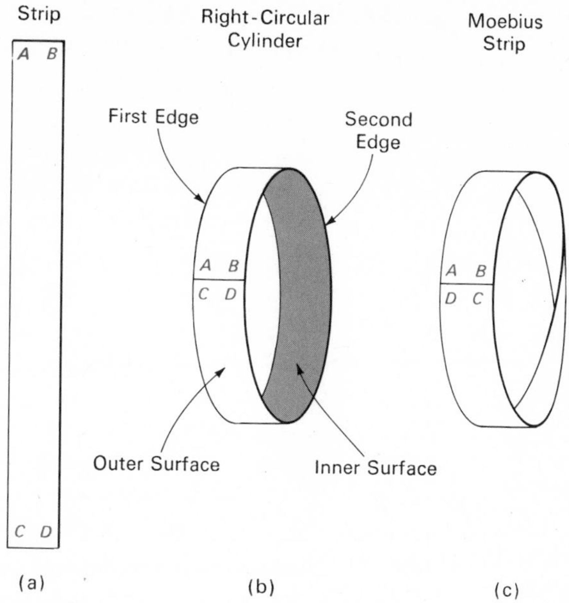

In 1858 a German, A. F. Moebius (1790–1868), varied this construction by taking a half-twist in the strip before taping the ends together. He joined the four vertices, as shown in Figure 5.27(c). The surface that results is called the **Moebius strip** and has some unusual properties. First, this strip has no inside and no outside—it has only one side. To show this, select any point on the surface of the strip. With a pencil, start to move along this surface, as shown in Figure 5.28. You will find that in doing this you traverse the entire strip and come back to the point at which you started. While traversing the surface in this way, you do not cross over an edge and you must conclude that the surface is one-sided. Second, this surface has only one edge. Start at any point on the edge and traverse along the edge. You will arrive back at your starting place and in the meantime you will have traversed the entire edge of the strip.

The Moebius strip and the right circular cylinder are not topologically equivalent. Both the number of sides of a figure and the number of edges of a figure are topological invariants. Since the cylinder and the strip do not have the same number of sides (or the same number of edges), these surfaces cannot be topologically the same.

Figure 5.28

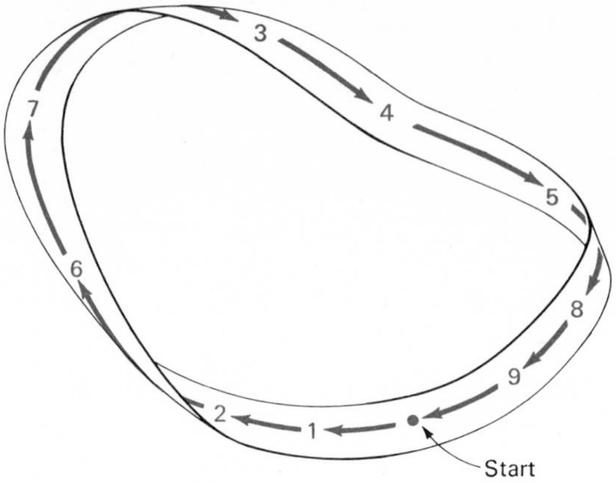

The **punctured Klein Bottle** was invented by Felix Klein in 1882. It is possible to make a physical model of the punctured Klein bottle, but this would require a certain amount of talent. We must be content with planar pictures of this bottle, which are necessarily somewhat difficult to visualize. The drawings in Figure 5.29 demonstrate how to make a punctured Klein bottle. Begin with an ordinary bottle that is made out of a completely elastic

Figure 5.29

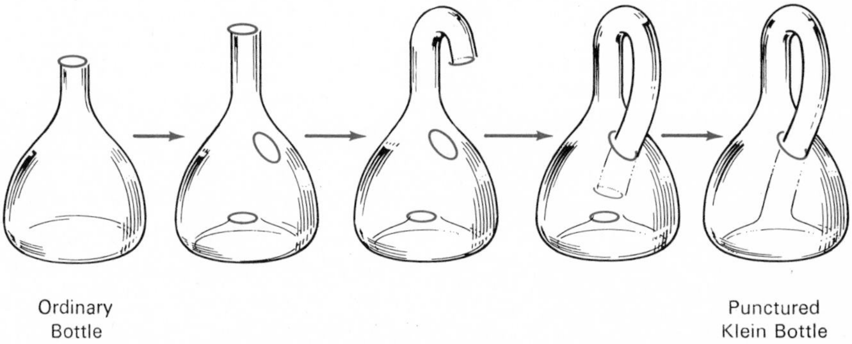

glass. Then make a hump in the bottom and cut off the top of this hump. Also cut a hole in the side of the bottle. Now stretch out the neck of the bottle and pull it around and pass it through the hole you cut in the side of the bottle. Join the mouth of the bottle neatly to the edge formed when you cut the hole in the bottom of the bottle. The resulting surface is called the punctured Klein bottle.

The punctured Klein bottle has only one edge, the edge formed when you cut the hole in the side of the original bottle. Also, the bottle has no outside or inside—it is a one-sided surface. To see this, study the illustration until you are convinced that you can trace from any one point on the surface to any other point on the surface without crossing over the edge of the surface.

The punctured Klein bottle is not topologically equivalent to the ordinary bottle because the ordinary bottle has two sides and the punctured Klein bottle has only one side. As both the Moebius strip and the punctured Klein bottle have one edge and one side, on the basis of these two invariants alone we cannot distinguish between these two figures. In order to show that these two figures are not topologically the same, we shall introduce another invariant.

By a **loop** on a surface we mean a simple closed curve on the surface which does not cross over an edge of the surface. Examples of loops are shown in Figure 5.30.

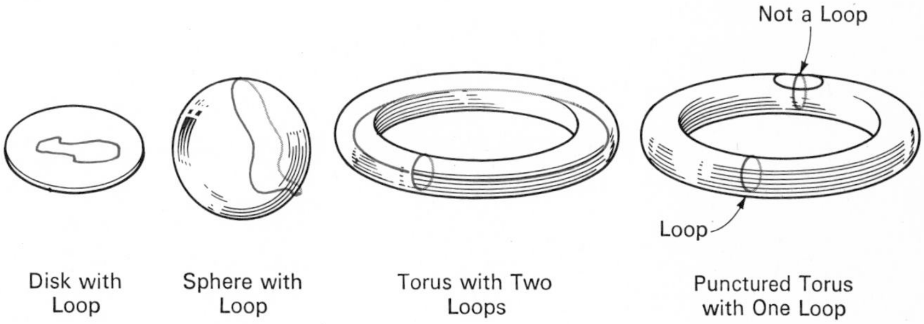

Figure 5.30

The largest number of loops that can be cut in a *one-edged surface* without separating that surface into two or more pieces is a topological invariant. Let us call this number the **loop number** of a one-edged surface. For example, the disk is one-edged and has loop number 0 since any one loop cut will separate the disk into two pieces. The punctured torus (like an inner tube with the valve stem removed) is a one-edged surface with loop number 1. The reason for this is that any two loop cuts will separate the punctured torus into two separate pieces, but it is possible to cut one loop in the figure without separating it into two pieces.

Using your paper Moebius strip, you can see for yourself that, if you make a loop cut that runs right down the middle of the strip, the strip is not separated into two pieces. The surface that results is shown in Figure 5.31. It follows that the loop number of the Moebius strip is at least 1. But, as

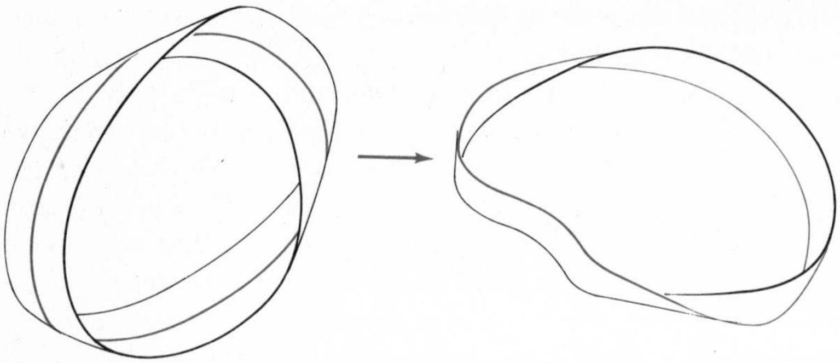

Figure 5.31

soon as you make another loop cut, the surface will separate into two pieces. You can experiment and see that this is true. Hence the loop number of the strip is 1.

If you do not have a model of the punctured Klein bottle to work with, it is harder for you to see that the loop number of the punctured Klein bottle is 2, but such is the case. For example, the two loop cuts shown in Figure 5.32 do not separate the punctured Klein bottle, but any three loop cuts will separate the bottle into two pieces. Hence the loop number is 2.

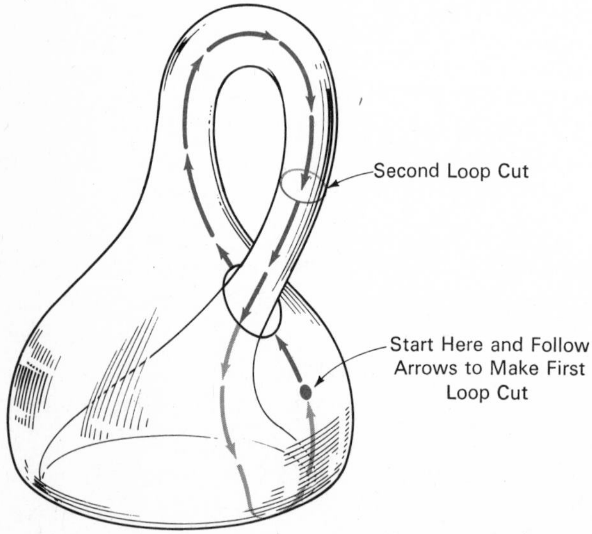

Figure 5.32

Since the strip and the bottle have different loop numbers, these surfaces are not topologically equivalent.

We have got a glimpse of just a few topological invariants in this and the preceding section. The last one, the loop number, illustrates how far removed topology is from Euclidean geometry. Of these two geometries, topology is far and away the more interesting and useful to the modern mathematician. Topology is the object of intense study by researchers, whereas almost no one does research in Euclidean geometry any more. Euclidean geometry, like Latin, is not thriving, but it is always around us and is always in use. Topology is more like a living language, constantly changing and expanding to satisfy new needs.

Exercises 5.6

1. The Moebius strip has one side and one edge. How many sides and edges do the spatial surfaces shown below have?

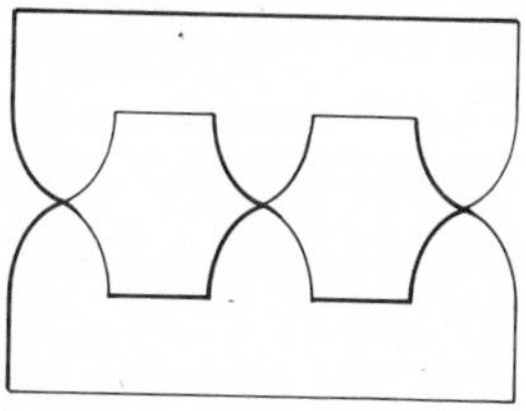

(a)

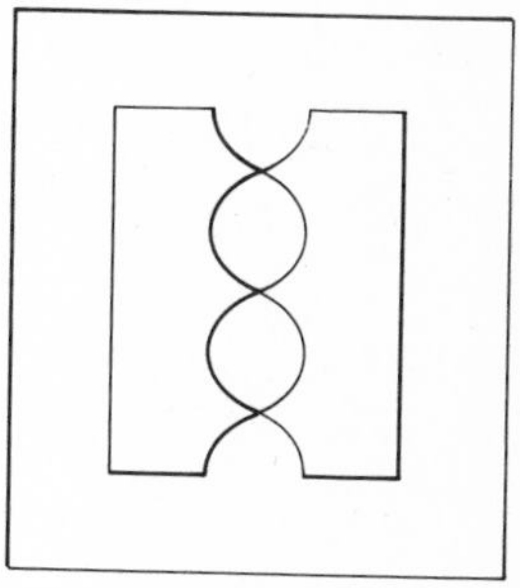

(c)

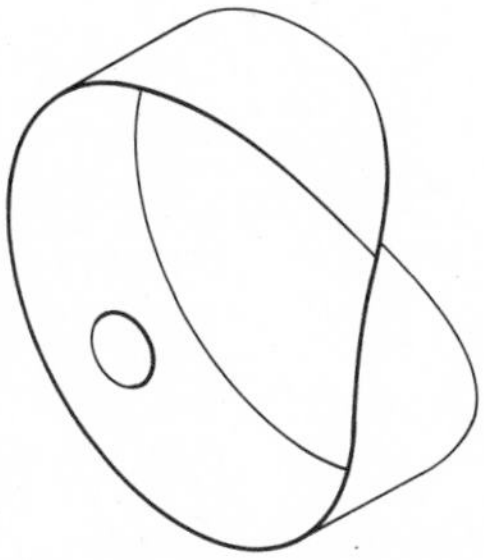

(b)

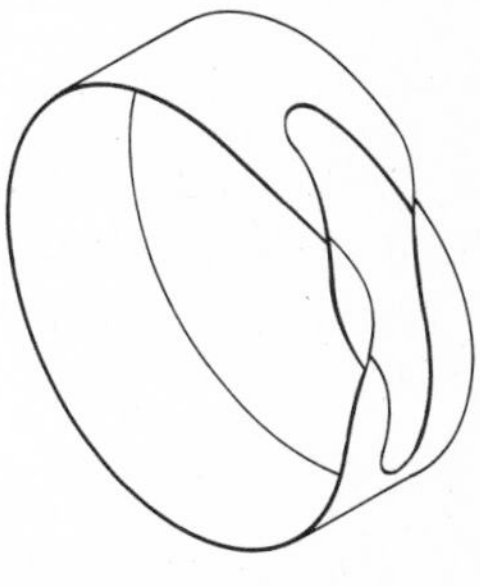

(d)

2. Is it possible to cut a loop in the Moebius strip that separates the figure into two separate pieces. Find such a loop cut. Why doesn't this mean

that the loop number of the Moebius strip is 0? (*Hint*: Don't cut down the middle.)

3. Find two loop cuts that separate the punctured Klein bottle into two separate pieces. Why doesn't this mean that the loop number of this figure is 1?
4. If you were to rip this page out of this book, you would be holding a one-edged surface in your hand. What would be the loop number of that surface?

In order to answer the following exercises you will need to make models. Strips of paper about 2 inches wide and 2 feet long would be best.

5. You can make a Moebius strip from a strip of paper by taking a half turn in it before taping the ends together. Suppose that you take two strips of paper laid together, and keeping these pieces together, take a half turn in them and then tape the pairs of ends together. You get what looks like two Moebius strips nestled together. Now keeping these strips together observe that you can run your finger around between them with no obstructions. Release the fi⌐ure and see what you have. Compare what you have with the figure on the right side of Fig. 5.31. How many edges and sides does this figure have? This figure can be made from a strip of paper by taking how many half turns in the strip before taping?

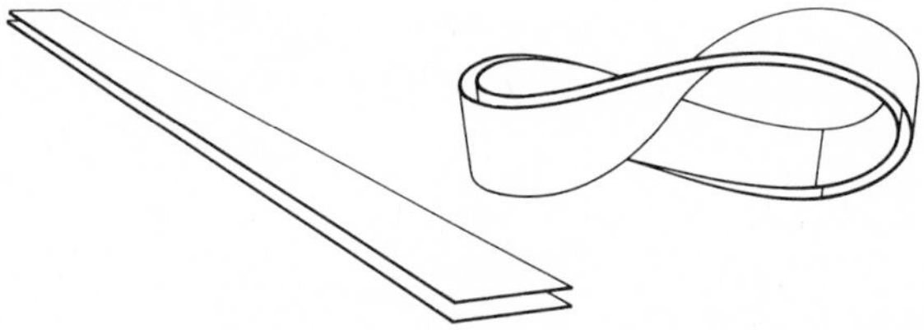

6. Take a strip of paper and instead of taking one half turn in it before taping (this would give you a Moebius strip) take one full turn before taping. How many edges and sides does this figure have? Then make a loop cut down the middle of this figure. What happens? How do the strips that result from this loop cut compare to the original strip?
7. Take a strip of paper and make one and one half turns in it before taping the ends together. How many edges and sides does this figure have?

Make a loop cut down the center of the strip and see what happens. Surprise! How many edges and sides does the resulting figure have? What is the loop number of the strip that you made?

8. We saw that making a loop cut down the middle of a Moebius strip did not separate the figure. Make a loop cut about one third of the way from one edge of the Moebius strip and see how the strip separates. Analyze each of the two strips so obtained. How many turns does each contain?

6 Extending the Concept of Number

IN THIS CHAPTER we shall continue from Chapter 3 the discussion of the notion of number. We shall carry the development of the number concept from its beginnings in the system of whole numbers to its first-stage culmination in the system of real numbers. Our concern in this chapter will be only partly with the usual computational aspects of working with numbers. Much of our attention will be directed toward the number systems themselves rather than just to the numbers that are the objects of the systems. By so doing, we shall be introducing some of the most basic ideas of that part of modern mathematics called "abstract algebra."

6.1 The System of Integers

Something about the idea of negative numbers makes them hard to accept as being legitimate numbers—at least this is the lesson taught us by history. In 274 A.D. the equation $4x + 20 = 4$ was called absurd (it has a negative solution). Negative numbers were called *numeri absurdi* by at least one important German mathematician of the early sixteenth century. As late as the end of the sixteenth century, some mathematicians, when discussing solutions of equations, studiously ignored the existence of solutions that were negative numbers. Descartes (of whom we will have more to say in Chapter 7) referred to positive solutions of equations as "true" solutions and to negative solutions as "false" solutions. By the eighteenth century, however, negative numbers were accepted, but they were still not well understood. For instance, some textbooks of the period taught that it was impossible to multiply two negative numbers together. Even in the nineteenth century we can find many instances of negative numbers which, although understood, were simply ignored for no good mathematical reason. The whole history of these numbers seems to be one of rejection until the middle nineteenth century, when new developments in mathematics made it finally and abundantly clear that the negative numbers were as necessary to mathematics as the familiar positive numbers. In this section we shall introduce some negative numbers into the system of whole numbers and, as a result, produce the number system called "the system of integers."

As our first step toward enlarging the number system, we shall augment the set of whole numbers with the numbers that are called **negative integers**. These are the numbers whose most familiar names are -1, -2, -3, -4, and so on. The negative integer -1 is defined to be that number which gives 0 when 1 is added to it; that is, -1 is the solution of the equation $x + 1 = 0$. The negative integer -2 is the solution of the equation $x + 2 = 0$; -3 is the solution of the equation $x + 3 = 0$; and so on. For consistency of terminology, we shall now rename the nonzero whole numbers and call them **positive integers**. The number 0 is an integer, but is neither positive nor negative. By an **integer** we mean a number that is zero, a positive integer, or a negative integer.

We can identify the integers with points on the number line. We begin by selecting two distinct points, which we call the **origin** and the **unit** and with which we associate the integers 0 and 1. Then we locate the other integers on the number line by marking off unit distances to the right and to the left of the origin (see Figure 6.1).

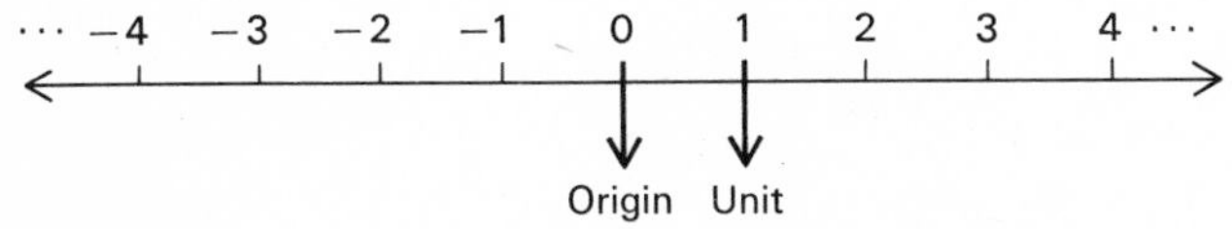

Figure 6.1

Like the system of whole numbers, the system of integers is equipped with two binary operations called "addition of integers" and "multiplication of integers." These operations, defined on the set of integers, are extensions of the corresponding operations defined on the set of whole numbers. That is, the result of applying addition of integers (or multiplication of integers) to two nonnegative integers (that is, whole numbers) is the same as the result of applying addition (or multiplication) of whole numbers to those two numbers. These binary operations possess the following basic properties.

1. Addition of integers:
   A. Is commutative: $x + y = y + x$.
   B. Is associative: $x + (y + z) = (x + y) + z$.
   C. Has the identity 0: $x + 0 = 0 + x = x$.
2. Multiplication of integers:
   A. Is commutative: $x \cdot y = y \cdot x$.
   B. Is associative: $x \cdot (y \cdot z) = (x \cdot y) \cdot z$.
   C. Has the identity 1: $x \cdot 1 = 1 \cdot x = x$.
3. Addition and multiplication of integers share the left and right distributive properties:
   A. $x \cdot (y + z) = (x \cdot y) + (x \cdot z)$.
   B. $(x + y) \cdot z = (x \cdot z) + (y \cdot z)$.

In the system of whole numbers, addition and multiplication possess these same properties. The difference between these two number systems is that addition in the system of integers possesses one additional property of great importance.

1.D. Each integer possesses an inverse with respect to addition.

This means that corresponding to each integer x there is another integer y, called the **additive inverse** of x, such that $x + y = y + x = 0$. For example, the additive inverse of 6 is -6 and the additive inverse of -5 is 5. Zero is its own additive inverse. If we denote the additive inverse of an integer x by the symbol $-(x)$, then we can render these statements symbolically as $-(6) = -6$, $-(-5) = 5$, and $-(0) = 0$. We shall see that it is this property 1D that makes the system of integers much more useful than the system of whole numbers.

Let us demonstrate by means of a few examples how these properties are used to verify addition and multiplication facts in the system of integers.

Example 1: Explain why $-3 + -4 = -7$.

SOLUTION: The sum of -3 and -4 must equal -7 since, when we add 7 to $-3 + -4$, the result is 0 and -7 is the only number with this property.

Observe:

$$\begin{aligned}
(-3 + -4) + 7 &= (-3 + -4) + (4 + 3) && (7 = 4 + 3)\\
&= -3 + [-4 + (4 + 3)] && (1B)\\
&= -3 + [(-4 + 4) + 3] && (1B)\\
&= -3 + [0 + 3] && (-4 \text{ and } 4 \text{ are additive inverses})\\
&= -3 + 3 && (1C)\\
&= 0. && (-3 \text{ and } 3 \text{ are additive inverses})
\end{aligned}$$

Example 2: Explain why $-3 + 5 = 2$.

SOLUTION: We write $5 = 3 + 2$ and proceed as shown:

$$\begin{aligned}
-3 + 5 &= -3 + (3 + 2) && (5 = 3 + 2)\\
&= (-3 + 3) + 2 && (1B)\\
&= 0 + 2 && (-3 \text{ and } 3 \text{ are additive inverses})\\
&= 2. && (1C)
\end{aligned}$$

Example 3: Explain why $-7 + 4 = -3$.

SOLUTION: We write $-7 = -3 + -4$ (see Example 1) and proceed as follows:

$$\begin{aligned}
-7 + 4 &= (-3 + -4) + 4 && (\text{From Example 1})\\
&= -3 + (-4 + 4) && (1B)\\
&= -3 + 0 && (-4 \text{ and } 4 \text{ are additive inverses})\\
&= -3. && (1C)
\end{aligned}$$

Example 4: We already know that 0 is an annihilator for whole numbers. Zero is also an annihilator for the negative integers. For example, consider the product of -3 and 0. We argue as follows:

$$\begin{aligned}(-3)(0) &= (-3)(0) + 0\\ &= (-3)(0) + (3)(0)\\ &= (-3 + 3)(0)\\ &= (0)(0)\\ &= 0.\end{aligned}$$

You should justify each of the steps in this argument.

Example 5: Explain why $(-3)(5) = -15$.

SOLUTION: This product must be equal to -15 because when we add 15 to it we get 0:

$$\begin{aligned}(-3)(5) + 15 &= (-3)(5) + (3)(5) && (15 = (3)(5))\\ &= (-3 + 3)(5) && \text{(3B)}\\ &= (0)(5) && (-3 \text{ and } 3 \text{ are additive inverses})\\ &= 0. && (0 \text{ is an annihilator})\end{aligned}$$

Example 6: Explain why $(-3)(-5) = 15$.

SOLUTION: Since when we add -15 to this product we get 0, this product must be equal to 15:

$$\begin{aligned}(-3)(-5) + -15 &= (-3)(-5) + (-3)(5) && \text{(From Example 5)}\\ &= (-3)(-5 + 5) && \text{(3A)}\\ &= (-3)(0) && (-5 \text{ and } 5 \text{ are additive inverses})\\ &= 0. && \text{(Zero is an annihilator)}\end{aligned}$$

Finally, let us note that the product of two integers is 0 if and only if at least one of the integers is itself equal to 0. That is, $nm = 0$ if and only if either $n = 0$ and or $m = 0$.

Subtraction is defined in the system of integers just as it was defined in the system of whole numbers. Thus, if x and y are integers, then by $x - y$ we mean that integer d such that $x = y + d$. That is, $x - y = d$ if and only if $x = y + d$. Let us prove an important and useful theorem relating subtraction of integers to the concept of additive inverse.

Theorem: *If x and y are integers, then $x - y = x + -(y)$. That is, to subtract y from x, add the additive inverse of y to x.*

PROOF: Let us begin by writing

$$x - y = d.$$

Then according to the definition of subtraction,

$$x = y + d.$$

Now add $-(y)$ to both sides of this equation and obtain

$$x + -(y) = (y + d) + -(y).$$

Then, by using property 1A, we get

$$x + -(y) = (d + y) + -(y),$$

and by using property 1B we get

$$x + -(y) = d + (y + -(y)).$$

But $y + -(y) = 0$, so

$$x + -(y) = d + 0 = d.$$

Combining the first and last equations, we obtain the statement of the theorem.

Example 7: $-3 - 7 = ?$ $\quad -3 - -7 = ?$

SOLUTION: According to the preceding theorem, $-3 - 7 = -3 + -(7)$. Then $-3 + -(7) = -3 + -7 = -10$. Similarly, $-3 - -7 = -3 + -(-7)$ by the theorem, so that $-3 - -7 = -3 + 7 = 4$.

Because every integer has an additive inverse, the symbols x and $-(y)$ have meaning for all integers x and y. Since addition is binary operation, therefore, the symbol $x + -(y)$ has meaning for all integers x and y. According to the preceding theorem, this means that $x - y$ has meaning for all integers x and y. Consequently, we see that because every integer has an additive inverse, subtraction in the system of integers is a binary operation. This is the single most significant property of the system of integers and is the reason for the usefulness of this number system.

Finally, subtraction shares both the right and left distributive properties with multiplication:

$$x \cdot (y - z) = (x \cdot y) - (x \cdot z)$$

and

$$(x - y) \cdot z = (x \cdot z) - (y \cdot z).$$

Exercises 6.1

1. How is -7 distinguished from all other numbers? That is, what can you say about -7 that you can't say about any other number?
2. What are the additive inverses of 18, -123, 67, 0, and -111?
3. As in Example 1, show why the equation $-5 + -2 = -7$ is true.
4. As in Example 2, show why the equation $11 + -4 = 7$ is true.
5. As in Example 3, show why the equation $-111 + 63 = -48$ is true.
6. As in Example 4, show why the product of -6 and 0 is 0.
7. As in Example 5, show why $(-4)(5) = -20$. Then, as in Example 6, show why $(-4)(-5) = 20$.
8. Use the Theorem relating addition and subtraction to help you solve these equations.
   (a) $x = 6 - -4$. **(c)** $x = 3 - (-4 - -5)$.
   (b) $2x = -4 - -6$.
9. Use the integers -4, 5, and -3 to demonstrate that addition and multiplication share both the right and left distributive properties.
10. The relation *is less than* is defined for integers just as it was for whole numbers: $x < y$ means that there exists a positive integer p such that $x + d = y$. Use this definition to prove that
    (a) $-3 < -2$. **(b)** $-1000 < -10$.
11. Let x, y, and z be integers and suppose that $x < y$.
    (a) If $z > 0$, then how are xz and yz related?
    (b) If $z < 0$, then how are xz and yx related?

12.* If we think of the integers as located on the number line, we can define the **absolute value** of an integer to be the distance of that integer from the origin. The absolute value of an integer x is denoted by $|x|$. For example, $|-8| = 8$ since -8 is located 8 units from the origin.

(a) What are the absolute values of the integers $-66, 45, 0, -1, -23$, and 14?

(b) For what values of x is the equation $|-3| \cdot |x| = 6$ true?

(c) If a positive integer and a negative integer are to be added, and if the absolute value of the negative integer is larger than the absolute value of the positive integer, then is the sum of the integers positive or negative?

13. The set of all integers can be described using the bracket notation as $\{0, 1, -1, 2, -2, 3, -3, 4, -4, 5, -5, 6, -6, \ldots\}$. Use this listing of the integers to set up a one-to-one correspondence between the set of integers and the set of whole numbers. What then is the cardinal number of the set of integers? Are there more integers than there are whole numbers?

6.2 Algebraic Structure: Groups

It was an Englishman, George Boole (1815–1864), who first clearly saw that mathematics might concern itself with properties of mathematical systems rather than just with properties of the objects of those systems. His idea, quickly followed by similar insights from other mathematicians, was that "pure" mathematics should concern itself with the study of the form of mathematical systems rather than with the content of such systems. Bertrand Russell has called this new understanding of the purpose of mathematical investigation the single greatest achievement of pure mathematics in the nineteenth century. In this section we shall discuss these ideas.

Suppose that S is a set of objects and that $*$ is a binary operation defined on the objects of S possessing the following properties:

1. **A.** $*$ is commutative.

   B. $*$ is associative.

   C. There is a $*$-identity $i \in S$. That is, there is a special object i belonging to the set S such that $x * i = i * x = x$ for every $x \in S$.

   D. Each object in S has a $*$-inverse. That is, corresponding to each object $x \in S$, there is an object $\tilde{x} \in S$ such that $x * \tilde{x} = \tilde{x} * x = i$.

George Boole (1815–1864)

Then the set S together with the binary operation $*$ is called a **commutative group**. We have already seen many examples of sets equipped with binary operations which are commutative groups.

Example 1: The set of integers together with the binary operation of addition is a commutative group. The identity object is 0 and the inverse of an object x is $-(x)$.

Example 2: The set $\{0, 1, 2, 3, 4, 5\}$ together with the binary operation called 6-addition (see Section 2.6) is a commutative group. The operation of 6-addition is both commutative and associative and the 6-additive identity is the object 0. Each object in the set has a 6-additive inverse. The 6-additive inverse of 0 is 0, of 1 is 5, of 2 is 4, of 3 is 3, of 4 is 2, and of 5 is 1.

Example 3: The set of whole numbers together with the operation of addition is not a commutative group. The operation is commutative and associative and there is an identity, but the operation fails to possess property 1D. Indeed, it was to obtain a number system with an addition operation that would possess property 1D that we were required to introduce the negative integers.

Example 4: Let the set S be the set $\{a,b,c,d\}$ and let a binary operation $*$ be defined by means of the operation table in Table 6–1. In the table the entry in row x and column y is the object $x * y$. It can be shown that this table defines an operation that is both commutative and associative. The $*$-identity

Table 6–1

Columns

Rows: $*$	a	b	c	d
a	a	b	c	d
b	b	d	a	c
c	c	a	d	b
d	d	c	b	a

is the object a since $x * a = a * x = x$ for $x \in S$. (Examine the table to verify this.) The $*$-inverse of a is a itself, of b is c, of c is b, and of d is d, since $a * a = a$, $b * c = c * b = a$, and $d * d = a$. Hence this four-object set, together with the operation defined by means of the table, is a commutative group.

Example 5: Let a point P be fixed in the plane. Then corresponding to each angle α there is a rotation r_α of the plane about the point P through α degrees. If $\alpha > 0$, then the rotation r_α is in the counterclockwise direction. If $\alpha < 0$, then the rotation is in the clockwise direction. Now we can define a binary operation (symbolized by $*$) on the set S of all such rotations as follows: Given two rotations r_α and r_β, the result of operating upon them (in the given order) is the rotation $r_{\alpha+\beta}$. This operation can be described by means of the equation

$$r_\alpha * r_\beta = r_{\alpha+\beta}$$

and is called **composition of rotations**. The set S of all rotations, together with this binary operation $*$, is a commutative group.

1. A. $*$ is commutative. For if r_α and r_β are any two rotations, then $r_\alpha * r_\beta = r_{\alpha+\beta} = r_{\beta+\alpha} = r_\beta * r_\alpha$.
   B. $*$ is associative. For if r_α, r_β, and r_γ are any three rotations, then $r_\alpha * (r_\beta * r_\gamma) = r_\alpha * r_{\beta+\gamma} = r_{\alpha+(\beta+\gamma)} = r_{(\alpha+\beta)+\gamma} = r_{\alpha+\beta} * r_\gamma = (r_\alpha * r_\beta) * r_\gamma$.
   C. The $*$-identity is the rotation through 0 degrees, r_0: $r_0 * r_\alpha = r_\alpha * r_0 = r_\alpha$.
   D. The $*$-inverse of a rotation r_α is the rotation $r_{-\alpha}$ since $r_\alpha * r_{-\alpha} = r_{\alpha+-\alpha} = r_0$ and $r_{-\alpha} * r_\alpha = r_{-\alpha+\alpha} = r_0$.

We worked with the objects of this commutative group in our discussion of the congruence and similarity relations in Chapter 5.

By a **group** we mean a set S together with a binary operation $*$ which possesses properties 1B, 1C, and 1D. We have not seen any examples of groups that are not also commutative groups, but such noncommutative groups abound in mathematics. Our concern, however, will be only with commutative groups.

The notion of a group was studied by a young Frenchman, Evariste Galois (1811–1832). Although the idea that mathematics could deal with such abstract ideas was not original with him, he was the first to specifically discuss the notion. (He died in a duel at the age of twenty-one.) The properties that define a group are called structural properties. Very roughly speaking, by a **structural property** of a mathematical system, we mean a property of that system which has nothing whatsoever to do with the particular nature of the objects of that system. For example, the property of being a commutative group is a structural property of a mathematical system. The study of such properties is called **modern** or **abstract algebra**. The abstract algebraist is concerned only with structural properties of mathematical systems and is not at all concerned with the specific nature of the objects of the systems that he studies. If two systems possess exactly the same structural properties, then they are called **isomorphic systems**.

Exercises 6.2

1. Consider the set $\{\alpha, \beta\}$ together with the binary operation defined by the following table:

$*$	α	β
α	α	β
β	β	α

Everiste Galois (1811–1832)

(a) Is the operation commutative? What is the $*$-identity? What is the $*$-inverse of α? What is the $*$-inverse of β?

(b) In order to establish that this operation is associative it is necessary to verify that each of the following equations is true. Do so by direct computation.

$$(\alpha * \alpha) * \beta = \alpha * (\alpha * \beta) \qquad (\alpha * \beta) * \beta = \alpha * (\beta * \beta)$$

$$(\alpha * \beta) * \alpha = \alpha * (\beta * \alpha) \qquad (\beta * \alpha) * \beta = \beta * (\alpha * \beta)$$

$$(\beta * \beta) * \alpha = \beta * (\beta * \alpha) \qquad (\beta * \alpha) * \alpha = \beta * (\alpha * \alpha)$$

$$(\alpha * \alpha) * \alpha = \alpha * (\alpha * \alpha) \qquad (\beta * \beta) * \beta = \beta * (\beta * \beta)$$

Conclude that this set together with the binary operation $*$ is a commutative group.

2. In Exercise 1 we saw an example of a group that contained only two objects. It was not an accident that this group was commutative for it can be proved that any group that contains just two objects must be a commutative group. Can you prove this?
3. In Example 1 we saw a table defining a binary operation that makes the set $\{\alpha,\beta\}$ into a group. Do any of the following tables define binary operations which make $\{\alpha,\beta\}$ into a group? (*Hint:* You may want to use the result of Exercise 2.)

◆	α	β
α	α	α
β	α	β

▲	α	β
α	α	α
β	β	α

●	α	β
α	α	α
β	β	β

■	α	β
α	α	β
β	β	β

4. The set $\{a,b,c,d,e,f\}$ together with the operation defined by means of the following table is a group.

$*$	a	b	c	d	e	f
a	a	b	c	d	e	f
b	b	c	a	f	d	e
c	c	a	b	e	f	d
d	d	e	f	a	b	c
e	e	f	d	c	a	b
f	f	d	e	b	c	a

(a) Use the two triples d, b, and c and a, f, and b to illustrate the associativity of this operation.

(b) Find the $*$-identity and find the $*$-inverse of each object of the group.

(c) Prove by means of a counterexample that this group is not commutative.

5. It is a theorem that if a set S of objects together with a binary operation $*$ is a group, then the operation $*$ has the right cancellation property:

$x * z = y * z$ implies $x = y$. Prove this theorem. (*Hint*: Consider somehow using the $*$-inverse of z.)

6. Suppose we were to change the entry in Row c and Column d of the operation table in Exercise 4 by replacing e by c. Using Exercise 5, explain why the operation defined by the changed table would not make the set $\{a,b,c,d,e,f\}$ into a group. (*Hint*: If it were still a group, then you could obtain a contradiction to Exercise 5.)

6.3 The System of Rational Numbers

The notion of a positive rational number is a very ancient one. As early as about 2000 B.C. the Egyptians were working with positive rational numbers whose numerators were equal to one and the Chinese were involved with such numbers as $247\frac{933}{1460}$. It would appear that such positive rational numbers were regarded as being much more natural than the negative integers. At any rate, they were accepted as legitimate numbers long before negative integers were. In this chapter we shall augment the system of integers with such numbers and the number system we obtain as a result is called "the system of rational numbers."

In Section 6.1 we defined the integers to be those numbers that are solutions of equations of the form $x + a = 0$, where a is a nonzero whole number. In a similar way we now define the **rational numbers** to be those numbers that are solutions of equations of the special form $b \cdot x = a$, where a and b are integers and b is different from zero. The solution of this equation is symbolized by a/b. For example, the rational number that is the solution of the equation $2x = 1$ is symbolized by the familiar symbol $\frac{1}{2}$ and, being the solution of the equation $2x = 1$, is that number which when multiplied by 2 yields 1. The rational number whose symbolic name is $\frac{2}{3}$ is the number which when multiplied by 3 yields 2; that is, $\frac{2}{3}$ names the solution of the equation $3x = 2$. The solution of the equation $5x = -2$ is symbolized by the symbol $\frac{-2}{5}$ and is that number which when multiplied by 5 yields -2.

We can also think of rational numbers as being numbers associated with certain points of the number line. For example, suppose that the unit distance (the distance between the origin and the unit) is subdivided into three equal parts and that two of these equal parts are measured off to the right of the origin. The point so determined is associated with the rational number $\frac{2}{3}$ (refer to Figure 6.2). Thus $\frac{2}{3}$ can be regarded (in terms of the number line) as being two of three equal parts of the unit distance. If these two equal parts are measured to the left of the origin, the point so determined is the point associated with the rational number $\frac{-2}{3}$.

Figure 6.2

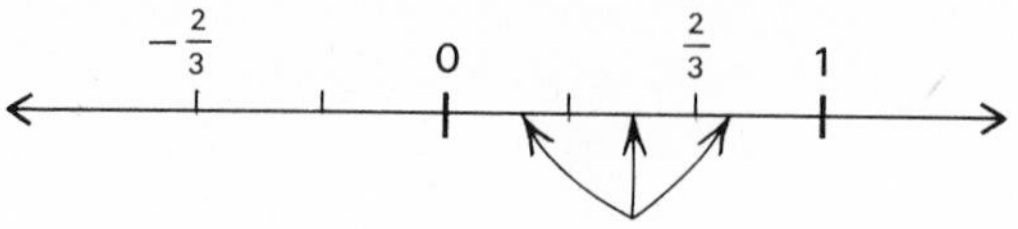

It should be clear that every integer is also a rational number. For example, the integer -6 is a rational number since -6 is the solution of the equation $1x = -6$ and, by definition, the solution of this kind of equation is a rational number. Thus the set of integers is a proper subset of the set of rational numbers.

The symbols of the form a/b are called **fractions**. The number a is called the numerator of the fraction and b is called the denominator of the fraction. An aspect of this method for naming rational numbers which causes a certain amount of difficulty is that many different fractions can name the same rational number. For example, each of the fractions $\frac{1}{2}$, $\frac{-1}{-2}$, $\frac{2}{4}$, $\frac{-2}{-4}$, $\frac{3}{6}$, $\frac{-3}{-6}$, $\frac{4}{8}$, $\frac{-4}{-8}$, and so on, names the same rational number. Two fractions a/b and c/d name the same rational number if and only if $ad = bc$. We write $a/b = c/d$ to indicate that the fractions name the same rational number.

Suppose that a/b names a certain rational number and c is a nonzero integer. Then a/b and ac/bc name the same rational number ($a/b = ac/bc$) because $(a)(bc) = (b)(ac)$. This means that we can multiply or divide both the numerator and the denominator of a fraction by the same nonzero integer without changing the meaning of the fraction. This fact has three important applications to the rewriting of fractions.

1. *To rewrite fractions with positive denominators.* For example, $\frac{5}{-4}$ can be written with a positive denominator by multiplying both numerator and denominator by the integer -1: $\frac{5}{-4} = \frac{-5}{4}$.

2. *To rewrite fractions in lowest terms.* A fraction is said to be written in lowest terms when its numerator and denominator are relatively prime. That is, a fraction is in lowest terms when the greatest common divisor of its numerator and denominator is 1 (for example, $\frac{2}{3}$ and $\frac{4}{5}$ are in lowest terms but $\frac{4}{14}$ and $\frac{-6}{9}$ are not). To write a fraction in lowest terms, divide both numerator and denominator by the GCD of these integers.

3. *To rewrite two or more fractions so that they have the same denominator.* The easiest way to do this is to compute the least common multiple of all the denominators and then to multiply both numerator and denominator of each fraction by an appropriate integer so that the denominator will equal this least common multiple. For example, to rewrite the fractions $\frac{7}{18}$ and $\frac{5}{24}$

so that they have the same denominator, compute the LCM of the denominators $2 \cdot 3^2$ and $2^3 \cdot 3$. This LCM is $2^3 \cdot 3^2$. Then

$$\frac{7}{2 \cdot 3^2} = \frac{7 \cdot 2^2}{(2 \cdot 3^2)(2^2)} = \frac{7 \cdot 2^2}{2^3 \cdot 3^2} = \frac{28}{72}$$

and

$$\frac{5}{2^3 \cdot 3} = \frac{5 \cdot 3}{(2^3 \cdot 3)(3)} = \frac{5 \cdot 3}{2^3 \cdot 3^2} = \frac{15}{72}$$

Up to now we have been careful to distinguish between rational numbers and the fractions that name them, but we shall fail to make this distinction in what follows unless there is a good reason for making it. Thus we may speak of "the rational number $\frac{2}{3}$" or "the numerator of the rational number" when we really mean "the rational number named by the fraction $\frac{2}{3}$" and "the numerator of the fraction which names the rational number."

Before going on to discuss the important operations in this number system, let us define the inequality relations. If two rational numbers are to be compared using the inequality relations, then first rename these numbers so that they have the same positive denominator. Suppose that a/b and c/b are two such numbers. Then $a/b < c/b$ if and only if $a < c$. Also $a/b > c/b$ if and only if $a > c$. The reason the common denominator must be positive is that this definition gives absurd results otherwise. For example, if we disregarded the requirement of a positive denominator, then $-4 < -3$ would imply that $-4/-1 < -3/-1$, from which it would follow that $4 < 3$, which is absurd.

The binary operations of addition and multiplication which are defined in the system of rational numbers are extensions of the corresponding operations in the system of integers in the sense that, given two integers, we can add or multiply them either by using addition or multiplication in the system of integers or by using addition or multiplication in the system of rational numbers and we get the same sum or product no matter which we do. Addition of rational numbers is easy to perform once the summands have been renamed so that their denominators are the same. We use the rule

$$\frac{a}{b} + \frac{c}{b} = \frac{a + c}{b}$$

to perform addition. Multiplication is even easier, since no renaming is necessary before the operation can be applied to a pair of rational numbers:

$$\frac{a}{b} \cdot \frac{c}{d} = \frac{ac}{bd}.$$

It can be proved that these two operations possess the same properties as addition and multiplication of integers. Thus addition has (see page 144) properties 1A (commutivity), 1B (associativity), 1C (identity), and 1D (inverses). Multiplication has properties 2A (commutivity), 2B (associativity), and 2C (identity). The two operations together possess the two distributive properties 3A and 3B. In addition to these, multiplication possesses one additional property of great importance that distinguishes the rational number system from the other number systems we have studied.

2.D. Every nonzero rational number possesses an inverse with respect to multiplication.

By this we mean that, given any nonzero rational number x, there is a rational number y, called the **multiplicative inverse** of x, such that $x \cdot y = y \cdot x = 1$. For example, the multiplicative inverses of $\frac{3}{4}$, $\frac{-5}{4}$, and 9 are $\frac{4}{3}$, $\frac{-4}{5}$, and $\frac{1}{9}$, respectively. We shall denote the multiplicative inverse of a nonzero rational number x by the symbol $(x)^{-1}$. Thus $(\frac{3}{4})^{-1} = \frac{4}{3}$, $(\frac{-5}{4})^{-1} = \frac{-4}{5}$, and $(9)^{-1} = \frac{1}{9}$. Zero has no multiplicative inverse.

Subtraction of rational numbers is performed upon rational numbers that have already been renamed so that they have the same common denominator according to the rule

$$\frac{a}{b} - \frac{c}{b} = \frac{a-c}{b}.$$

If a/b and c/b are any two rational numbers that have been written with the same denominator, then since the symbol $a - c$ represents a unique integer, the symbol $\frac{a-c}{b}$ names a unique rational number. This means that subtraction in the system of rational numbers is a binary operation.

We are now ready to define the division process. As usual, if a/b and c/d represent rational numbers, and if c/d is different from 0 (division by 0 is never possible), then by the symbol $(a/b) \div (c/d)$ we mean that rational number q such that $(a/b) = (c/d) \cdot q$. That is, $a/b \div c/d = q$ if and only if $a/b = c/d \cdot q$.

Theorem:

$$\frac{a}{b} \div \frac{c}{d} = \left(\frac{a}{b}\right) \cdot \left(\frac{c}{d}\right)^{-1}$$

PROOF: Suppose that a/b and c/d are rational numbers and that c/d is different from 0. Let

$$\frac{a}{b} \div \frac{c}{d} = q$$

Then according to our definition of division

$$\frac{a}{b} = \frac{c}{d} \cdot q.$$

Since $c/d \neq 0$, $(c/d)^{-1}$ exists and we can write

$$\begin{aligned}
\frac{a}{b} \cdot \left(\frac{c}{d}\right)^{-1} &= \left(\frac{c}{d} \cdot q\right) \cdot \left(\frac{c}{d}\right)^{-1} \\
&= \left(q \cdot \frac{c}{d}\right) \cdot \left(\frac{c}{d}\right)^{-1} \\
&= q \cdot \left(\frac{c}{d} \cdot \left(\frac{c}{d}\right)^{-1}\right) \\
&= q \cdot 1 \\
&= q.
\end{aligned}$$

Combining the first and last equations, we get the statement of the theorem and the proof is complete.

Division by nonzero rational numbers is always possible; this is the most significant property of the system of rational numbers. Suppose that a/b and c/d are two rational numbers and $(c/d) \neq 0$. Then the multiplicative inverse of c/d exists and, since multiplication is a binary operation, $(a/b) \cdot (c/d)^{-1}$

has a unique meaning. According to the last theorem, $(a/b)\cdot(c/d)^{-1}$ has exactly the same meaning as $(a/b) \div (c/d)$. Hence $(a/b) \div (c/d)$ has a unique meaning and division by nonzero rational numbers is always possible; the result is always a unique rational number. Although division in this number system is not a binary operation, it comes as near to being one as any division process can come.

Exercises 6.3

1. Draw a number line and locate the rational numbers $\frac{3}{4}, \frac{5}{4}, \frac{1}{7}, \frac{-3}{7}$, and $\frac{16}{7}$. Then locate the additive inverses of these numbers. Finally, locate the multiplicative inverses.
2. Write the rational numbers $\frac{4}{6}, \frac{-16}{24}, \frac{198}{144}$, and $(2^2\cdot 3^4\cdot 5\cdot 7^3\cdot 11)/(2^3\cdot 3^2\cdot 5^2\cdot 7\cdot 13)$ in lowest terms.
3. Solve these equations.
   (a) $2x - \frac{3}{4} = \frac{5}{7}$.
   (b) $x = \frac{2}{3} \div (\frac{1}{2} - \frac{-2}{3})$.
   (c) $\frac{4}{7}x - \frac{1}{3} = \frac{1}{2}$.
   (d) $2x = (\frac{3}{4} \div \frac{-3}{4}) \div \frac{1}{5}$.
4. Arrange these numbers from left to right in order of increasing size: $\frac{2}{3}, \frac{-2}{3}, \frac{4}{5}, \frac{4}{-5}, \frac{1}{5}, \frac{-1}{9}, 0, \frac{1}{2}, \frac{-1}{16}, -7$, and 12.
5. Is there a smallest positive rational number? Is there a smallest positive integer? Is there a largest negative rational number? Is there a largest negative integer?
6. Prove that between every pair of distinct rational numbers there is a third rational number. (*Hint*: Consider two rational numbers a/b and c/d with $a/b < c/d$. Average these numbers and show that this average is greater than a/b and less than c/d.)
7. Complete the following.
   (a) $a/b + c/d = ?/bd$.
   (b) $a/b - c/d = ?/bd$.
8.* The Egyptians worked only with positive rational numbers whose numerators were equal to 1. Use the fact that

$$\frac{1}{n} = \frac{1}{n+1} + \frac{1}{n(n+1)}$$

to write the following rational numbers as sums of distinct rational numbers whose numerators are equal to 1.
(*Hint*: $\frac{2}{3} = \frac{1}{3} + \frac{1}{3} = \frac{1}{3} + (\frac{1}{4} + \frac{1}{12}) = \frac{1}{3} + \frac{1}{4} + \frac{1}{12}$.)
(a) $\frac{2}{7}$. (b) $\frac{3}{7}$. (c) $\frac{4}{5}$.
Your answers should make it clear why the Egyptians were able to

work only very simple problems involving rational numbers. As simple a number as $\frac{4}{5}$ must have been regarded by them as a most complicated number because their name for it was the sum of 15 numbers with numerators equal to 1.

9. Prove the fact used in the preceding exercise:

$$\frac{1}{n} = \frac{1}{n+1} + \frac{1}{n(n+1)}$$

by adding the summands on the right side and simplifying.

10.* We have seen that the cardinal number of the set of integers is $\aleph_0$ so that there are just as many whole numbers as there are integers. Even more surprising is the fact that the set of positive rational numbers also has cardinal number $\aleph_0$. In other words there are no more positive rational numbers than there are whole numbers. (Incidentally it can be proved from this that the cardinal number of the set of all rational numbers is also $\aleph_0$.) Here is the outline of the proof of this fact.

(a) Arrange the fractions in an "infinite" array as shown below. Explain why every fraction representing a positive rational number occurs somewhere in this array of fractions. Where would you find the fraction $\frac{56}{78}$ in this array?

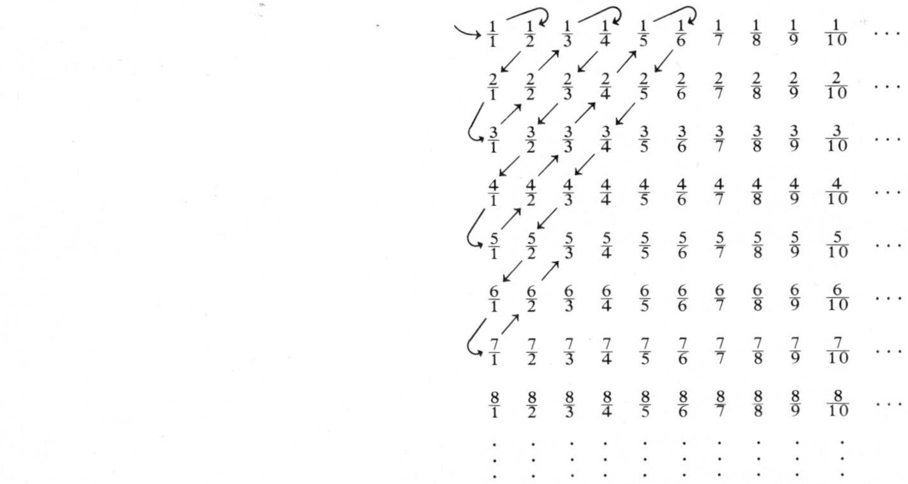

(b) By tracing along the path as indicated we set up a correspondence between the whole numbers and the positive rationals which looks like this for small whole numbers:

0	1	2	3	4	5	6	7	8	9	10	11	12	...
$\updownarrow$	$\updownarrow$	$\updownarrow$	$\updownarrow$	$\updownarrow$	$\updownarrow$	$\updownarrow$	$\updownarrow$	$\updownarrow$	$\updownarrow$	$\updownarrow$	$\updownarrow$	$\updownarrow$	
1	$\frac{1}{2}$	2	3	$\frac{1}{3}$	$\frac{1}{4}$	$\frac{2}{3}$	$\frac{3}{2}$	4	5	$\frac{1}{5}$	$\frac{1}{6}$	$\frac{2}{5}$	...

As we moved along the path we occasionally skipped a positive rational. Why? Explain why our procedure sets up a pairing between the whole numbers and the positive rational numbers that is a one-to-one correspondence. Find the positive rational numbers that correspond to the whole numbers 13 through 50.

6.4 Algebraic Structure: Fields

In this section we shall continue our discussion of algebraic structure of mathematical systems by defining the concept of a field.

The set of rational numbers together with the binary operation of addition is a commutative group, but this number system has more structure than this. The subset of objects different from the additive identity 0 forms a commutative group with respect to multiplication. Also, the addition and multiplication operations are connected by means of the distributive properties. Any mathematical system with these properties is called a field. A **field**, then, is a mathematical system consisting of a set S of objects together with two binary operations $*$ and $\circ$ which possess the following properties:

1. **A.** $*$ is commutative.
   B. $*$ is associative.
   C. There is a $*$-identity i in the set S: $x * i = i * x = x$.
   D. Each object $x \in S$ has a $*$-inverse $\tilde{x}$ in the set S: $x * \tilde{x} = \tilde{x} * x = i$.
2. **A.** $\circ$ is commutative.
   B. $\circ$ is associative.
   C. There is a $\circ$-identity e (different from i) in the set S: $x \circ e = e \circ x = x$.
   D. Each object $x \in S$ different from i has a $\circ$-inverse $\bar{\bar{x}}$ in the set S: $x \circ \bar{\bar{x}} = \bar{\bar{x}} \circ x = e$.
3. These left and right distributive properties connecting the operations $*$ and $\circ$ hold:
   A. $x \circ (y * z) = (x \circ y) * (x \circ z)$.
   B. $(x * y) \circ z = (x \circ z) * (y \circ z)$.

As we have just said, the system of rational numbers possesses each of these properties (when S means the set of rational numbers, $*$ means addition and $\circ$ means multiplication) and so the system of rational numbers is a field. Here is an example of a field containing only a finite number of objects.

Example 1: The system of arithmetic modulo five is a field. The objects of this system are the objects of the set $\{0,1,2,3,4\}$ and the operations are 5-addition ($\oplus$) and 5-multiplication ($\otimes$). These operations are performed upon two objects by first adding or multiplying the objects using ordinary addition or multiplication of whole numbers and then casting out fives from the resulting sums or products. What remains after fives have been cast out is the 5-sum or 5-product of the objects. For example, $3 \oplus 4 = 2$ and $3 \otimes 4 = 2$. The operations $\oplus$ and $\otimes$ are both commutative and associative and they share the distributive properties. (We could verify these statements, but we shall not bother to do so.) The $\oplus$-identity is 0 and the $\otimes$-identity is 1. The $\oplus$-inverses of all objects and the $\otimes$-inverses of objects different from the $\oplus$-identity are listed in Table 6–2.

Table 6–2

Object	$\oplus$*-Inverse*	$\otimes$*-Inverse*
0	0	—
1	4	1
2	3	3
3	2	2
4	1	4

Since all the field properties hold in this system, arithmetic modulo five is a field.

Example 2: The system called arithmetic modulo six is not a field because not every object (different from the $\oplus$-identity 0) has a $\otimes$-inverse. For example, 3 has no $\otimes$-inverse in this system ($3 \otimes 0 = 0$, $3 \otimes 1 = 3$, $3 \otimes 2 = 0$, $3 \otimes 3 = 3$, $3 \otimes 4 = 0$, $3 \otimes 5 = 3$ and so there is no object $\bar{\bar{x}}$ in the system such that $3 \otimes \bar{\bar{x}} = \bar{\bar{x}} \otimes 3 = 1$, and therefore 3 has no $\otimes$-inverse.) What is the difference between arithmetic modulo five and arithmetic modulo six? Why should one of them be a field and the other not? The answer lies in the fact that 5 is a prime but 6 is composite. It can be proved that if p is a prime number, then arithmetic modulo p is a field, but that if c is composite, then arithmetic modulo c is not a field.

Example 3: The system of integers is not a field because property 2D fails to hold in this system. It was to obtain a number system possessing property 2D that the rational numbers were introduced.

There is another structural property possessed by the field of rational numbers called "the order property." This property can be phrased for an arbitrary field, but let us be content with its statement for the field of rational numbers.

4. The field of rational numbers is equipped with an order relation $<$ such that
   A. $0 < x$ and $0 < y$ imply $0 < x + y$ and $0 < x \cdot y$.
   B. If $0 < x$, then $-(x) < 0$.
   C. Exactly one of these statements is true: $0 < x$, $x < 0$, $x = 0$.

Because the system of rational numbers is a field with property 4, we call the field of rational numbers an **ordered field.**

We shall continue our discussion of structural properties of mathematical systems in Section 6.6.

Exercises 6.4

1. Consider the set $\{a,b,c\}$ together with the two operations defined by means of these tables:

$*$	a	b	c
a	a	b	c
b	b	c	a
c	c	a	b

$\circ$	a	b	c
a	a	a	a
b	a	b	c
c	a	c	b

You may assume that each of these operations is associative and that the operations share the two distributive properties given in Property 3. Verify that the rest of the properties (1A, 1C, 1D, 2A, 2C, and 2D) hold and thus that this set together with these operations is a field.

2. Arithmetic modulo four (that is, the set $\{0,1,2,3\}$ together with 4-addition and 4-multiplication) is a group (with respect to 4-addition) but is not a field because one of the properties 2A, 2B, 2C, 2D, 3A, and 3B fails to hold. Find the property that does not hold for arithmetic modulo four.
3. Does the group of integers possess the order property? The system of whole numbers does not possess this property. Why not?
4. Is it correct to say that property 4C means that either $0 < x$ or $x < 0$ or $x = 0$?

6.5 Decimal Numerals and Rational Numbers

We have been naming rational numbers with fractions. Now we want to discuss the naming of such numbers by decimal numerals.

Given a fraction name of a rational number, it is easy enough to find the decimal numeral name for that number. The procedure is simply to long divide the numerator of the fraction by its denominator. For example, 3 long divided by 8 is .375 and so $\frac{3}{8} = .375$. Such numerals as .375 are called **terminating numerals** because they have only a finite number of digits to the right of the decimal point. But not all rational numbers can be named with terminating numerals. For example, 5 long divided by 6 yields the nonterminating numeral $.83333\cdots$. This numeral is called **nonterminating** because a digit appears in every place to the right of the decimal point. Another example is $\frac{41}{333} = .123123123123\cdots$.

The nonterminating numerals $.83333\cdots$ and $.123123123123\cdots$ are called **repeating numerals** because each consists of a block of digits which is repeated over and over to form the entire numeral. This repeating block does not have to begin repeating at the tenths place (as does $.123123123\cdots$) and may begin to repeat at any place. The numeral $.83333\cdots$ has a repeating block consisting of the single digit 3, which begins to repeat in the hundredths place.

We could examine a great many rational numbers and we would see that in every case the decimal numeral name is either a terminating numeral or a nonterminating but repeating numeral. In fact, the converse of this is true as well. That is, a decimal numeral names a rational number if and only if the numeral is either terminating or nonterminating but repeating.

If we are given the decimal numeral name of a rational number, then we can find a fraction name for that number. This is particularly easy to do if the given decimal numeral is terminating. For example, consider the terminating numeral 1.56. We use the fact that such terminating numerals are really nothing more than abbreviations for the sums of their place values. Thus

1.56 is a symbol that abbreviates the sum $1 + \frac{5}{10} + \frac{6}{100}$ and so

$$1.56 = 1 + \frac{5}{10} + \frac{6}{100} = \frac{100}{100} + \frac{50}{100} + \frac{6}{100}$$

$$= \frac{100 + 50 + 6}{100} = \frac{156}{100} = \frac{39}{25}.$$

In the case of nonterminating numerals, however, the situation is complicated by the fact that, since we cannot add infinitely many numbers, we cannot regard nonterminating numerals as the sum of their place values. We need another procedure in these instances. This procedure is demonstrated in the following two examples.

Example 1: The decimal numeral $.4545454545\cdots$ is nonterminating but repeating and so we know that it names a rational number. Let x represent this rational number so that we can write $x = .4545454545\cdots$. Multiplying both sides of this equation by 100, we get the equation $100x = 45.45454545\cdots$. Now we can subtract these equations,

$$\begin{aligned} 100x &= 45.4545454545\cdots \\ x &= .4545454545\cdots \\ \hline 99x &= 45.00000\cdots = 45 \end{aligned}$$

and see that $99x = 45$ so that $x = \frac{45}{99} = \frac{5}{11}$. Hence $.4545454545\cdots = \frac{5}{11}$.

The length of the repeating block dictates the power of 10 that must be used to multiply the first equation. In Example 1 the length of the block was 2 and so we multiplied the first equation by 100. If the repeating block had had length 3, then we would have multiplied by 1000. Example 1 was fairly simple because the repeating block began to repeat in the tenths place. If such is not the case, then proceed as in the next example.

Example 2: Find a fraction naming the rational number $5.6454545\cdots$.

SOLUTION: Write $x = 5.645454545\cdots$. This numeral does not begin to repeat in the tenths place, so we multiply by 10 and look at $10x = 56.454545\cdots$.

Now we have a numeral that begins to repeat in the tenths place. The length of the repeating block is 2 and so we multiply this equation by 100 and subtract as shown below:

$$\begin{aligned} 100(10x) &= 5645.45454545\cdots \\ 10x &= 56.45454545\cdots \\ \hline 990x &= 5589.0000\cdots = 5589 \end{aligned}$$

Hence $x = \frac{5589}{990} = \frac{621}{110}$. That is, $5.645454545\cdots = \frac{621}{110}$.

Exercises 6.5

1. Find fractions that name the rational numbers named by these decimal numerals.
(a) $.22222\cdots$.
(b) $4.3232323232\cdots$.
(c) $12.1622222\cdots$.
(d) $.1365757575757\cdots$.

2. A rational number that is represented by a fraction a/b written in lowest terms has a terminating decimal numeral if and only if the prime factorization of b has the special form $2^x \cdot 5^y$. Which of the following have terminating decimal numerals? Verify your answer by finding the decimal numerals of all of these rational numbers.
(a) $\frac{4}{10}$. **(b)** $\frac{4}{9}$. **(c)** $\frac{3}{17}$. **(d)** $\frac{1}{125}$.

3. Let T denote the set of all rational numbers that can be named by terminating decimal numerals. If $x \in T$ and $y \in T$, is $x + y \in T$? Is $x \cdot y \in T$? Is $x - y \in T$? Is $x \div y \in T$?
(*Hint*: The theorem mentioned in Exercise 2 bears on this exercise.)

4. What would happen if you were to set the problem "Divide 45 by 20" into a desk calculator? What would happen if you set the problem "Divide 45 by 18" into the machine? If you set the problem "Divide 20 by 45" into the machine?

5. Show that the repeating blocks of the decimal numerals for $\frac{1}{7}$, $\frac{5}{7}$, and $\frac{13}{7}$ all have the same length. This comes as a result of the theorem: If $1/q$ has a repeating block of length n, and if p and q are relatively prime, then p/q also has repeating block of length n.

6. Verify that $\frac{1}{99}$ and $\frac{33}{99}$ have repeating blocks of different lengths. Why is this not a counterexample to the theorem stated in Exercise 5? Can you find another pair of rational numbers whose denominators are the same but that have repeating blocks of different lengths?

6.6 The System of Real Numbers

For the very ancient Greeks (prior to about 700 B.C.), the rational numbers were the only numbers there were, but sometime before about 600 B.C. (these dates are impossible to establish with any kind of accuracy) the existence of numbers that were not rational was discovered. Euclid knew that there were such irrational numbers, but their development was slow and it was not until late in the nineteenth century that they were finally given the careful mathematical treatment they required. This work was done largely by Cantor (whom we met in Chapter 4 in connection with set theory) and the German mathematician J. W. R. Dedekind (1831–1916). These numbers, together with the rational numbers, comprise the most significant number system in mathematics and are the basis for a most important part of modern mathematics, called "analysis." In this section we shall discuss these numbers and the number system to which they give rise.

In Section 6.3 we saw how the rational numbers may be located along the number line. Let us suppose that each time we locate a rational number on the line we color its point red. Then we would see that these red points are strung all along the number line and that there are no segments of the number line which do not contain red points. This is not particularly difficult to understand. But what is considerably less obvious is that not every point of the number line is in this way colored red. That is, there exist points at which no rational number is located. Here is how to find one of these nonred points of the number line.

As shown in Figure 6.3, construct a square of side one unit distance and place it along the number line. Then the diagonal $\overline{OP}$ decomposes the square into two right triangles. Centering attention on either one of these triangles, we can use the Pythagorean theorem to conclude that the length of the diagonal $\overline{OP}$, d, is given by the equation $d^2 = 1^2 + 1^2$ or $d^2 = 2$. Thus the length of the diagonal $\overline{OP}$ is the number we call the square root of 2 and denote by the symbol $\sqrt{2}$. There is an elementary proof (known to Euclid) which proves that this number, $\sqrt{2}$, is not a rational number. Thus the point P cannot correspond to a rational number and so is one of the nonred points.

Figure 6.3

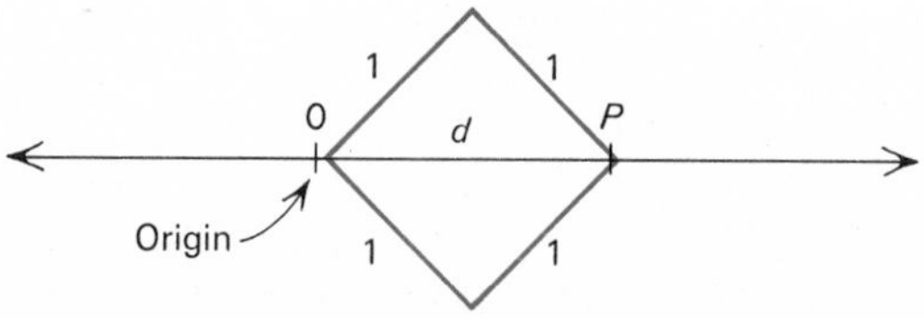

The conclusion we draw from the existence of nonred points is that if the only numbers we have available to us are the rational numbers, then there are line segments whose lengths cannot be measured—which do not have a length at all if a length is something that can be measured.[1] This means that we need to introduce still more numbers into our number system if all segments are to have measurable length. The number $\sqrt{2}$ is an example of just such a number. We call these new numbers **irrational numbers**. These irrational numbers are the numbers needed to measure the lengths of segments whose lengths cannot be measured using rational numbers. In terms of the number line, they are numbers that correspond to the nonred points.

There are three ways to think of an irrational number. We have just identified the irrational numbers as those numbers that correspond to the nonred points on the number line—to the points to which no rational number corresponds. We can also think of an irrational number as one that cannot be expressed as the quotient of two integers. A third way to think of an irrational number is by using decimal numerals. We observed in the preceding section that the decimal numeral name for a rational number is either terminating or nonterminating and repeating. It then follows that the decimal numerals that are nonterminating and nonrepeating must name some kind of number other than a rational number. Such numerals name the irrational numbers. Here are some decimal numerals, each of which names an irrational number:

$$1.123456789101112131415161718\cdots$$

$$1.0100100010000100000100000001\cdots$$

$$1.1223334444555556666667777777 8\cdots.$$

These numerals are nonterminating (obviously) and do not repeat (less obviously) so each must name an irrational number.

We have stated that the number $\sqrt{2}$ is an irrational number. The fact is that the square root of any positive integer that is not a perfect square is an irrational number. Hence the numbers $\sqrt{2}, \sqrt{3}, \sqrt{5}, \sqrt{6}, \sqrt{7}, \sqrt{8}, \sqrt{10}, \ldots,$ are all irrational. The cube root of any positive integer that is not a perfect cube is also irrational and so $\sqrt[3]{2}, \sqrt[3]{3}, \sqrt[3]{4}, \sqrt[3]{5}, \sqrt[3]{6}, \sqrt[3]{7}, \sqrt[3]{9}, \ldots$ are irrational. In general, the nth root of any positive integer which is not a perfect nth power is irrational.

[1] We could measure the approximate length of the segment $\overline{OP}$ using only rational numbers, but here we are talking about the exact length of this segment.

The number π is irrational. It follows that the decimal numeral for π is nonterminating and nonrepeating. This numeral begins like this:

$$3.14159265358979323846264338327950\cdots.$$

There is no discernible pattern to the occurrence of the digits in this numeral. In recent years computers have been used to find many thousands of the digits in this numeral but the complete numeral is unknown.

By a **real number**, we mean a number that is either rational or irrational. Hence the set of all real numbers is the union of the set of rational numbers and the set of irrational numbers. The set theoretic relationships between the various sets of numbers that we have studied is shown in Figure 6.4.

Figure 6.4

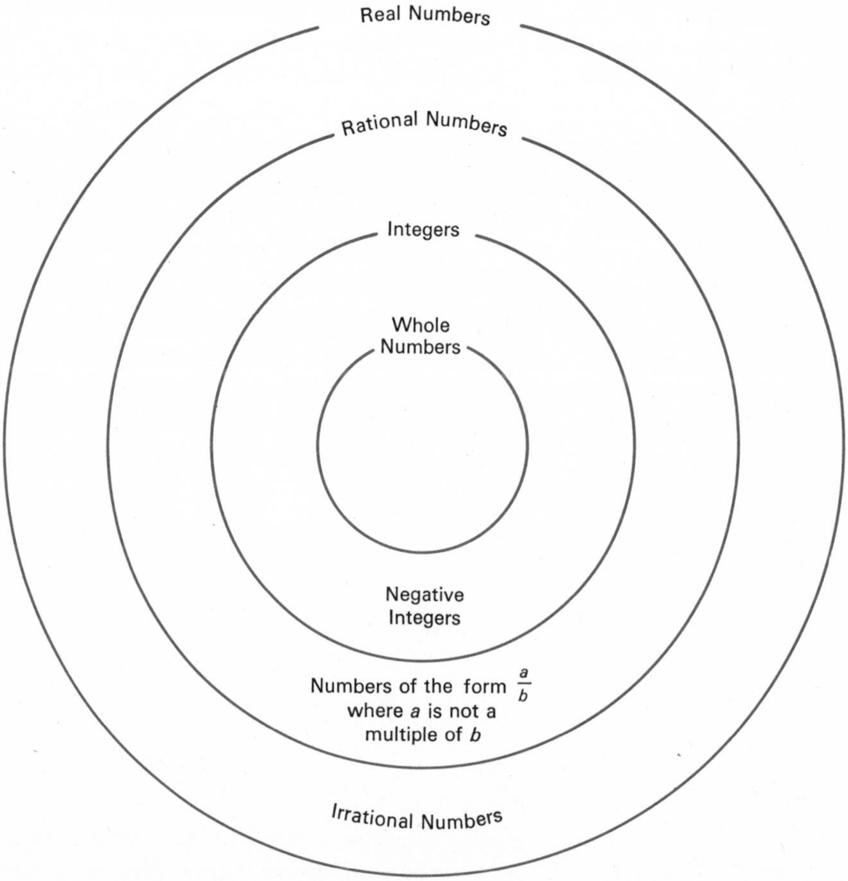

In our later work, we shall most often want to think of the real numbers as being those numbers that correspond to the points of the number line. It is often convenient to identify the real numbers with their corresponding points and thus to think of the real numbers as actually being points. For this reason, we often refer to the number line as the real number line.

Let us remark that there exist numbers that are not real numbers. For example, the number $\aleph_0$ (the smallest infinite cardinal number and the cardinal number of the set of whole numbers) is a number that is not a real number. We can see that $\aleph_0$ is not a real number by observing that there is no point of the number line which is located an infinite distance from the origin, and so no point of the line can be associated with the infinite cardinal number $\aleph_0$. Therefore, $\aleph_0$ is not a real number. There are other kinds of numbers which are not real numbers as well, but we shall not discuss such numbers in this book.

Computations involving real numbers are usually performed by using the decimal numeral names for these numbers, but since all of our computational work in later chapters will involve rational numbers alone, we shall ignore this aspect of the system of real numbers. We should, however, note the structural properties of this system. The set of real numbers together with the binary operations of addition and multiplication possess the following properties (see pages 162 and 164): 1A, 1B, 1C, 1D, 2A, 2B, 2C, 2D, 3A, 3B, 4A, 4B, and 4C. Consequently, the system of real numbers is an ordered field. On the basis of these structural properties alone, we cannot distinguish between the system of rational numbers and the system of real numbers. That is, on the basis of the ordered field properties alone, structurally speaking these two number systems are the same. But there is another structural property possessed by the system of real numbers which is not possessed by the system of rational numbers and which can be used to differentiate between these two number systems. This property is called the **completeness property**. We shall discuss this property in some detail in Chapter 10. For the time being, however, let us be content with a very rough description of this important but somewhat complicated property.

Suppose that we locate all the rational numbers on the number line and then throw away all the points of the line that do not correspond to a rational number. For example, we would throw away the point corresponding to $\sqrt{2}$. Then, after we had done this, the line would have gaps or holes in it. In other words, the line would not be *complete*. But if, after locating all the real numbers on the line, we threw away those points not corresponding to any real number, there would be no such gaps or holes in the line because we would not have thrown any points away. That is, the real number line is complete. Every point corresponds to a real number and every real number corresponds to a point—there is a one-to-one correspondence between the set of all points on the line and the set of all real numbers.

We call the field of real numbers a **complete ordered field**. The field of rational numbers is not a complete ordered field. In fact, the only complete ordered field is the field of real numbers. More precisely, it can be proved in advanced courses in abstract algebra that if F is any complete ordered field, then F cannot be distinguished from the field of real numbers on the basis of structural properties alone.

Exercises 6.6

1. The irrational number $\sqrt{5}$ is the length of the diagonal of a rectangle of length 2 and width 1. Use this fact to locate the number $\sqrt{5}$ on the number line. Find the points of the number line which correspond to the irrational numbers $\sqrt{10}$ and $\sqrt{13}$.
2. Describe how you would locate the point $\sqrt{3}$ on the number line using a right triangle whose hypotenuse has length 2 and one of whose legs has length 1.
3. Prove that there does not exist an isosceles right triangle whose sides are integers.
4.* Here is Euclid's proof of the irrationality of $\sqrt{2}$.

Theorem: $\sqrt{2}$ *is not a rational number (and therefore is irrational).*

PROOF: (By indirect method.) We begin by assuming that $\sqrt{2}$ is a rational number. Then $\sqrt{2}$ can be named by a fraction. Moreover, like all rational numbers, $\sqrt{2}$ can be named by a fraction which has been written in lowest terms. Let us therefore write $\sqrt{2} = a/b$, where a and b are relatively prime. Now explain why these statements follow.

(1) $\sqrt{2} \cdot b = a$.
(2) $2b^2 = a^2$.
(3) a^2 is divisible by 2.
(4) a is divisible by 2.
(5) $a = 2x$.
(6) $2b^2 = 4x^2$.
(7) $b^2 = 2x^2$.
(8) b^2 is divisible by 2.
(9) b is divisible by 2.

Statements 4 and 9 together give us a contradiction. Why? Hence the initial assumption that $\sqrt{2}$ was rational is false and so $\sqrt{2}$ is not a rational number and this means that $\sqrt{2}$ is an irrational number.

5. Repeat the proof given in Exercise 4 making the appropriate changes so as to obtain a proof that $\sqrt{3}$ is irrational.

6. Which of the following are irrational numbers.

(a) $\sqrt{2} + 1$. **(c)** $(\sqrt{2} + 1)(\sqrt{2} - 1)$.

(b) $(\sqrt{2} \cdot \sqrt{2}) + 3$. **(d)** $(\sqrt{2})^2 - 1$.

7. Explain why the decimal numeral 1.0100100010000100000100 ··· is nonrepeating. (*Hint:* Assume it is repeating and note that the repeating block, which has some definite length, must contain both 0's and 1's. Argue to a contradiction.)

8. Is the sum of two irrational numbers necessarily irrational? Is the product of two irrational numbers necessarily irrational? (*Hint:* Study Exercise 6.)

9. Insert "Yes" or "No" in the blanks as appropriate.

	Whole Numbers	*Integers*	*Rational Numbers*	*Real Numbers*	*Arithmetic Modulo 6*	*Arithmetic Modulo 5*
Addition						
Commutative						
Associative						
Identity						
Inverses						
Multiplication						
Commutative						
Associative						
Identity						
Inverses						
Distributivity of Addition and Multiplication						
$nm = 0$ if and only if $n = 0$ or $m = 0$						
Order Property						
Completeness Property						

7 Analytic Geometry

IN OUR STUDY of the real numbers we saw that the real numbers may be placed in one-to-one correspondence with the points on a line. This one-to-one correspondence allows us to think of points as being numbers or to think of numbers as being points whenever it is convenient to do so. What we have established is a connection between arithmetic on the one hand and geometry on the other. As tenuous as this connection may appear to be, when fully developed it provides a strong and extremely useful tool for the study of both Euclidean geometry and algebra. The name of this tool is analytic geometry and we shall be studying some of the basic ideas about this part of mathematics in this chapter.

Analytic geometry stems from the work of the two most important seventeenth century mathematicians, Pierre de Fermat (French, 1601–1665) and René Descartes (French, 1596–1650). Fermat made significant contributions to the subject, but unfortunately he did not publish during his lifetime. Descartes, who probably made his discoveries at roughly the same time as did Fermat (about 1629), published a manuscript in which he dealt with connections between algebra and geometry, and it is this work that is usually regarded as the beginning of the subject. As a matter of fact, Fermat's work more nearly resembles modern analytic geometry than does Descartes', but because he published and Fermat did not, it is Descartes' name that is associated with the subject.

7.1 The Cartesian Coordinate System

We are able to locate the solutions of such equations as $3x + 5 = 8$ on the real number line and so give a kind of geometric picture of these solutions. The reason we can do this is that we earlier found a way to attach

René Descartes (1596–1650)

"number meaning" to each of the points of a line. Before we get involved in analytic geometry, it will be necessary for us to do the same thing in the plane. We must find a way of giving each point of the plane a kind of "number meaning."

The names we shall give to points in the plane are called **ordered pairs** of real numbers. An ordered pair is a two-object set whose two objects are given in a specified order. The ordered pair consisting of the two real numbers 2 and 3, given in that order, is denoted by (2,3). The symbol (3,2) means the two-object set consisting of 3 and 2, given in that order. Two ordered pairs (a,b) and (c,d) are the same ordered pair if and only if their left-hand parts are the same and their right-hand parts are the same: $(a,b) = (c,d)$ if and only if $a = c$ and $b = d$.

Here is how we find the ordered name of a point in the plane. Select a pair of perpendicular lines in the plane. For convenience, make one of them vertical and the other horizontal. These lines are called the **coordinate axes**. The horizontal line is called the **x-axis** and the vertical line is called the **y-axis**. Their point of intersection is called the **origin**. Next, using the origin as the point corresponding to the real number 0, and using some convenient unit distance, set up a one-to-one correspondence between the points on each axis and the real numbers. We have done this in Figure 7.1 where we have indicated a few points on the axes which correspond to integers.

Figure 7.1

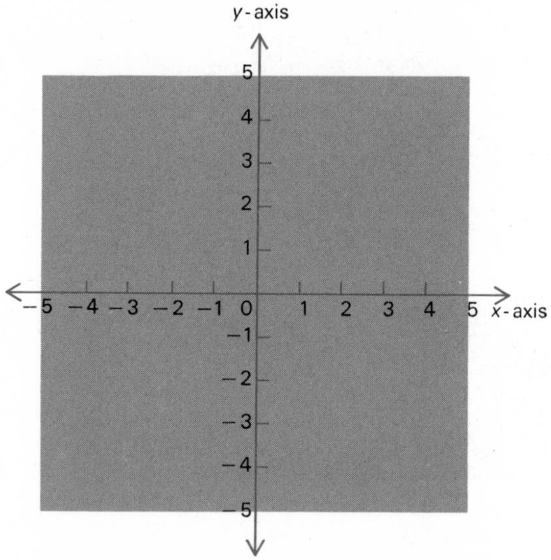

In effect, we have placed two real-number lines in the plane so that they are perpendicular to each other and intersect at their origins. Using these axes, we can assign an ordered pair of real numbers to each point of the plane. If P is a point (refer to Figure 7.2), we construct lines through P perpendicular to the coordinate axes. The left-hand part of the ordered pair name for P is the number assigned to the point on the x-axis determined by the vertical line through P. The right-hand part of the ordered pair name for P is the real number assigned to the point on the y-axis determined by the horizontal line through P. In Figure 7.3 we have located a few points and have given their ordered pair names.

This method for giving ordered pair names to points of the plane sets up a one-to-one correspondence between the set of all points in the plane and the set of all ordered pairs of real numbers. That is, each point has exactly

Figure 7.2

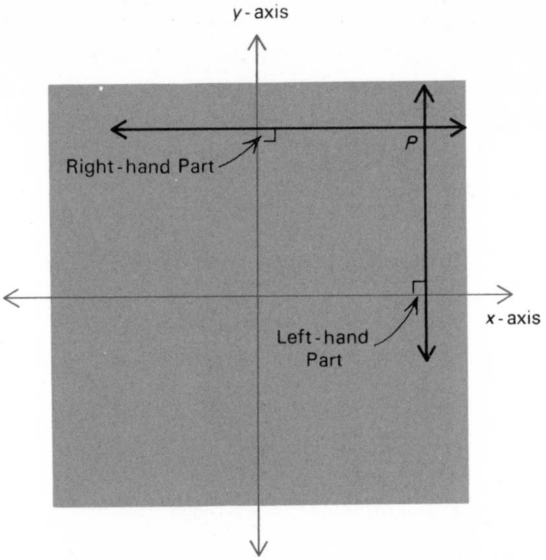

one ordered pair name and each ordered pair names exactly one point. We call the ordered pair name of a point the **coordinate** of that point. The left-hand part of the coordinate is called the ***x*-coordinate** and the right-hand part is called the ***y*-coordinate**.

Figure 7.3

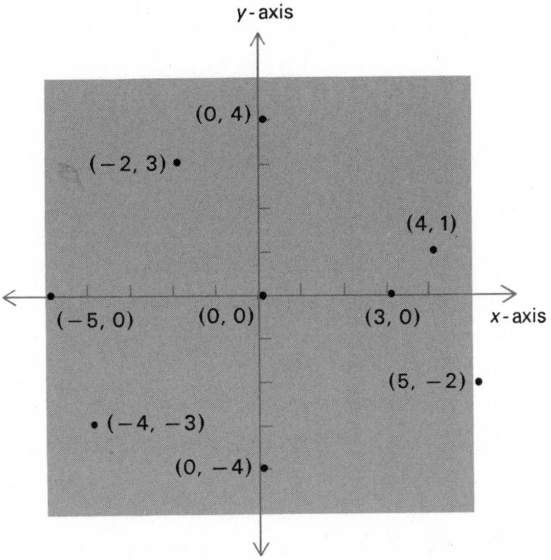

The coordinates of points in the plane can be used for a great many different purposes, one of which is to find the distance between points. If two points belong to a line that is parallel to one of the coordinate axes, then it is very easy to find the distance between them. Consider these examples.

Example 1: Find the distance between the points (1,2) and (−2,2).

SOLUTION: These points determine a line parallel to the x-axis (see Figure 7.4). Thus the distance between them is found by subtracting the smaller x-coordinate from the larger x-coordinate. In this case the difference is $1 - (-2)$ or 3. Hence these two points are 3 units apart.

Figure 7.4

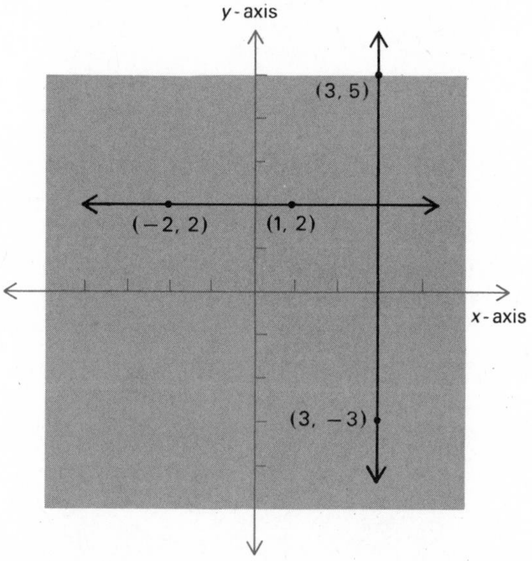

Example 2: The distance between the points (3, −3) and (3,5) (see Figure 7.4) is found by subtracting the smaller y-coordinate from the larger y-coordinate. The distance between these points is $5 - (-3) = 8$ units.

If the line through the two given points is not parallel to a coordinate axis, then the problem of finding the distance between the points is somewhat more complicated. For example, if P and Q are as shown in Figure 7.5, then we first construct a right triangle, as shown in that illustration. This right triangle should have the line segment $\overline{PQ}$ as its hypotenuse and should

Figure 7.5

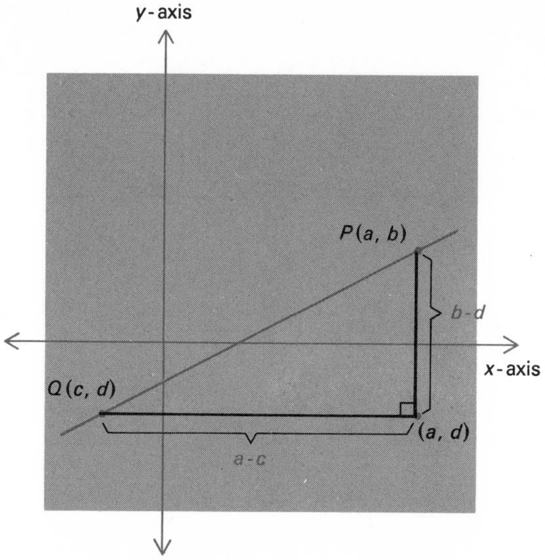

have its legs parallel to the coordinate axes. Since the legs of this triangle are parallel to the coordinate axes, we may find their lengths as in the two examples above. Once the lengths of these two legs are known, the Pythagorean theorem can be used to find the length of the hypotenuse.

Example 3: Find the distance between the points (5,2) and (1, – 1).

SOLUTION: Construct a right triangle as shown in Figure 7.6. (Actually there are two right triangles that could be constructed; either one can be

Figure 7.6

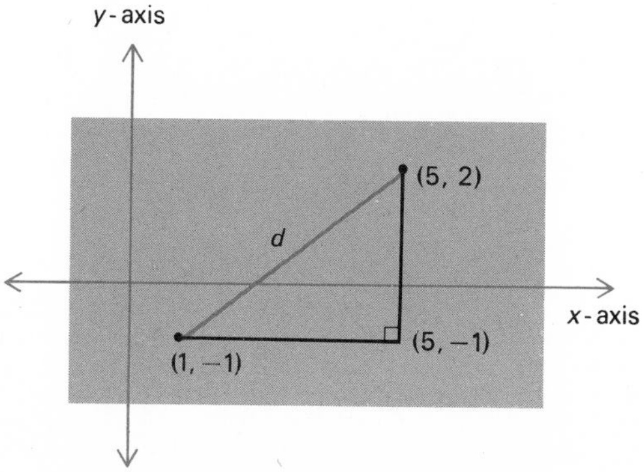

used.) The coordinate of the third vertex is $(5,-1)$, the length of the vertical leg is $2-(-1)=3$, and the length of the horizontal leg is $5-1=4$. According to the Pythagorean theorem, if the length between the given points is denoted by d, then

$$d^2 = 3^2 + 4^2.$$

Hence $d^2 = 25$ and so $d = 5$.

Exercises 7.1

1. Find the distance between the points
   (a) $(0,3)$ and $(4,-3)$.
   (b) $(-1,3)$ and $(-3,2)$.
   (c) (a,b) and (c,d), where $a < c$ and $b < d$.
2. What can you say about the coordinate (x,y) of a point P which lies above the x-axis? Below the x-axis? To the left of the y-axis? To the right of the y-axis?
3. Three of the vertices of a square are located at the points $(3,1)$, $(3,-3)$, and $(-1,-3)$. Find the coordinate of the fourth vertex and the coordinate of the center of the square.
4. The base of an isosceles triangle has endpoints $(-2,2)$ and $(4,2)$. The height of the triangle is 5. What is the coordinate of the third vertex?
5. Draw the circle whose center is at the point $(3,1)$ and that passes through the point $(7,-2)$. What is the radius of this circle?
6. A triangle has its vertices at the points $(-2,2)$, $(7,2)$, and $(2,-2)$. Is this triangle a right triangle or not?
7. Prove that the points $(-1,2)$, $(4,-3)$, and $(5,3)$ are the vertices of an isosceles triangle.
8. Do the points $(8,5)$, $(-4,-11)$, and $(-6,2)$ all lie on the same circle with center at $(2,-3)$?

7.2 Lines and Linear Equations

We have observed the connection between the geometric objects that are points and the arithmetic objects that are ordered pairs of real numbers. In this section we shall discuss the connection between the geometric objects that are lines and the arithmetic objects that are equations of a certain type.

Consider the line shown in Figure 7.7. We have identified a few points of this line by giving their coordinates. Is there anything special or unusual about these coordinates? Do they display any kind of pattern? If the x- and y-coordinates are added, the sum is 4. That is, if (x,y) is one of these points,

Figure 7.7

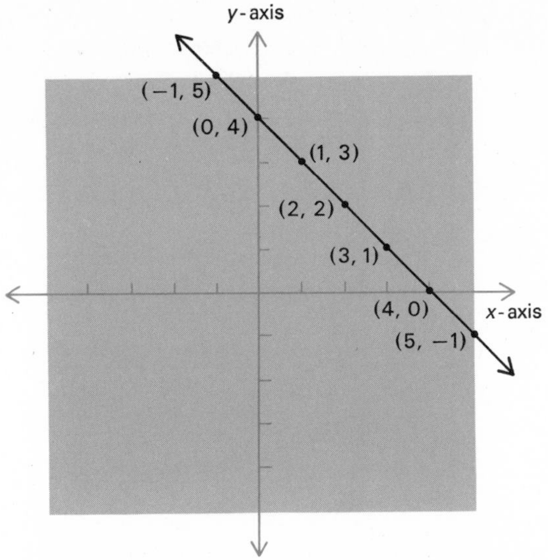

then $x + y = 4$. This may not appear startling, but see what has happened: We began with a geometric object (the line) and have produced an algebraic object (the equation $x + y = 4$). Here is another example of how we can produce an equation from a line.

Figure 7.8

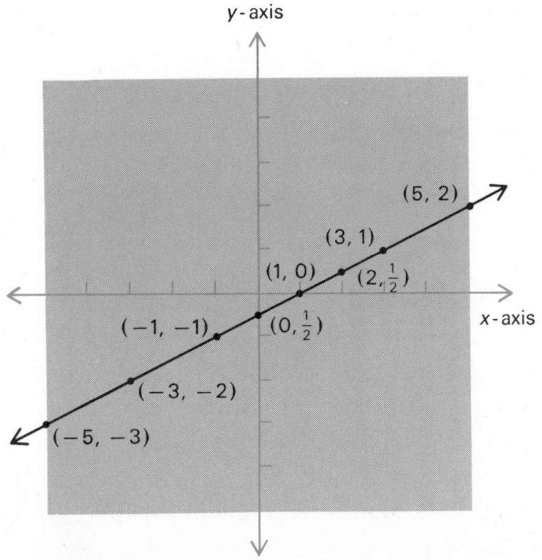

Example 1: In Figure 7.8 we have identified a line and some of the points of that line. The special relationship between the x- and y-coordinates of these points is not so obvious, but a careful examination will reveal this relationship. It is that the x-coordinate made smaller by 1 is equal to twice the y-coordinate. Thus, if we denote a typical point of the line by (x,y), then we may conclude that $x - 1 = 2y$. Once again a line has given rise to an equation.

Let us examine the equations we obtained in these two examples. The first equation was

$$x + y = 4$$

and the second equation (rewritten) was

$$x - 2y = 1.$$

These equations have the form of what is called a linear equation. A **linear equation** is one that can be rewritten in the general form

$$ax + by = c,$$

where a, b, and c are real numbers and not both a and b are zero. Other examples of linear equations are $3x - 2y = -5$, $y = 5 - 2x$, $y = 2x$, $2x = 5$, and $y = 1$. The preceding two examples would seem to suggest that each line in the plane gives rise to a linear equation, and this is indeed true. By examining the coordinates of the points of a line, we can always find a linear equation. In these two examples we found the equations by inspection. There is a routine procedure for finding the equation of a line; however, for the time being, the inspection method will suffice.

By a **solution** of a linear equation we mean numerical values of the variables x and y which produce a true statement. For example, $x = 2$ and $y = 1$ together comprise a solution of the linear equation $x - y = 1$ because $(2) - (1) = 1$ is a true statement. We write this solution in the form of an ordered pair: $(2,1)$. The left-hand part of the ordered pair is the x value of the solution and the right-hand part is the y value of the solution. The ordered pair $(4,3)$ is another solution of $x - y = 1$ since $(4) - (3) = 1$ is a true statement. It should be clear that linear equations in two variables have infinitely many solutions. Among the solutions of the equation $x - y = 1$ are the solutions (2,1), (3,2), (4,3), (5,4), and so on.

Example 2: Some solutions of the linear equation $x - 2y = 1$ are $(0,-\frac{1}{2})$, $(2,\frac{1}{2})$, $(3,1)$, $(-3,-2)$, and $(18,\frac{17}{2})$. These solutions were found by giving various values to x and then determining the corresponding values of y. Of course we can just as well give values to y and then compute the corresponding values of x. For instance, when $y = 0$, we get the equation $x - 2(0) = 1$, so that the ordered pair (1,0) is also a solution.

Example 3: Find five solutions of the linear equation $2x = 4$.

SOLUTION: If we first rewrite this equation in the form $ax + by = c$, it will be clearer what the solutions are. When we rewrite $2x = 4$ in this form we get

$$2x + 0y = 4.$$

Now it should be clear that any ordered pair $(2,y)$ (where y is any number at all) is a solution. Five solutions are (2,1), (2,2), (2,3), (2,4), and (2,5).

We have seen that lines give rise to linear equations. The reverse is true as well. That is, if the solutions of a linear equation are located in the

Figure 7.9

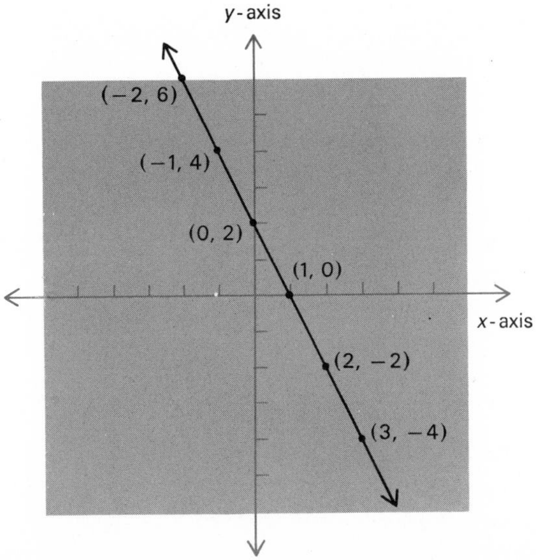

coordinate plane, then these solutions form a straight line. For example, consider the linear equation $2x + y = 2$. A few solutions of this equation are $(0,2)$, $(1,0)$, $(-1,4)$, $(2,-2)$, $(-2,6)$, and $(3,-4)$. We have located the points named by these ordered pairs in Figure 7.9. The reader will not have to stretch his imagination very far to conclude that these points do in fact belong to the same straight line and that if we were to identify more solutions of the linear equation, then these solutions would also belong to this same line. We call the line that is formed by the solutions of a linear equation the **graph** of the equation. Thus the line shown in Figure 7.9 is the graph of the linear equation $2x + y = 2$.

Example 4: Find the graph of the equation $x - 2y = 3$.

SOLUTION: Since a line is determined by any two of its points, all we need to do is to find two solutions of this equation and locate these in the plane. The line determined by these two points is the graph of the given equation. The easiest solutions to find are those in which either x or y is 0. If $x = 0$, then $y = -\frac{3}{2}$ and so $(0,-\frac{3}{2})$ is a solution. If $y = 0$, then $x = 3$ and so $(3,0)$ is a solution. The unique line passing through these two points is the graph of the linear equation (see Figure 7.10).

The two points found in Example 4 are called the **intercepts** of the line. The point $(0,-\frac{3}{2})$ is called the ***y*-intercept** of the line and $(3,0)$ is called the ***x*-intercept** of the line.

Figure 7.10

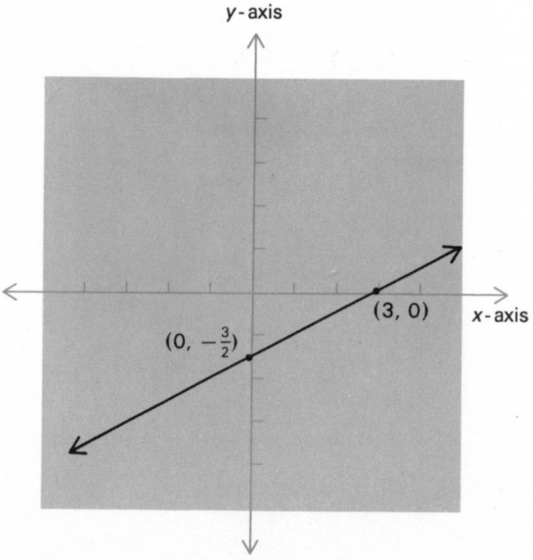

We have seen that there is an intimate connection between lines and linear equations. The connection between a line and its equation is that the set of coordinates of the points of the line is equal to the set of solutions of the linear equation. This connection may be used to the mutual advantage of both geometry and algebra. However, in practice, the invention of analytic geometry has resulted in the subversion of geometry to the advantage of algebra. Problems that prior to the introduction of analytic geometry would have been solved geometrically were solved algebraically after the introduction of analytic geometry. There are a number of reasons for this, but perhaps the most significant one is that geometric arguments tend to stress inventiveness and cleverness more than do algebraic arguments. On the whole, algebraic arguments are more routine and what must be done to complete one is more self-evident than is the case with geometric arguments.

Exercises 7.2

1. Find the equation of the line which passes through the points
(a) $(1,-1)$, $(3,1)$, and $(5,3)$.
(b) $(-1,4)$, $(0,2)$, $(1,0)$, $(2,-2)$, and $(3,-4)$.

2. Write each of these linear equations in the form $ax + by = c$.
(a) $3 - 2y = 4x$. **(b)** $6x = 17$. **(c)** $3y + 6 = -2x$.

3. Find two solutions of each equation and use these solutions to graph the line corresponding to each equation.
(a) $5x - 3y = -1$. **(b)** $3x + 2y = 4$.

4. Graph these equations by locating their x- and y-intercepts.
(a) $4x - 2y = 1$. **(b)** $6x = 14$. **(c)** $3x - 7y = -4$.

5. What can you say about the graph of an equation each of whose solutions has the same x-coordinate? Each of whose solutions has the same y-coordinate?

6. What can you say about the graph of the equation $ax + by = 0$?

7. Graph the equations $2x - y = 3$ and $4x - 2y = 6$. Can you find other equations that have the same line for their graph? Given a line, how many equations are there which have that line for their graph?

7.3 The Slope of a Line

We know that a line is completely determined as soon as two of its points are given. Certainly one point alone does not determine a line. Thus to say, "Consider the line determined by the point (1,2)" is nonsense because there are infinitely many different lines passing through the point (1,2). But, if we identify one of the line's points and also give some indication as to the slope of that line, then the line is determined. For example, we could say, "Consider the line passing through the point (1,2) and making an angle of 45° with the x-axis." This does describe a unique line, the line shown in Figure 7.11. (Incidentally, angles are usually measured in the counter-clockwise direction.) So one way to describe the slope of a line is to describe the angle that that line makes with the x-axis. But there is another way to describe the slope that is more useful because it relates directly to the equation of the line. We shall study this method of describing the slope of a line in this section.

Figure 7.11

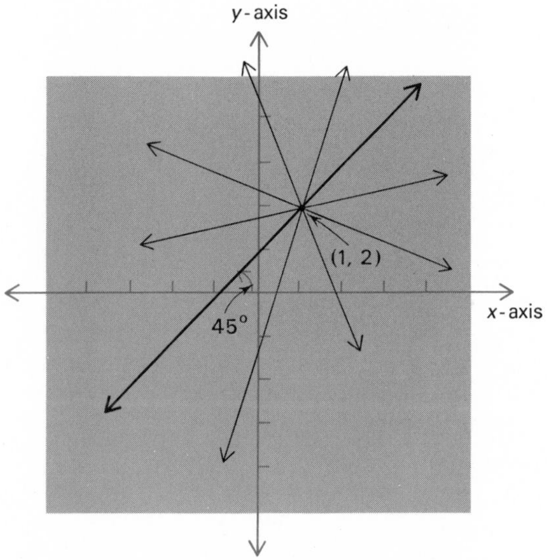

A common way to measure the degree of incline or decline of a highway is to measure the amount of vertical rise or fall over a certain horizontal distance. For example, a highway that rises vertically 10 feet over a horizontal distance of 1000 feet would be said to have slope of 10/1000 or 1/100. If the highway fell 10 feet vertically for every 1000 feet horizontally, then the highway would have slope $-10/1000$ or $-1/100$. We use this same idea to measure the slope of a line. To determine the slope of a line, select any two distinct points (it does not matter which two points you choose), say the points (x_1,y_1) and (x_2,y_2). The slope of the line (refer to Figure 7.12) is then defined to be the quotient

$$\frac{y_2 - y_1}{x_2 - x_1}.$$

Figure 7.12

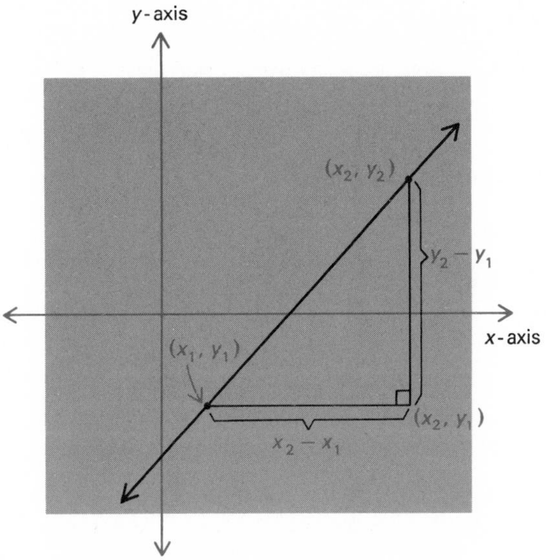

Here are some examples of how the slope of a line is computed.

Example 1: The line m in Figure 7.13 passes through the points (1,2) and (3,5) and so has slope $\frac{5-2}{3-1} = \frac{3}{2}$. The slope of line ℓ in Figure 7.13 is $\frac{3 - -1}{-4 - -2} = \frac{4}{-2} = -2$.

Example 2: Draw a picture of a line that is parallel to the x-axis. If (x_1,y_1) and (x_2,y_2) are points of this line, then since $y_1 = y_2$, the expression for the slope is $0/(x_2 - x_1) = 0$. Hence a line parallel to the x-axis has slope of zero.

Example 3: If a line is parallel to the y-axis, and if (x_1,y_1) and (x_2,y_2) are two points of the line, then since $x_1 = x_2$, the expression for the slope of the line is $(y_2 - y_1)/0$. This symbol is meaningless and so lines parallel to the y-axis have no slope at all.

Figure 7.13

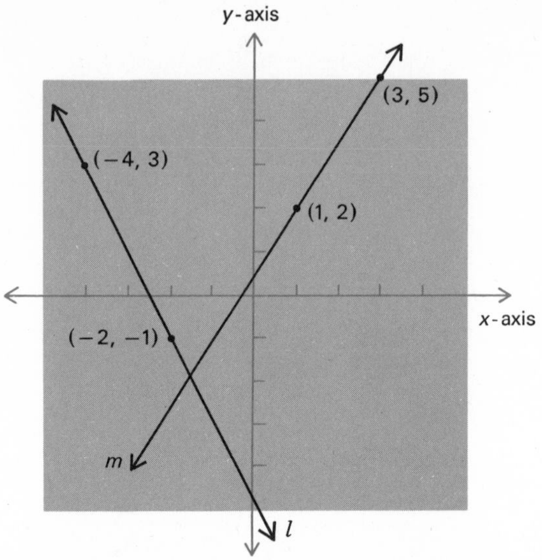

Examples 2 and 3 show that to say a line has zero slope is very different from saying that the line has no slope.

If a line is not parallel to the y-axis (that is, is not vertical) then its equation can be written in the special form

$$y = mx + b$$

where m and b are real numbers. Now if $x = 0$, then $y = b$ and so $(0,b)$ is the y-intercept of the line. In addition, the number m is the slope of the line. We can see this as follows: Suppose that (x_1, y_1) and (x_2, y_2) are points of this line. Then these pairs are solutions of the linear equation $y = mx + b$ and so we can write the equations

$$y_2 = mx_2 + b \qquad \text{and} \qquad y_1 = mx_1 + b.$$

By subtracting the second equation from the first, we can obtain

$$\begin{aligned} y_2 - y_1 &= (mx_2 + b) - (mx_1 + b) \\ &= mx_2 - mx_1 \\ &= m(x_2 - x_1). \end{aligned}$$

Consequently, $m = (y_2 - y_1)/(x_2 - x_1)$ and m is the slope of the line. This means that we can identify the slope and the y-intercept of a nonvertical line simply by writing its equation in the form $y = mx + b$. For this reason, we call this form of the equation of a line the **slope-intercept form** of that equation.

Example 4: Find the slope and y-intercept of the line $2x - 3y = 6$.

SOLUTION: Writing this equation in the slope-intercept form, we get $y = \frac{2}{3}x - 2$ and so the line has slope $\frac{2}{3}$ and y-intercept $(0, -2)$. The line is shown in Figure 7.14.

Figure 7.14

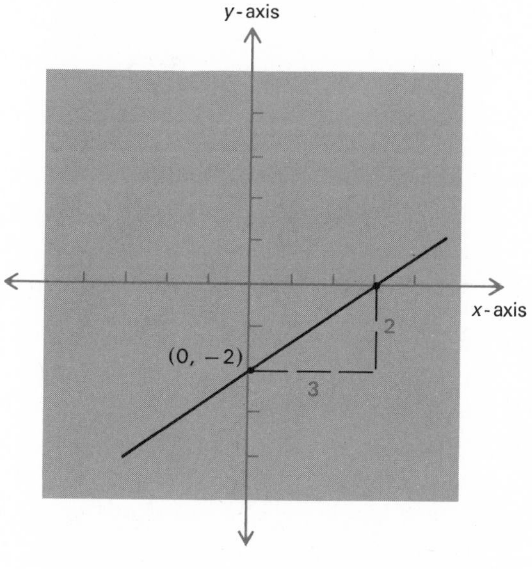

Example 5: A line has slope $\frac{3}{2}$ and passes through the point (1,2). Find its equation.

SOLUTION: We know that the equation of the line has the form

$$y = \frac{3}{2}x + b$$

since the slope was given to us. It remains only to determine the number b.

But since the line is known to pass through the point (1,2), we know that (1,2) is a solution of the equation we are looking for. That is

$$2 = (\tfrac{3}{2} \cdot 1) + b.$$

From this equation we see that $b = 2 - \frac{3}{2} = \frac{1}{2}$. Hence the equation of the line is

$$y = \tfrac{3}{2}x + \tfrac{1}{2}$$

or $3x - 2y = -1$.

Since parallel lines must have the same slopes, we can tell whether or not two lines are parallel by examining their equations.

Example 6: Which of the lines $x - y = -1$ and $3x - y = 6$ is parallel to the line $x - y = 2$?

SOLUTION: Rewriting these equations in slope-intercept form, we are asking which of the lines $y = x + 1$ and $y = 3x - 6$ is parallel to the line $y = x - 2$. The line $y = x + 1$ has the same slope as the line $y = x - 2$ (both have slope 1) and so these lines are parallel. The line $y = 3x - 6$ has slope 3 and so is not parallel to $y = x - 2$ (see Figure 7.15).

Figure 7.15

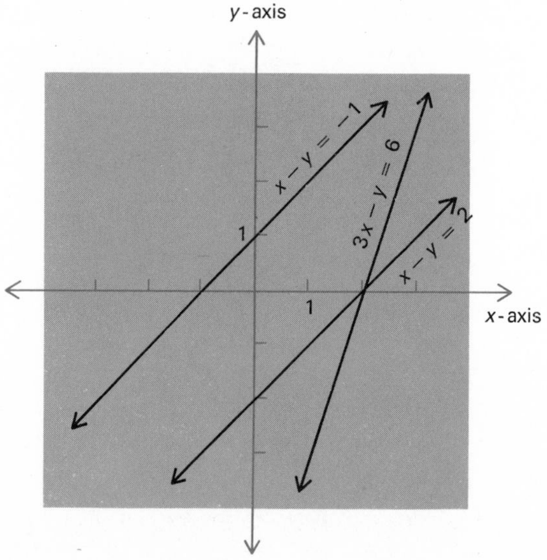

We can also tell whether or not two lines are perpendicular by looking at their equations. It can be proved that two lines are perpendicular if and only if the product of their slopes is equal to -1.

Example 7: Which of the lines $y = -2x - 3$ and $y = 3x - 1$ is perpendicular to the line $y = \frac{1}{2}x + 3$?

SOLUTION: The line $y = 3x - 1$ is not perpendicular to $y = \frac{1}{2}x + 3$ since the product of the two slopes is not equal to -1. But $y = -2x - 3$ is perpendicular to $y = \frac{1}{2}x + 3$ since the product of their slopes (-2 and $\frac{1}{2}$) is equal to -1. These lines are shown in Figure 7.16.

Figure 7.16

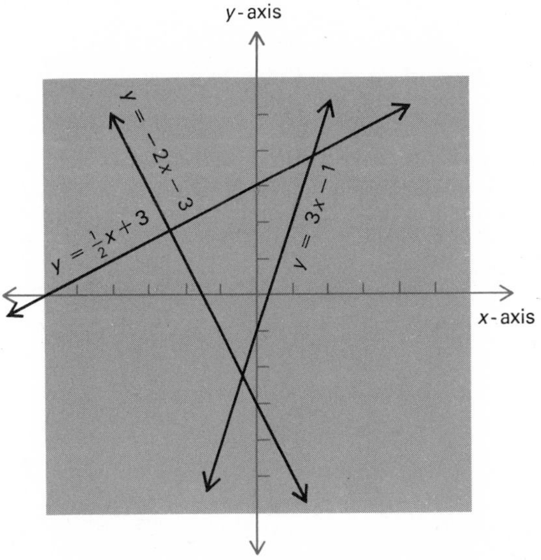

Exercises 7.3

1. A line passes through the points given. What is the slope of the line?
   (a) (2,2) and (4, −2). **(b)** (−1,2) and (−4,0).
2. Determine the slope of each line by locating two points belonging to the line.
   (a) $2x + y = 7$. **(b)** $2x - y + 2 = 0$.
3. What can you say about a line that has no slope? What can you say about a line that has slope equal to 0? If a line has positive slope, then does the line rise or fall as you move along the line from left to right? Does the line rise or fall if its slope is negative?

4. A line passes through the point $(-1,3)$ and has slope $-\frac{1}{2}$. Graph the line and find its equation.
5. An isosceles right triangle has its legs parallel to the coordinate axes. What can you say about the slope of its hypotenuse?
6. Find three linear equations whose graphs form a right triangle.
7. Describe how you could use the idea of slope to prove that three given points were collinear. Test your idea by showing that the points $(-1,-5)$, $(2,1)$, and $(3,3)$ are collinear.
8. The vertices of a triangle are A: $(-4,2)$, B: $(6,6)$, and C: $(-3,-4)$. Find the equation of the altitude (that is, perpendicular) from the vertex A to the side $\overline{BC}$.
9. In 1965 the population of Foosland, Illinois, was 13. In 1967 the population was 24. Assuming that the town's rate of growth is linear, what would you predict the population to be in 1971?

7.4 The Conic Sections, I

The study of lines and linear equations is only the first part of the study of analytic geometry. The next curves of interest are called "the conic sections." These curves were studied by the Greeks, but their treatment using algebra had to await the invention of the coordinate plane. In this section we shall describe these curves without reference to the coordinate plane. In the next section we shall discuss them using the methods of analytic geometry.

A (right-circular) **cone** is a spatial surface, as shown in Figure 7.17. The cone may be thought of as consisting of the totality of all lines in space that pass through a fixed point P called the **vertex** of the cone and which make a fixed angle α with a fixed line that passes through this vertex and is called the **axis** of the cone. A cone is a surface, not a solid, and extends without limit in two directions.

By cutting through this cone with planes, we form plane curves called sections of the cone or **conic sections**. If the cutting plane is held so that it is perpendicular to the axis of the cone, then the section so formed is a **circle** (see Figure 7.18(a)). Thus a circle is a conic section. If the cutting plane is held as shown in Figure 7.18(b), then the resulting section is a sort of elongated circle called an **ellipse**. Holding the cutting plane as shown in Figure 7.18(c) produces a curve that is not closed and that extends without limit in two directions. This curve is called a **parabola**. The fourth conic section is formed by holding the cutting plane so that it is parallel to the axis of the cone. The curve produced in this case (Figure 7.18(d)) consists of two branches, each of which somewhat resembles a parabola. This two-piece curve is called a **hyperbola**.

These definitions in terms of cuts of the cone are purely geometric in nature. We want to apply the methods of analytic geometry to these curves, however, and so we would prefer to have definitions that may more easily be translated into algebraic language. We already have such a definition of the circle. We know that a circle consists of all points in the plane that are a given distance away from a given point. We shall use this alternate definition of the circle in the next section to find an equation for the circle.

The other conic sections also have alternate definitions similar to the above alternate definition of a circle. An ellipse can be defined as the set of all points in the plane the sum of whose distances from two given points is equal to a given distance greater than the distance between the two given points. Refer to Figure 7.19. In this illustration the given points are P and Q and the given distance is shown on the left and is called d. Notice that d is greater than the distance between P and Q. Each of the points A, B, C, and D is a point of the ellipse, since each of these points has the property that its distance from P plus its distance from Q is equal to the distance d. The points P and Q are called the **foci** of the ellipse.

A parabola is defined in terms of a given line and a given point. A parabola consists of all points in the plane whose distances from a given point are equal to their distances from a given line. Refer to Figure 7.20. The given point is P and the given line is ℓ. Each point of the parabola has the same

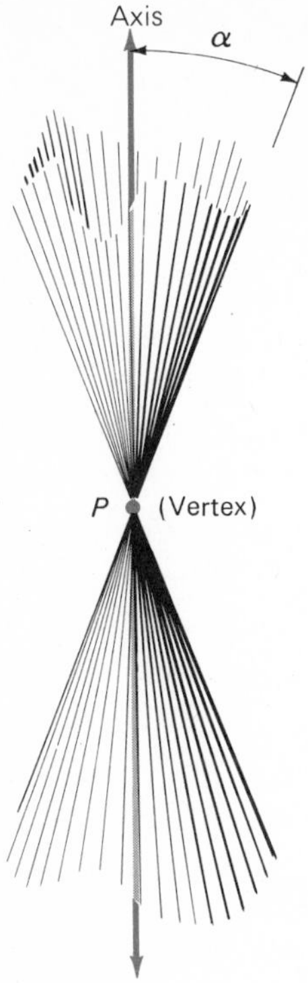

Figure 7.17

Figure 7.18

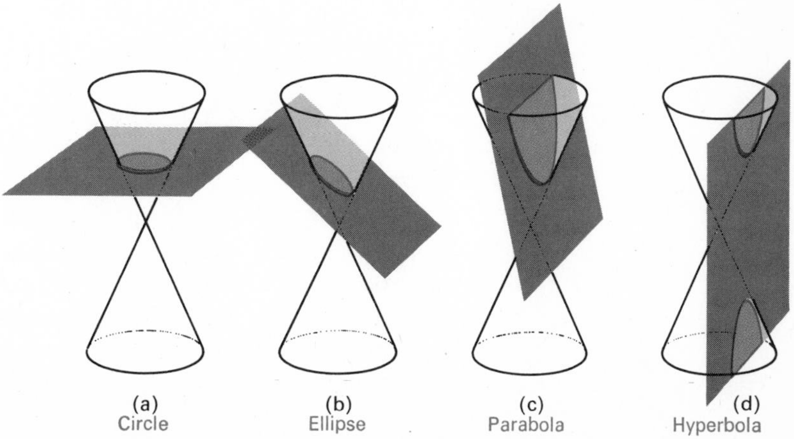

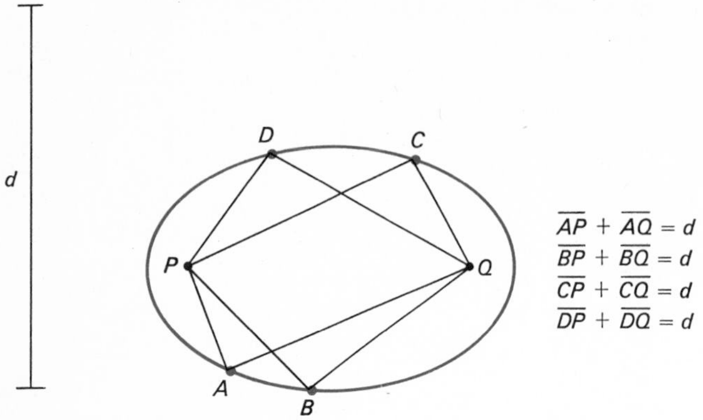

Figure 7.19

Figure 7.20

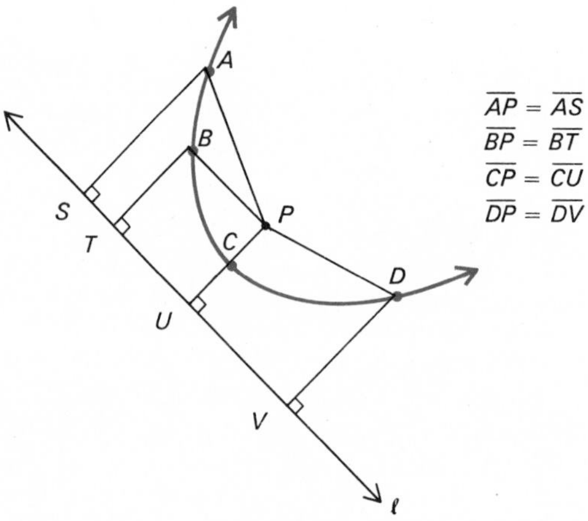

distance from P as it does from the line ℓ. The point P is called the **focus** of the parabola and the line ℓ is called the **directrix**.

A hyperbola (like an ellipse) is defined in terms of two points and a given distance. A hyperbola consists of all points in the plane the difference of whose distances from two given points is equal to a given distance less than the distance between the two given points. In Figure 7.21, P and Q are the given points and d is the given distance. Each point of the hyperbola (which consists of two separate branches) has the property that the difference of its distances from P and from Q is equal to d.

Figure 7.21

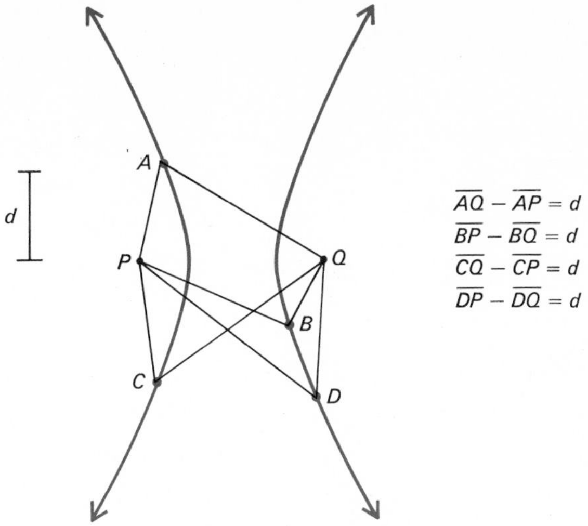

The conic sections have innumerable important physical properties that make knowledge of them essential to an understanding of physics, astronomy, and many other sciences. Let us mention just a few of these.

1. If you wanted to enclose one acre of grazing land with a fence as cheaply as possible, you should make the fence circular. This is because a circle encompasses a given area with the least perimeter.
2. The reflectors of automobile headlights are parabolic in cross section because when the light source is located at the focus, the parabola reflects this light in parallel beams, thus maximizing the lighting effect (Figure 7.22).

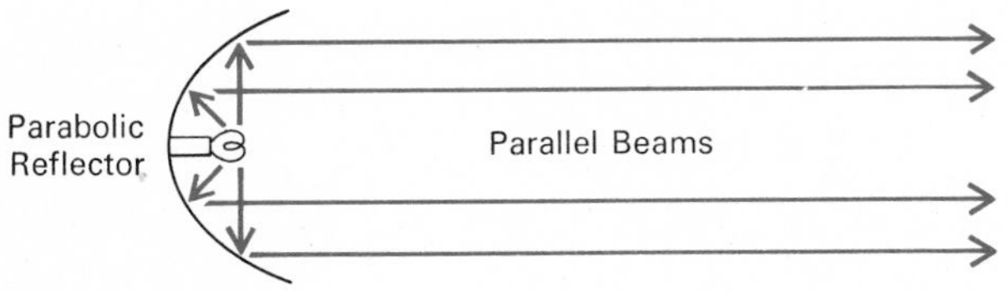

Figure 7.22

3. If one person stands at one focus of an elliptically shaped room and whispers very softly, he will be heard by another person standing at the

other focus because of a reflecting property of ellipses. Sounds emitted from one focus are reflected by the ellipse to the other focus (Figure 7.23).

Figure 7.23

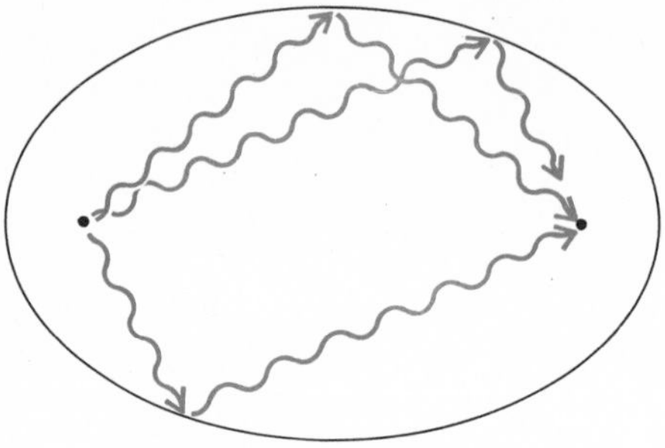

4. The planets travel around the sun on elliptical paths. In each case the sun is located at one of the foci of these paths.
5. Meteors travel on paths which are conic sections, mainly ellipses.

Exercises 7.4

1. Can you think of a way to generate a cone by using rigid motions in space?
2. If we think of the light beams emitted by a flashlight as forming half of a cone, then the conic sections can be reproduced by shining a flashlight against a wall. For example, a circle can be produced by holding the flashlight at right angles to the wall. How would the other conic sections be demonstrated in this way?
3. Place two thumb tacks in a flat surface and attach a piece of string to the tacks. (Make the length of the string about double the distance between the tacks.) Now place a pencil so as to stretch the string and make it taut. Move the pencil about the surface in such a way as to keep the string taut at all times. The curve traced out is what kind of conic section?
4. How would you trace out a circle using string, tacks, and a pencil?
5. Draw a line on a piece of paper and locate a point 2 inches away from the line. Now locate ten points whose distances from the line equal their distances from the point. Connect these points by a smooth curve. What kind of a conic section have you constructed?
6. Locate two points P and Q on a piece of paper so that they are 3 inches apart. Now locate a number of points that have the property that their distance from P less their distance from Q is equal to 1 inch. Locate a number of points with the property that their distance from Q less their

distance from P is 1 inch. By connecting these points with smooth curves you will have constructed a hyperbola.

7. The four conic sections we have described are called **nondegenerate conics.** The degenerate conics are the point, the line, and the figure consisting of two intersecting lines. Explain how these degenerate conics can be obtained by cutting a cone with a plane. The point is a degenerate case of what kinds of conic sections? The line is a degenerate case of which conic? The pair of intersecting lines is a degenerate case of what kind of conic?

8. *Pascal's Theorem* states that if six points A, B, C, D, E, and F are chosen on a conic section, and if the lines $\overleftrightarrow{AB}$, $\overleftrightarrow{BC}$, $\overleftrightarrow{CD}$, $\overleftrightarrow{DE}$, $\overleftrightarrow{EF}$, and $\overleftrightarrow{FA}$ are drawn, then the intersections of the lines $\overleftrightarrow{AB}$ and $\overleftrightarrow{DE}$, $\overleftrightarrow{BC}$ and $\overleftrightarrow{EF}$, and $\overleftrightarrow{CD}$ and $\overleftrightarrow{FA}$ are collinear. Illustrate this using a circle. Repeat the illustration using a parabola.

7.5 The Conic Sections, II

We have seen how the conic sections can be defined in terms of cuts of a cone and how they can be defined in terms of points, lines, and distances. These later definitions lend themselves to the techniques of analytic geometry because points are easily changed into ordered pairs, lines into linear equations, and distances into numbers. In this section we shall demonstrate how equations can be found for some of the conic sections using the point-line-distance definitions given in the last section.

Let us begin by finding the equation of the circle whose center is at the point (a,b) and whose radius is r units. Refer to Figure 7.24. If we let (x,y) be the coordinate of a typical point P on this circle, then according to the definition of a circle, the distance between (x,y) and (a,b) is equal to r. We therefore are able to determine the lengths of the three sides of the right triangle shown in Figure 7.24. Using the Pythagorean theorem, we may then write the equation

$$(x - a)^2 + (y - b)^2 = r^2.$$

We have found an equation in two variables the solutions of which are the coordinates of the points belonging to this circle. Conversely, every point belonging to this circle has a coordinate that is a solution of this equation. Just as we were able to establish a connection between straight lines and linear equations, now we have been able to establish a connection between

Figure 7.24

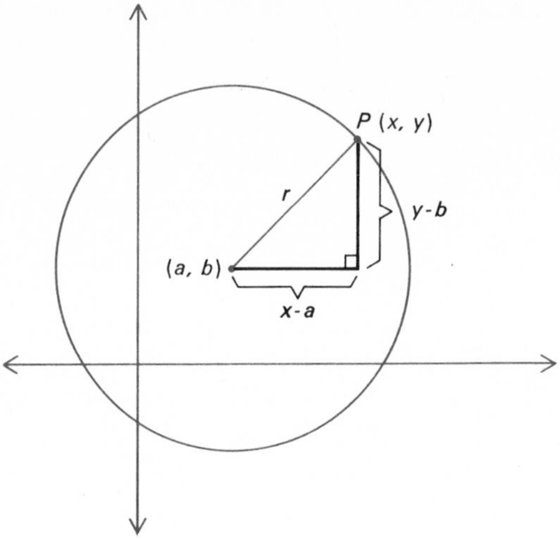

circles and equations of the form $(x - a)^2 + (y - b)^2 = r^2$, where a, b, and r are real numbers.

Example 1: What is the equation of the circle whose center is at the origin and which has a radius of 4 units?

SOLUTION: We use the equation $(x - a)^2 + (y - b)^2 = r^2$ with $a = 0$, $b = 0$, and $r = 4$. We get $(x - 0)^2 + (y - 0)^2 = 4^2$ or $x^2 + y^2 = 16$.

Example 2: The equation $(x + 4)^2 + (y - 1)^2 = 25$ is the equation of a circle. Find the center and radius of the circle.

SOLUTION: To find the center and radius, we must rewrite this equation in the form $(x - a)^2 + (y - b)^2 = r^2$. When we do so we get $(x - -4)^2 + (y - 1)^2 = (5)^2$ so that the circle has its center at $(-4, 1)$ and has a radius of 5 units.

We shall not derive the equations of ellipses or hyperbolas because to do so requires more algebraic manipulation than we wish to become involved with. But working with parabolas is not too much, so let us consider the problem of finding the equation of a parabola. Recall that a parabola is the set of all points that are equidistant from a fixed point and a fixed line. For example, if the fixed point is the point (0,2) and the fixed line is the x-axis (the line $y = 0$), then there is defined a parabola consisting of all the points of the plane whose distance from (0,2) is equal to their distance from $y = 0$. We let (x,y) be the coordinate of a typical point P of this parabola and compute the lengths of the segments $\overline{PA}$ and $\overline{PB}$ as shown in Figure 7.25:

$$(\overline{PA})^2 = (2 - y)^2 + x^2$$

$$\overline{PB} = y.$$

Figure 7.25

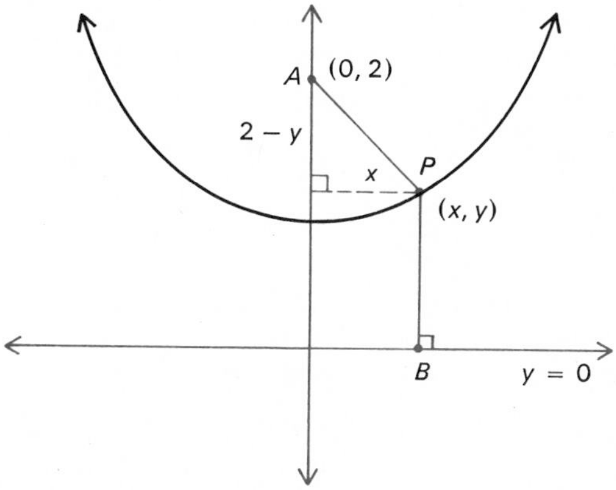

By definition of the parabola, the point (x,y) belongs to the parabola if and only if $\overline{PA} = \overline{PB}$. Thus

$$\sqrt{(2 - y)^2 + x^2} = y,$$

or, upon squaring both sides of this equation,

$$(2 - y)^2 + x^2 = y^2.$$

This is the equation of the parabola. A point belongs to the parabola if and only if the coordinate of that point is a solution of this equation. We would usually want to simplify this equation like this:

$$(4 - 4y + y^2) + x^2 = y^2$$

$$4 - 4y + x^2 = 0.$$

All of the equations we have seen in this section are of the same general form. They are all **equations of degree 2** by which we mean an equation that can be rewritten in the special form

$$ax^2 + bx + cy^2 + dy + e = 0,$$

where a, b, c, d, and e are real numbers and where not both a and c are equal to zero. (If both a and c were zero, then this equation would be a linear equation.) It can be proved that every equation of degree 2 is the equation of some conic section and, conversely, that every conic section has an equation that is an equation of degree 2. We shall not give details, but a great deal of information about the conic sections can be obtained from their equations. Indeed, all of the geometric information about these conic sections is contained one way or another in their equations.

Finally, let us use the following examples to illustrate the way that plotting points can help in graphing conic sections.

Example 3: The equation $4x^2 + y^2 = 16$ has degree 2 and so its graph is a conic section. In this case the conic section is an ellipse. To sketch this ellipse (since we know what its general shape is), we need only identify a few solutions of the equation, locate these solutions in the coordinate plane, and then connect these points together with a smooth curve. Some solutions are presented in table form[1] and the graph is sketched in Figure 7.26.

Figure 7.26

x	y
0	4, −4
2	0
−2	0
1	3.4, −3.4
−1	3.4, −3.4

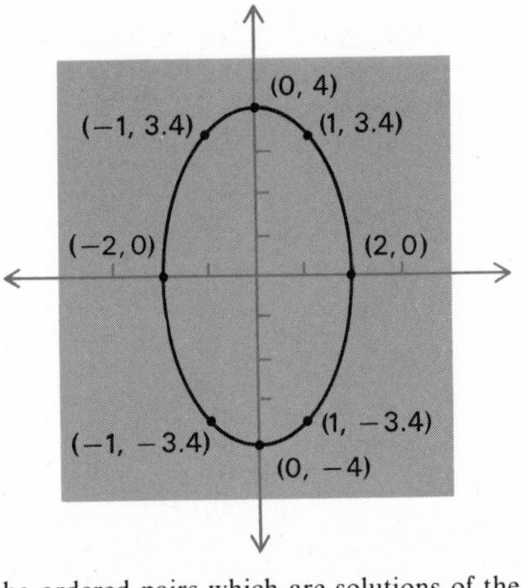

[1] This table is a convenient listing of some of the ordered pairs which are solutions of the given equation and conveys the information that the following ordered pairs are solutions of the equation: (0,4), (0,−4), (0,0), (−2,0), (1,3.4), (1,−3.4), (−1,3.4), and (−1,−3.4). We are using 3.4 as an approximate value for $\sqrt{15}$.

Example 4: Sketch the graph of the parabola whose equation is $y = x^2$.

SOLUTION: We know what the general shape of a parabola is, so we need only locate enough points of this parabola to be able to determine its particular shape. In Figure 7.27 we have tabulated some points and sketched the parabola.

Figure 7.27

x	y
0	0
1	1
−1	1
2	4
−2	4

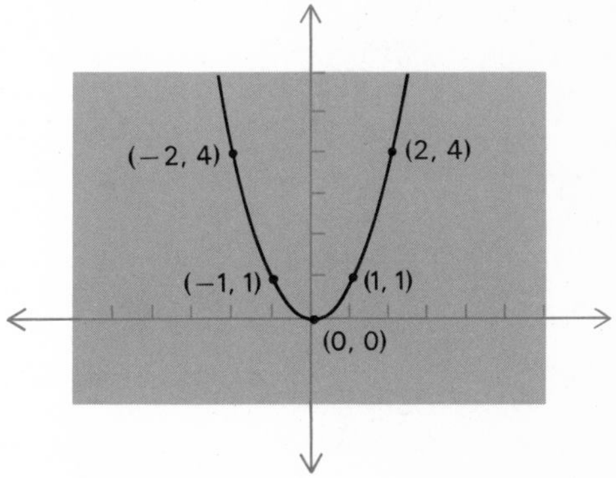

Example 5: Sketch the hyperbola which is the graph of the equation $x^2 - y^2 = 4$.

SOLUTION: See Figure 7.28. Do not forget that a hyperbola consists of two branches.

Figure 7.28

x	y
0	No Values
± 2	0
$\pm\sqrt{5} \doteq 2.2$	± 1
$\pm\sqrt{8} \doteq 2.8$	± 2
$\pm\sqrt{13} \doteq 3.9$	± 3

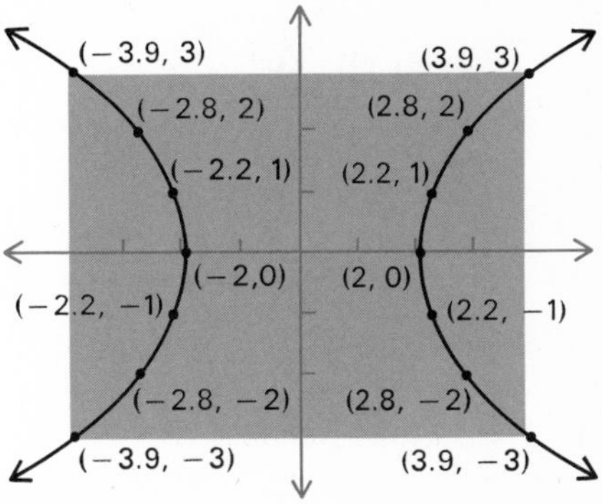

Exercises 7.5

1. Write the equation of the circle with the given point as center and the given distance as radius.
   (a) (1,5); 6. **(b)** (−3, −5); distance between (1,8) and (−2,5).

2. Identify the center and radius of each of these circles.

(a) $(x + 1)^2 + (y - 1)^2 = 16$. **(b)** $(x - 5)^2 + (y + 4)^2 = 10$.

3. Find the equation of the parabola defined by the line $x = 0$ and the point (2,3).

4. Graph these equations.

(a) $x^2 - y^2 = 4$. (Hyperbola). **(e)** $4x^2 + 3y^2 = 12$.

(b) $9x^2 + 25y^2 = 225$. (Ellipse). **(f)** $16y^2 - 9x^2 = 144$.

(c) $y^2 = 8x$. (Parabola). **(g)** $x^2 = 8y$.

(d) $y^2 = -8x$. **(h)** $x^2 = -8y$.

5. What can you say about the general shape of the parabola $x^2 = ay$ if $a > 0$? What if $a < 0$? What is the general shape of the parabola $y^2 = ax$ if $a > 0$? What if $a < 0$? (*Hint*: Consider various parts of Exercise 4.)

8 Functions

THE WORD "function" has a number of different meanings outside of mathematics, but its meaning in mathematics is exact. We have been involved with functions from the beginning of our study, but it has not been necessary to specifically point this out. Now is a convenient time to discuss the concept since this discussion is made easier and more natural once the Cartesian coordinate plane is available. The study of functions comprises one of the largest and most important branches of mathematics and the idea pervades every part of mathematics. The power of the concept lies with its almost total generality, but in our work we shall be dealing exclusively with a kind of function called a "real-valued function."

8.1 Black Boxes

We shall introduce the concept of function by means of a physical analogy called "the black box." All of the important ideas related to the concept of function can be illustrated using this analogy.

A **black box** is a mysterious-looking device something like the object shown in Figure 8.1. This box has an opening in its top called the "input opening" and a spout near its bottom called the "output spout." One puts things into the top and things come out of the bottom. What comes out depends upon what was put into the box and upon the particular internal construction of the black box. The inputs are the objects that are put into the box at the top and the outputs are the objects that come out of the box at the bottom.

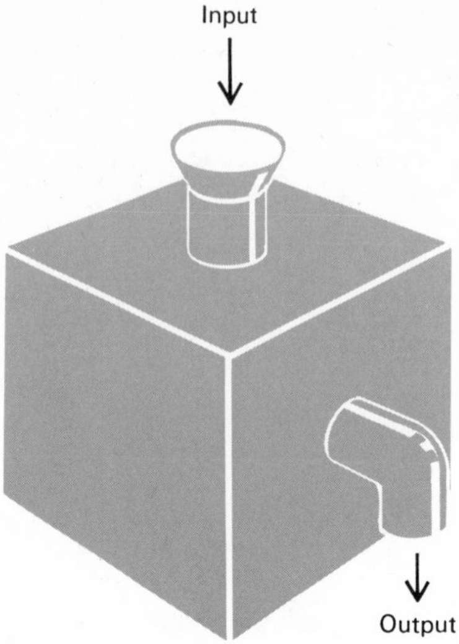

Figure 8.1

Example 1: There is a black box that uses whole numbers as inputs and produces whole numbers as outputs. This box is constructed in such a way that if you put the number 1 into the box, the number 4 drops out the output spout. If you put 16 into the box, 19 comes out the bottom. The input 234 results in the output 237. Perhaps it is clear from these examples that this particular black box works by adding 3 to any inputs that are inserted into the box. We might call this particular box the "add 3" black box.

The black box discussed in Example 1 has a property common to all properly constructed black boxes. Given one input there is produced by the box *exactly one* output. Put one object into the box and exactly one object comes out the bottom. This is an especially important property of a black box.

Example 2: In 1532 a German alchemist named O. Zeltmacher invented a black box that worked as follows: You would take a piece of paper and draw on it the picture of a polygon. Then you would put this paper into the input opening. After some whirrings, out from the box would drop another piece of paper on which was written the number of vertices of the polygon you had inserted into the box. If you put in a picture of a square, the output would be a piece of paper with the number "four" written on it. This box took polygons as input and gave out whole numbers as output.

The same Zeltmacher as mentioned in Example 2 tried to invent a black box that would work the reverse of his successful "vertex counting" box. He tried to design a box that would take as input pieces of paper with whole numbers greater than three written on them. The output was supposed to be a piece of paper with a picture of a polygon having as many vertices as the input number. To test the box Zeltmacher inserted a piece of paper with the word "three" written on it. The box began to pour out all sorts of triangles. In trying to produce all of the infinitely many different triangles, the box overheated and blew up. That is all we hear of Zeltmacher. The trouble was that he tried to design a black box that gave more than one output for a given input.

Example 3: There is a black box that eats typewriters as input and gives out whole numbers as output. It might be called the "serial number" black box. If the typewriter on which this book was typed were put into this box, the number 61554409 would come out.

There need be no special relationship between the inputs and the outputs of a black box. These boxes (being after all quite imaginary) can be constructed in any way at all. They can be made so as to accept anything at all as inputs and to produce anything at all as outputs. Of course in mathematics these black boxes usually "act" upon mathematical objects and "produce" mathematical objects. Here is an example of such a black box.

Example 4: The inputs for this black box are linear equations and the outputs are real numbers. Here are a few examples of how this particular black box works.

Inputs	$\rightarrow$	*Outputs*
$2x + y = 4$	$\rightarrow$	2
$y + 4 = -9$	$\rightarrow$	0
$y - 3x - 4 = 0$	$\rightarrow$	-3

Can you describe in words how this box works? It takes an input (a linear equation) and produces from it an output which is the real number which is the coefficient of the x term of the given input.

The black box in Example 4 is a properly constructed box because given one input there is produced exactly one output. You should be careful not to confuse this characteristic of a black box with the fact that different inputs may produce the same output. For example, this black box produces the same output, 2, from the two different inputs $2x + y = -1$ and $2x - 15y = 0$, but there is nothing wrong in this. Many different inputs may produce the same output, but one input may not produce many different outputs.

Each time we have described a black box, we have been careful to describe the kind of objects that could be used as inputs for that box. When describing a black box we must not only describe the effect of the box upon a given input, but we must also specify the kind of objects that can be used as inputs.

Example 5: There is a black box which can be called the "positive square root box." This black box operates upon an input number by producing the positive square root of that number. But note that this black box is legitimate only if the inputs are restricted to the set of nonnegative real numbers. For example, if we were to allow -1 to an input for this box, then no output would be produced (since there is no real number that is the square root of -1). Hence we must specifically state that this black box operates only upon nonnegative inputs.

In the next section we shall replace the notion of a black box with its mathematical equivalent—the notion of a function.

Exercises 8.1

1. There is a black box called the "negation box" that takes statements as inputs and gives out statements as outputs. What comes out of the box when these statements are put into it?
   (a) $2 + 2 = 5$.
   (b) $2 + 3 = 6 - 1$.
   (c) $\sim p \vee \sim q$.
2. Describe the internal workings of a black box that can take the objects of the first set as inputs and give out the objects from the second set as outputs.
   (a) {1,2,3,4,5,6,7,8}; {a,b,c,d,e,f,g,h}.
   (b) {bad, whole, ugly, evil, wicked, craven}; {incomplete, good, beautiful}.
   (c) {House, car, spigot, horseshoe, swatch}; {Man-O'-War, wrench, beer, needle, doormat}.

3. O. Zeltmacher tried to construct the following black boxes but they all blew up. Why?
   (a) A black box such that when a simple closed curve was put into the box another simple closed curve topologically equivalent to it would drop out the bottom.
   (b) A black box that when fed a whole number would produce a whole number less than the one put into the input spout.
   (c) A box such that whenever a woman was put into the top, there would drop out at the bottom the only man she ever loved.
   (d) A box such that when a letter was put into the input spout would drop a word containing that letter from the output spout.
4. Is the black box that when any real number is put into it produces the number 4 a legitimate black box?
5. Unless we carefully describe the kinds of input objects that can be used for the following black boxes they will not always produce an output object. Describe the set of permissible inputs for each box.
   (a) The box that when given a line produces its slope.
   (b) The box that when given a conic section produces the area contained by that conic.
   (c) The box that when given the equations of two lines produces the coordinates of their point of intersection.

8.2 The Concept of Function

We shall continue our introduction to the concept of function using mathematical terminology and notation.

The black boxes discussed in Section 8.1 are examples of functions. Each of these black boxes can be described as follows. A black box is a device by means of which, corresponding to each object in a certain set of input objects (this set depending upon the particular black box we are describing), there is produced exactly one output object. We call the black box a **function**, the set of inputs the **domain** of the function, and the set of outputs the **range** of the function. To describe a function, therefore, it is necessary to specify two sets, the domain and the range, and then to describe a rule or instruction by means of which, corresponding to each and every object in the domain set, there can be determined exactly one object in the range set. The idea of a function then involves three different ideas: the domain of the function, the range of the function, and the rule for performing the function. Usually, however, it is necessary to be concerned only about the domain and the rule—the range will take care of itself. That is, as soon as the domain and the rule are given, the range set is automatically determined.

Example 1: If the domain is the set $\{1,2,3\}$ and the rule for performing the function is "To perform the function upon a domain object, add 3 to that domain object," then the range of the function must be the set $\{1 + 3, 2 + 3, 3 + 3\}$ or $\{4,5,6\}$.

Example 2: The diagram

$a \to 3$

$b \to 1$

$c \to 2$

describes a function whose domain is the set $\{a,b,c\}$ and whose range is the set $\{1,2,3\}$. The arrows define the effect of the function upon each domain object.

Example 3: Consider the function defined on the domain of all real numbers and whose rule is: "To perform this function upon a domain object (that is, a real number), add 3 to that domain object." This function is different from the function in Example 1 above since it has a different domain from that function. Many students mistakenly think that because these two functions are performed according to the same rule, they are the same function. Two functions can be the same only if their domains and their rules are the same. We call the function in this example an *extension* of the function in Example 1.

Whenever possible we use equations to describe functions. For example, consider the function in Example 1 above. Denoting this function symbolically by the letter f (suggestive of the word "function"), we would symbolically describe the effect of this function upon the domain object 1 by writing

$$f(1) = 4.$$

The symbol $f(1)$ is read "f of 1." We would describe the effect of this function upon 2 and 3 by writing $f(2) = 5$ and $f(3) = 6$. Thus the three equations

$$f(1) = 4$$
$$f(2) = 5$$
$$f(3) = 6$$

completely describe this function. These equations tell us not only how the function works upon domain objects, but they also tell us what the domain objects are. (They tell us what the range objects are, too.) To describe the effect of the function generally, we would write

$$f(x) = x + 3, \text{ where } x \in \{1,2,3\}.$$

The function in Example 3 would be described using this notation by writing

$$f(x) = x + 3, \text{ where } x \text{ is a real number.}$$

Observe that we mention not only the rule, but also the domain. This notation is called *functional notation.* Here are more examples of functions described using this notation.

Example 4: The equation $f(x) = 2x + 3$ (where x denotes an integer) describes a function that acts upon integers by doubling them and then adding 3 to the result. The range objects produced by this function are integers and so we say that the function f is a function from the integers into the integers.

Example 5: If x is an integer, then the distance of that integer from the origin on the number line is called the **absolute value** of that integer. The absolute value of an integer x is denoted by the symbol $|x|$. For example, $|-6| = 6$ and $|9| = 9$. The function f defined according to the equation

$$f(x) = |x|, \text{ where } x \text{ is an integer,}$$

is a function whose domain is the set of all integers and whose range is the set of all nonnegative integers. For example, $f(-6) = 6$ and $f(9) = 9$. This function is called the **absolute value function**.

Example 6: If x is a real number, then the symbol $[\![x]\!]$ represents the greatest integer less than or equal to x. For example, $[\![1]\!] = 1$, $[\![\frac{2}{3}]\!] = 0$, $[\![\pi]\!] = 3$, and $-[\![19\frac{7}{8}]\!] = -20$. The function defined by the equation

$$f(x) = [\![x]\!], \text{ where } x \text{ is a real number,}$$

is a function whose domain consists of all real numbers and whose range is the set of all integers. This function is called the **greatest integer function**.

Not all functions can easily be described using equations, but all of the functions that we shall be working with can be. Also, most of our functions will have as their domains the set of all real numbers.

We remarked in the introduction to this chapter that we have been working with functions since the beginning of our study of mathematics. Here are two examples of functions that we have dealt with without specifically calling attention to the fact that we were doing so. The first is an example from arithmetic.

Example 7: Let f be the function whose domain consists of all *ordered pairs of integers* and which is described according to the equational rule

$$f((a,b)) = a + b.$$

This function acts upon ordered pairs of integers and produces integers according to the following rule: Add the left-hand and right-hand parts of the given ordered pair. The function acting upon the ordered pair (2,3) produces the integer 2 + 3 or 5, and so we write $f((2,3)) = 5$. Similarly, $f((-1,-5)) = -6$. This function is called the **addition of integers function.** To say that addition of integers is commutative means simply that this function acts the same way upon the pair (a,b) as it does upon the pair (b,a):

$$f((a,b)) = f((b,a)).$$

The operations of subtraction and multiplication of integers similarly can be regarded as functions from the domain of all ordered pairs of integers into the integers. The subtraction of integers function acts upon the ordered pair $(-2,-7)$ and produces the integer $2 - -7$ or 5. The multiplication of integers function acting upon this same ordered pair results in the integer 14.

Our next example comes from Euclidean geometry.

Example 8: Let the function f be defined on the set of all polygons as follows: If P is a polygon, then $f(P)$ is that real number which is the area of the polygon P. The domain objects for this function are polygons and the range objects are real numbers. Thus, for example,

$f($2 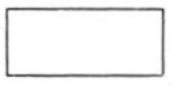 $) = 6$
3

and

$f($5  $) = 10.$
4

This function might be called the **area function.**

Exercises 8.2

1. In Example 8 we described a function whose domain consisted of all polygons and whose range was a subset of the real numbers. Describe another such function. Describe a function whose domain is the set of all circles and whose range is a subset of the set of all real numbers.

2. If f denotes the *absolute value function* with domain the integers, then what can you say about x if $f(x) = 5$?

3. If f denotes the *greatest integer function* with domain the real numbers, then what can you say about x if $f(x) = 2$?

4. Define a function whose domain is the set $\{a,b,c\}$ and whose range is a proper subset of the set $\{1,2,3\}$.

5. Let f denote the *subtraction of integers function.* This function has as its domain the set of all ordered pairs of integers and has as its range the set of integers. List ten ordered pairs (x,y) such that $f((x,y)) = 6$.

6. Let the *truth value function* be denoted by t. This function has as its domain the set of all statements and as its range the set {true, false}. Complete the following:

(a) t(All men are mortal) = ?

(b) $t(2 + 2 = 4) = ?$

(c) $t(p \wedge \sim p) = ?$

(d) $t(p \vee \sim p) = ?$

(e) t(Some implications have true converses) = ?
(f) t(All implications have true converses) = ?
(g) t(All implications have true contrapositives) = ?

7. Let p denote the *perimeter function* with domain the set of all polygons.
(a) Is 0 an object in the range of this function? Are there any negative numbers in the range of this function?
(b) Give three examples of polygons such that p(polygon) = 4.
(c) How many squares are there such that p(square) = 16?
(d) How many rectangles are there such that p(rectangle) = 16?
(e) Find a triangle and a rectangle such that p(triangle) = p(rectangle).

8. Define using functional notation functions that have as their domains the first of the given sets and have their ranges contained in the second of the given sets. (That is, the ranges need not be equal to the second sets.)
(a) $\{0,1,2,3\}$; $\{0,1,2,3\}$.
(b) $\{0,2,4,6,8, \ldots\}$; $\{0,1,2,3,4,5,6,\ldots\}$.
(c) {triangle, square, pentagon, hexagon}; $\{0,1,2,3,4,5,6,7,8\}$.
(d) $\{\frac{1}{2}, \frac{2}{3}, \frac{5}{3}, 17, \frac{21}{5}, 0\}$; $\{0, 4, 17, 1, 189, 32\}$.

8.3 Graphing Functions

It is particularly useful to visualize functions geometrically as curves in the coordinate plane. In fact, we did some of this in the last chapter when we graphed certain equations. Information about the function itself can be obtained from its geometric "picture."

Let us begin by examining the function $f(x) = 3x - 7$ (where x represents any real number). We can graph this function by constructing a coordinate system (just as in the last chapter) with one axis labeled the x-axis and the other labeled the $f(x)$-axis. Then we construct a table and compute a few values of $f(x)$:

x	-1	0	1	2	3
$f(x)$	-10	-7	-4	-1	2

We now know the coordinates of five points of the graph of this function. These points are shown in Figure 8.2. This function is called a **linear function**. In Chapter 7 we wrote this function as $y = 3x - 7$ instead of $f(x) = 3x - 7$.

Figure 8.2

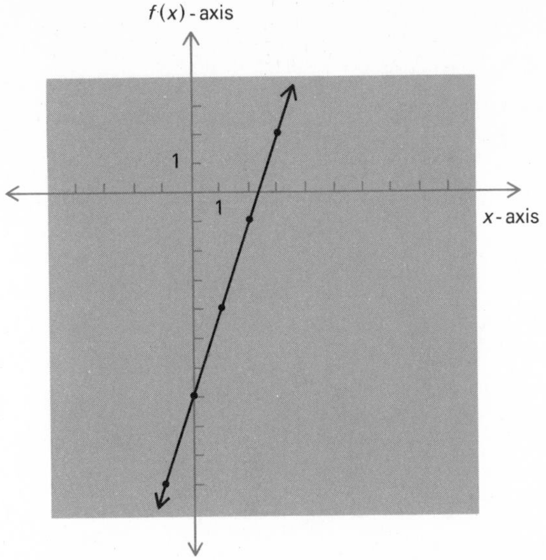

Example 1: Graph the function defined on the domain of all real numbers according to the equational rule $f(x) = 6x^2 - 1$. Plot points corresponding to every integer value of x between $x = -3$ and $x = 3$.

SOLUTION: We first construct a table of values:

x	-3	-2	-1	0	1	2	3
$f(x)$	53	23	5	-1	5	23	53

Then we plot the points we have found as shown in Figure 8.3. These points, if properly connected, will give us a rough idea as to the graph of the function. There are many possibilities for making a mistake when connecting these points, so one should be wary. If you are in doubt as to the correctness of your graph, try plotting a few additional points. Incidentally, note that different scales were used on the axes in Figure 8.3. If we had used the same scale on both axes, we could have plotted only a very few points on the page. After the table of values has been constructed, you should have a better idea as to the appropriate scales to use in order to get a more complete picture on the paper.

Figure 8.3

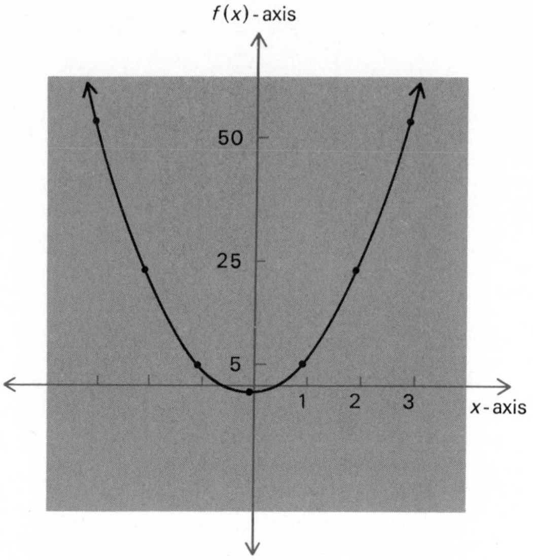

Example 2: Graph the function

$$f(x) = \frac{2}{x-1}.$$

SOLUTION: We begin by making a table of some values of $f(x)$ corresponding to convenient values of x:

x	-5	-3	-1	0	$\frac{1}{2}$	$\frac{2}{3}$	1	$\frac{3}{2}$	2	3	4	5
$f(x)$	$\frac{-1}{3}$	$\frac{-1}{2}$	-1	-2	-4	-6	No value	4	2	1	$\frac{2}{3}$	$\frac{1}{2}$

It is very important to note that there is no point of the graph which has an x-coordinate equal to 1. This means that the graph cannot cut the vertical line $x = 1$, and so it must consist of two separate branches. We have plotted these points and connected them with the correct curves in Figure 8.4. We call the line $x = 1$ a **vertical asymptote** for the curve and we call the x-axis a **horizontal asymptote** for the curve. Each branch of the graph gets closer and closer to these lines, but neither branch ever intersects either of the asymptotes.

Figure 8.4

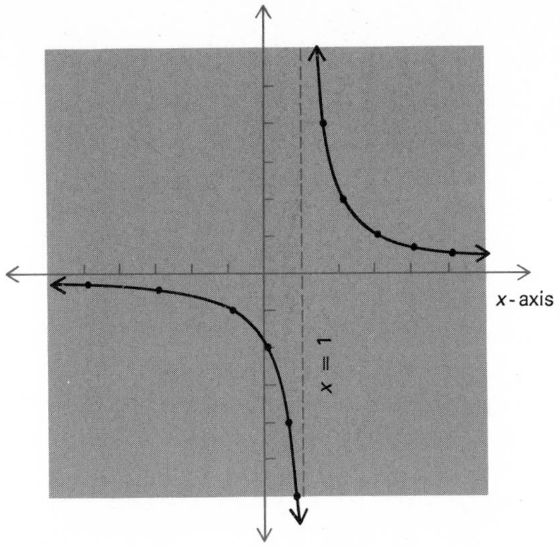

Plotting points to find the graph of a function is often the easiest way to find the graph, but the method is full of pitfalls. The trouble is that between some pair of plotted points, the graph may behave in some way that is not made apparent by the points actually plotted. One must be sure to plot enough points to correctly identify the graph.

Exercises 8.3

1.* Functions of the general form $f(x) = a_n x^n + a_{n-1}x^{n-1} + \cdots + a_1 x + a_0$, where n is a whole number and the coefficients $a_n, a_{n-1}, \ldots, a_1$, and a_0 are real numbers, are called **polynomial functions**. The graph of a polynomial function is a one-piece smooth curve. Sketch the graph of the following polynomial functions by plotting points for integers values of x from -5 to 5 and then by plotting more points as needed.

(a) $f(x) = x^2 - 2x - 5$. **(c)** $f(x) = x^4 - 2x^2$.

(b) $f(x) = x^3 - 3x^2 - 4x + 10$.

From these three examples can you spot any connection between the highest power of x occurring in the expression for the function and the way the graph moves up and down?

2.* Functions that have the form $f(x) = a^x$, where a is a real number, are called **exponential functions** and their graphs are one-piece smooth curves. Graph the following exponential functions on the same coordinate plane. Use a small scale on the $f(x)$-axis. Plot values of x from -6 to 6 and use the fact that by definition $a^{-6} = 1/a^6$, $a^{-5} = 1/a^5, \ldots,$ $a^{-1} = 1/a^1$.

(a) $f(x) = 1^x$.
(b) $f(x) = 2^x$.
(c) $f(x) = 3^x$.
(d) $f(x) = 4^x$.

3. Does the graph of the function $f(x) = 1/(x - 1)$ look like the curve on the left or the curve on the right?

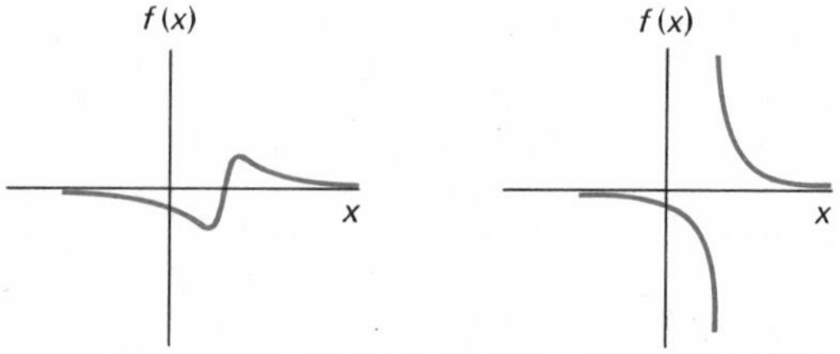

4. Each of the following functions has a graph consisting of two smooth branches. To find these graphs plot points between -4 and 4 as needed. Each of these graphs has both vertical and horizontal asymptotes.
(a) $f(x) = 1/x$.
(b) $f(x) = x/(x - 1)$.
5. Sketch the graphs of the following functions between $x = -10$ and $x = 10$. Plot points as needed.
(a) $f(x) = [\![x]\!]$.
(b) $f(x) = |x|$.

8.4 Applications of Graphing

The graph of a function may be used to reveal information about the function itself. In this section we shall use the graphs of functions in the solution of certain problems involving functions.

Our first application involves using the graph of a function to find the point at which the function is minimal.

Example 1: It is desired to construct a rectangle encompassing an area of 4 square inches. What should be the dimensions of the rectangle in order that it will have the smallest possible perimeter?

Figure 8.5

SOLUTION: Let the length of the rectangle be represented by x (see Figure 8.5). Then, since the area encompassed by the rectangle is 4, the width of the rectangle will be $4/x$. The perimeter of a rectangle of dimensions x by $4/x$ is

$x + x + 4/x + 4/+$ or $2x + 8/x$. That is, we are able to express the perimeter of the rectangle as a function of the length of the rectangle. Representing this function by P, we can express this functional relationship by the equation

$$P(x) = 2x + \frac{8}{x}.$$

Our problem now is to find that value of x for which $P(x)$ is as small as possible. We can find this value of x, approximately at least, by graphing this function and locating its minimum by inspection. The graph of this function is shown in Figure 8.6. Notice that we have plotted points only to

Figure 8.6

x	$P(x)$
$\frac{1}{4}$	$32\frac{1}{2}$
$\frac{1}{2}$	17
$\frac{3}{4}$	$12\frac{1}{6}$
1	10
$\frac{3}{2}$	$8\frac{1}{3}$
2	8
$\frac{5}{2}$	$8\frac{1}{5}$
3	$8\frac{2}{3}$
4	10

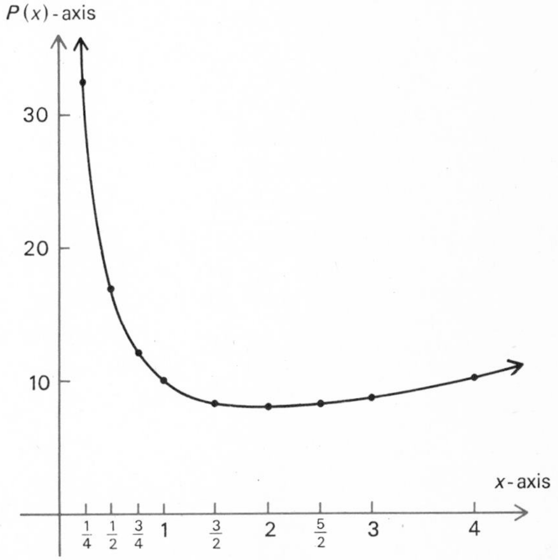

the right of the $P(x)$-axis, because negative values of x are not meaningful in this problem (since lengths cannot be negative), and so we need not concern ourselves with the part of the graph to the left of the $P(x)$-axis. Happily, we plotted the point for which $x = 2$, and this point appears to be a minimum point. That is, the point (2,8) appears from our sketch to be the minimum point of this graph. To test this, we might want to try a couple of values of x very near to 2 and on either side of 2 to make sure that their functional values are greater than 8. We compute and find that $P(1.9) = 8\frac{1}{95}$, which is greater than 8, and that $P(2.1) = 8\frac{1}{105}$, which is also greater than 8.

We may therefore feel rather secure in our conclusion that (2,8) is the minimum point. This means that the smallest perimeter that a rectangle of area 4 square inches can have is 8 inches. In this case the width of the rectangle is $\frac{4}{2}$ or 2 inches. This means that the rectangle that we should use is a square.

Example 1 illustrates the general fact that to encompass a given area with a rectangle of the least perimeter, use a square. The next example involves finding a maximum point.

Example 2: We have a piece of tin measuring 20 inches by 20 inches. It is required to make this into an open-topped box by cutting squares out of the corners and bending up the sides (see Figure 8.7). To the nearest half inch, what should be the dimensions of the pieces to be cut out in order that the resulting box will have the greatest possible volume?

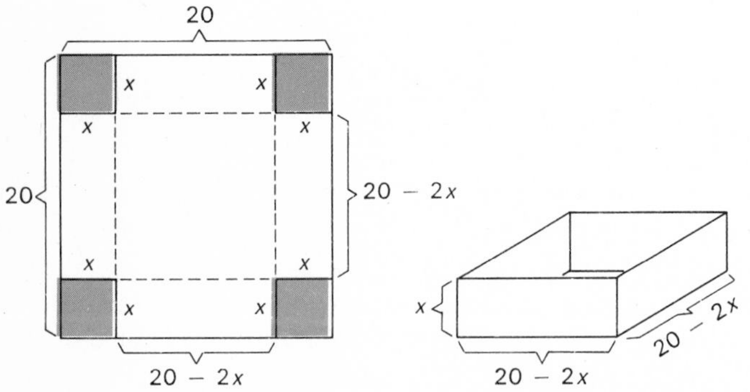

Figure 8.7

SOLUTION: If we represent the side of one of these smaller squares by x, then the volume of the resulting box is given by the expression

$$(20 - 2x)(20 - 2x)(x).$$

Thus the volume of this box can be expressed in terms of the length x and is therefore a function of x. If we represent this function by the letter V, then it can be described by the equation

$$V(x) = (20 - 2x)(20 - 2x)(x).$$

Our job now is to find that value of x for which $V(x)$ is as large as possible.

We can get an approximate value for x by graphing the function and observing its maximum point. This function is graphed in Figure 8.8. Since we are

Figure 8.8

x	$V(x)$
0	0
1	324
2	512
3	588
4	576
5	500
6	384
7	252
8	128
9	36
10	0

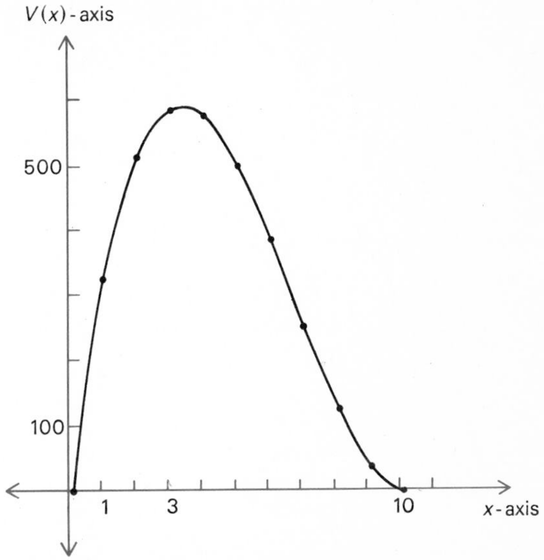

concerned only with values of x between 0 and 10 (no other values make sense in this problem), we need bother only with that portion of the graph between $x = 0$ and $x = 10$. On this portion of the graph, there appears to be a maximum in the vicinity of $x = 3$. Since we want to find x to the nearest half inch so that $V(x)$ is maximum, let us compute $V(2.5)$ and $V(3.5)$:

$$V(2.5) = (20 - 5)(20 - 5)(2.5) = 562.5$$

and

$$V(3.5) = (20 - 7)(20 - 7)(3.5) = 591.5.$$

Since $V(3) = 588$, we see that to the nearest half inch, $V(x)$ is greatest when $x = 3.5$ inches. This means that if the four corner squares are of dimensions 3.5 inches by 3.5 inches, then the resulting box will have the largest volume—591.5 cubic inches. [In order to be doubly sure that we have the correct answer, you might want to determine $V(4)$ also.]

One of the important uses of calculus is to solve such problems as these and obtain exact answers. Using elementary calculus, we could easily and quickly determine that our answer in Example 1 is exact and our answer to Example 2 is not. The exact dimensions of the squares to be removed in Example 2 should be $3\frac{1}{3}$ inches instead of $3\frac{1}{2}$ inches, but we asked for the dimensions to the nearest half inch, and so our answer is correct subject to the requirements of the example. (We shall discuss some of the basic ideas of calculus in Chapter 10.)

Exercise 8.4

1. What is the largest area that can be enclosed by a rectangle of perimeter 100 inches? (*Hint:* Express the area of the rectangle, $A(x)$, in terms of the length, x, of the rectangle. Plot the values $x = 0, 5, 10, \ldots$, and then plot more values of x as needed.)
2. In order to send a package through the mails the combined length and girth must not exceed 84 inches. Suppose we want to construct a box with a square cross section that has as large a volume as possible subject to the 84-inch restriction. To the nearest inch what should be the dimensions of the package? (*Hint:* Express the volume as a function of the length of a side of the square end. When you graph the function to find its maximum value, begin by graphing even integer values of x from 0 to 20. Then plot more points as necessary.)
3. We want to make a covered box to hold 64 cubic inches. The box is to have a square base. What should be the dimensions of the box if it is to have a minimal surface area? (*Hint:* Express the surface area in terms of the length of a side of the square bottom. Graph this function $A(x)$ by plotting some points corresponding to integral values of x. Then plot more points as needed.)
4. A book is to be designed and it has been decided that each page of the book should contain 32 square inches of print. There should be right and left margins of $\frac{1}{2}$ inches, a top margin of $\frac{3}{4}$ inches, and a bottom margin of $1\frac{1}{4}$ inches. What should be the dimensions of a page of this book in order that the least amount of paper is used?

8.5 Trigonometric Functions

An important class of functions the study of which is the central part of trigonometry is called "trigonometric functions." In this section and the next we shall discuss some of these functions.

The first trigonometric function we shall study is called the **sine function.** This function is defined using a circle and a moving radius. In Figure 8.9

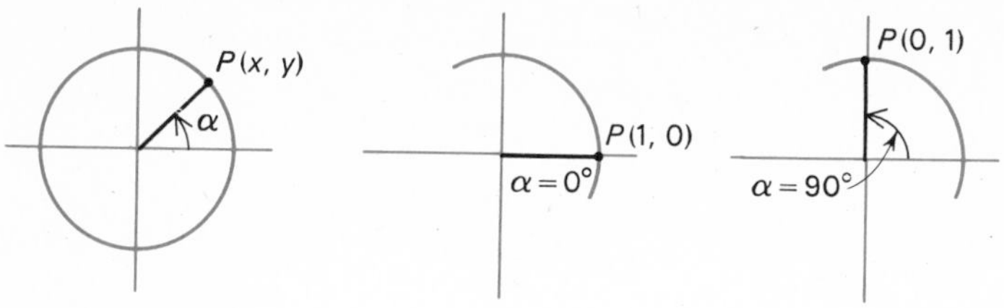

Figure 8.9

we have shown a circle of radius one unit situated so that its center lies at the origin of the coordinate plane. The segment $\overline{OP}$ is a typical radius of this circle. This radius makes an angle α with the positive x-axis.[1] As the angle α varies, the point P moves along the circumference of the circle. We want to center our attention upon the y-coordinate of the point P. As the angle α varies, say from 0° to 90°, the y-coordinate of the point P varies in turn. In fact, the y-coordinate of the point P is a function of the angle α. For example, when $\alpha = 0°$, the radius $\overline{OP}$ is coincident with the positive x-axis, the coordinate of P is (1,0), and so the y-coordinate of P is 0. When $\alpha = 90°$, the radius $\overline{OP}$ is coincident with the positive y-axis, the coordinate of P is (0,1) and so the y-coordinate of P is equal to 1 (see Figure 8.9). As the angle α varies from 0° to 90°, the y-coordinate of the point P varies from 0 to 1. Figure 8.10 will help you to visualize the way that the y-coordinate varies as α varies from 0° to 90°. The curve in Figure 8.10 is the graph of the functional relationship between the y-coordinate of P and the angle α for values of α from 0° to 90°.

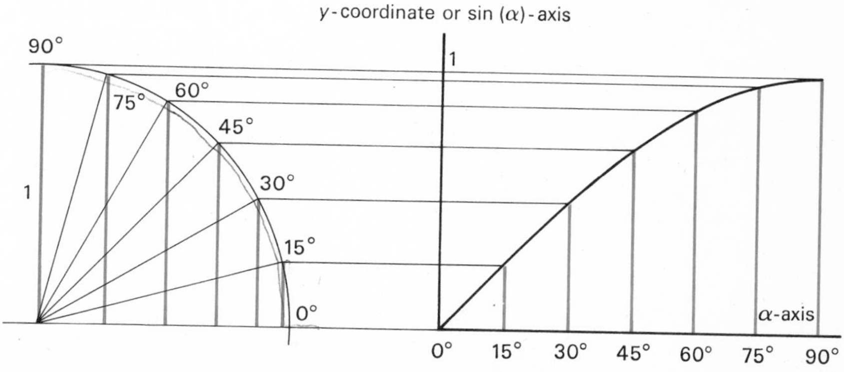

Figure 8.10

[1] By convention, an angle is termed positive if it is measured from the positive x-axis in a counterclockwise direction. Angles measured from the positive x-axis in a clockwise direction are termed negative angles.

The function just described is called the sine function and is symbolized by the special symbol **sin**. For example, since when $\alpha = 0°$, the y-coordinate of P is 0, we can write $\sin(0°) = 0$. Also, since when $\alpha = 90°$, the y-coordinate of P is 1, we write $\sin(90°) = 1$. In general, we write

$$\sin(\alpha) = y.$$

That is, the sine of an angle α is the y-coordinate of the point P when the radius $\overline{OP}$ makes an angle α with the positive x-axis.

Let us go on and see what this function looks like for other values of α. What happens to this y-coordinate as α varies from 90° to 180°? The sine of 180° is 0, since when $\alpha = 180°$ the radius $\overline{OP}$ is coincident with the negative x-axis, the coordinate of P is $(-1,0)$ and the y-coordinate of P is 0. Hence, as α varies from 90° to 180°, the y-coordinate (that is, $\sin(\alpha)$) varies from 1 (at 90°) to 0 (at 180°). See Figure 8.11, which shows the graph of the sine function from 0° to 180°. The sine of 270°, sin (270°), is equal to -1, since

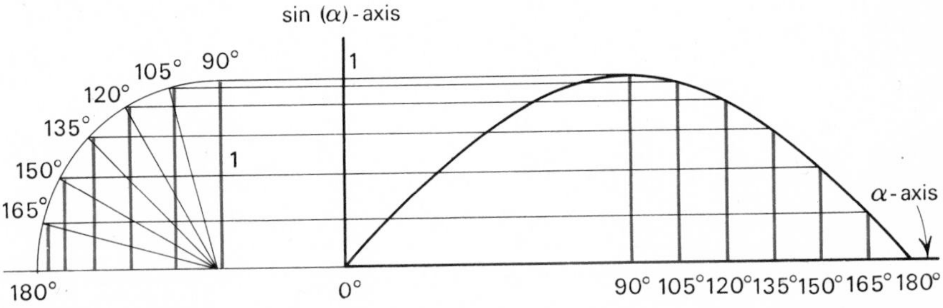

Figure 8.11

when $\alpha = 270°$ the radius $\overline{OP}$ is coincident with the negative y-axis and the y-coordinate of P is -1. The sine of 360° is 0 since, when $\alpha = 360°$, the radius $\overline{OP}$ is again coincident with the positive x-axis. Hence, as α varies

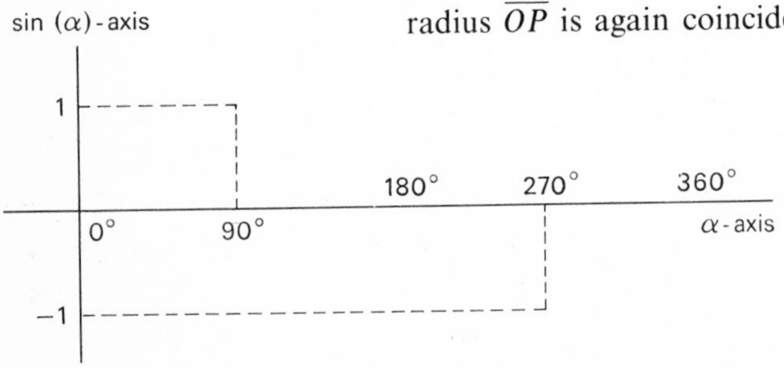

Figure 8.12

from 180° through 270° to 360°, the y-coordinate of P varies from 0 through -1 to 0 again. The graph in Figure 8.12 is the graph of the sine function for values of α from 0° to 360°.

Table 8–1 contains numerical values of the sine function for integral values of α from 0° to 90°. With a few exceptions these values have been rounded off to three decimal places.

Table 8–1

Angle	*Sine*	*Angle*	*Sine*	*Angle*	*Sine*	*Angle*	*Sine*
0°	.000	26°	.438	51°	.777	76°	.970
1°	.017	27°	.454	52°	.788	77°	.974
2°	.035	28°	.469	53°	.799	78°	.978
3°	.052	29°	.485	54°	.809	79°	.982
4°	.070	30°	.500	55°	.819	80°	.985
5°	.087	31°	.515	56°	.829	81°	.988
6°	.105	32°	.530	57°	.839	82°	.990
7°	.122	33°	.545	58°	.848	83°	.993
8°	.139	34°	.559	59°	.857	84°	.995
9°	.156	35°	.574	60°	.866	85°	.996
10°	.174	36°	.588	61°	.875	86°	.998
11°	.191	37°	.602	62°	.883	87°	.9986
12°	.208	38°	.616	63°	.891	88°	.9994
13°	.225	39°	.629	64°	.899	89°	.9998
14°	.242	40°	.643	65°	.906	90°	1.000
15°	.259	41°	.656	66°	.914		
16°	.276	42°	.669	67°	.920		
17°	.292	43°	.682	68°	.927		
18°	.309	44°	.695	69°	.934		
19°	.326	45°	.707	70°	.940		
20°	.342	46°	.719	71°	.946		
21°	.358	47°	.731	72°	.951		
22°	.375	48°	.743	73°	.956		
23°	.391	49°	.755	74°	.961		
24°	.407	50°	.766	75°	.966		
25°	.423						

In discussing the sine function, we centered our attention on the y-coordinate of the point P. If we had instead centered attention on the x-coordinate, then another function would have been defined, called the **cosine function**. Given an angle α, then the cosine of α, $\cos(\alpha)$, is defined to be the x-coordinate of the point P when the radius $\overline{OP}$ is making an angle of α with the positive x-axis. See Figure 8.13.

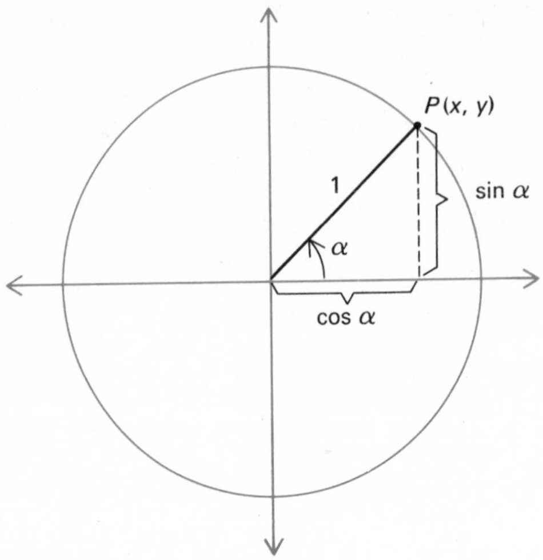

Figure 8.13

Example 1: What is the cosine of 0°?

SOLUTION: We see from Figure 8.14 that when $\alpha = 0°$, the x-coordinate of the point P is 1. Hence the cosine of 0° is 1, and we write $\cos(0°) = 1$.

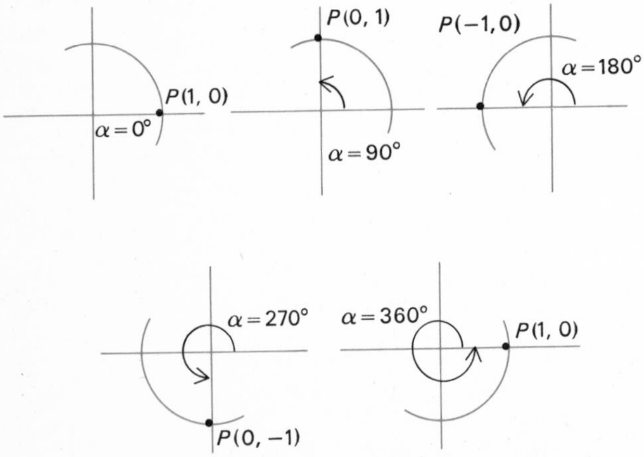

Figure 8.14

Example 2. Find the cosine of 90°, 180°, 270°, and 360°.

SOLUTION: We can use Figure 8.14 to see that the x-coordinate of P, when $\alpha = 90°$, is equal to 0. Hence $\cos(90°) = 0$. $\text{Cos}(180°) = -1$, since the x-coordinate of P, when $\alpha = 180°$, is -1. $\text{Cos}(270°) = 0$ and $\cos(360°) = 1$.

The graph of the cosine function for values of α from 0° to 360° is shown in Figure 8.15.

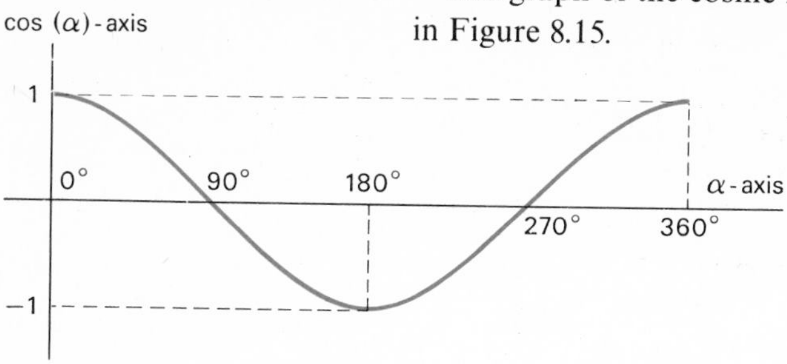

Figure 8.15

Table 8–2 lists approximate values of the cosine function for values of α from 0° to 90°. With three exceptions, these values have been rounded off to three decimal places.

Table 8–2 **Table of Cosines**

Angle	*Cosine*	*Angle*	*Cosine*	*Angle*	*Cosine*	*Angle*	*Cosine*
0°	1.000	26°	.899	51°	.629	76°	.242
1°	.9998	27°	.891	52°	.616	77°	.225
2°	.9994	28°	.883	53°	.602	78°	.208
3°	.9986	29°	.875	54°	.588	79°	.191
4°	.998	30°	.866	55°	.574	80°	.174
5°	.996	31°	.857	56°	.559	81°	.156
6°	.995	32°	.848	57°	.545	82°	.139
7°	.993	33°	.839	58°	.530	83°	122
8°	.990	34°	.829	59°	.515	84°	.105
9°	.988	35°	.819	60°	.500	85°	.087
10°	.985	36°	.809	61°	.485	86°	.070
11°	.982	37°	.799	62°	.469	87°	.052
12°	.978	38°	.788	63°	.454	88°	.035
13°	.974	39°	.777	64°	.438	89°	.017
14°	.970	40°	.766	65°	.423	90°	.000
15°	.966	41°	.755	66°	.407		
16°	.961	42°	.743	67°	.391		
17°	.956	43°	.731	68°	.375		
18°	.951	44°	.719	69°	.358		
19°	.946	45°	.707	70°	.342		
20°	.940	46°	.695	71°	.326		
21°	.934	47°	.682	72°	.309		
22°	.927	48°	.669	73°	.292		
23°	.920	49°	.656	74°	.276		
24°	.914	50°	.643	75°	.259		
25°	.906						

Besides the sine and cosine there are four other trigonometric functions called the **tangent**, **cotangent**, **secant**, and **cosecant** functions. All of these are defined in terms of a circle as were the sine and cosine functions, and for this reason these functions are sometimes called "circular functions." We shall not study these other functions.

Exercises 8.5

1. By examining the graphs of the sine and cosine functions between 0° and 90° you can see that these graphs intersect. Using the table of values find the angle at which they intersect; that is, find α such that $\sin \alpha = \cos \alpha$.
2. In the table of values of the sine function we rounded all values off to three decimal places to the right of the decimal point except for the values of the angles 87°, 88°, and 89°, which were rounded off to four decimal places. Why were we forced to round these values off to four places rather than to three places as we did for all the other values? (This same situation arises in the table of values for the cosine function.)
3. By analyzing the way the y-coordinate of the point P varies as α varies from 0° to 360°, we obtain the graph shown in Figure 8.12 for the sine function. How does this graph look for values of α from 360° to 720°?
4. In Figure 8.15 we have sketched the graph of the cosine function for values of α from 0° to 360°. What does this graph look like for values of α from 360° to 720°?
5. A high school mathematics club project is to build a "sine curve machine". This machine is to be designed so that by turning a crank a sine curve can be traced out on a piece of moving paper. How could such a machine be designed?
6. Prove that for any angle α between 0° and 90° the equation

   $$(\sin \alpha)^2 + (\cos \alpha)^2 = 1$$

   is true. (Actually this is a theorem and is true for all values of the angle α. Study Figure 8.13 to find the proof.)
7. Use the tables of values of the sine and cosine functions to verify that $\sin(90° - \alpha) = \cos \alpha$. Can you see why this is true by comparing the graphs of the sine and cosine functions?

8.6 Applications of the Trigonometric Functions

In this section we shall use the sine and cosine functions to solve certain kinds of problems involving the determination of distances that would be difficult or even impossible to find directly.

Consider the right triangle shown in Figure 8.16. This triangle has a hypotenuse of length 1 unit. Using the sine and cosine functions, we can

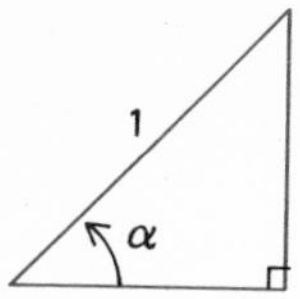

Figure 8.16

express the lengths of the two legs of this triangle in terms of the angle α. To see how to do this, place the right triangle inside a circle, as shown in Figure 8.17. This circle has radius 1 unit and so it follows that the vertical leg of the right triangle has length $\sin(\alpha)$ (since the length of this vertical leg is the y-coordinate of the point P). Also, since the length of the horizontal leg is the x-coordinate of the point P, the length of this leg is equal to $\cos(\alpha)$.

Figure 8.17

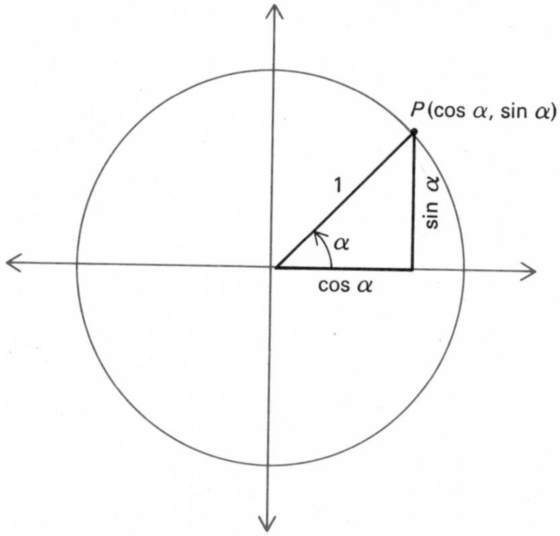

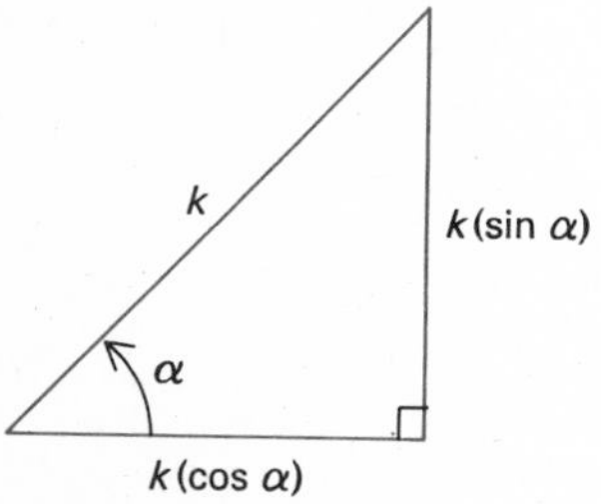

Figure 8.18

Now consider a right triangle whose hypotenuse has length k units (k a real number). Again the lengths of the legs of this triangle can be expressed in terms of the angle α. We use the fact that this triangle (Figure 8.18) is similar to the triangle in Figure 8.17, and so the sides of the two triangles have proportional lengths. Thus, since the hypotenuse of one triangle has length that is k times the length of the other triangle, the lengths of the legs of the one triangle are k times the lengths of the other triangle. This means that the vertical leg in Figure 8.18 has length $k[\sin(\alpha)]$ and the horizontal leg has length $k[\cos(\alpha)]$. In the following examples, we shall use this information to find inaccessible distances.

Example 1: A man lives in a cabin located on the side of a mountain at the base of which is a lake. It is known that the elevation of the lake is 6000 feet. The man must walk up the mountain a distance of 1 mile to reach his cabin from the lake. Also, the angle of incline of the mountain from the lake to the cabin is about 18°. What is the approximate elevation of the cabin?

SOLUTION: In Figure 8.19 we have drawn a sketch that conveys the information supplied in this problem. Also, we have drawn the right triangle that

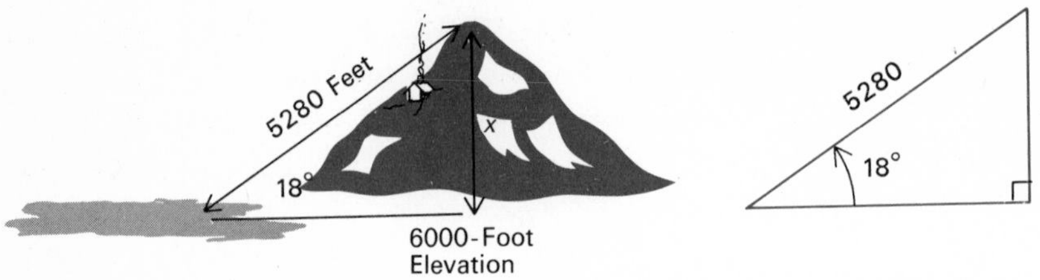

Figure 8.19

is the mathematical model of the problem. If we call the vertical distance of the cabin above the lake level x, then since this distance x is the length of the leg opposite the 18° angle, we can express x as a function of α by the equation

$$x = (5280)[\sin(18°)].$$

Using Table 8–1, we observe that $\sin(18°) = .309$ and so

$$x = (5280)(.309)$$
$$= 1631, \text{ approximately.}$$

Hence, the elevation of the cabin is 6000 + 1631 or 7631 feet, approximately.

Example 2: Two towers are located on either side of a river (see Figure 8.20). From a point 2000 yards downstream of one of the towers, the tower

Figure 8.20

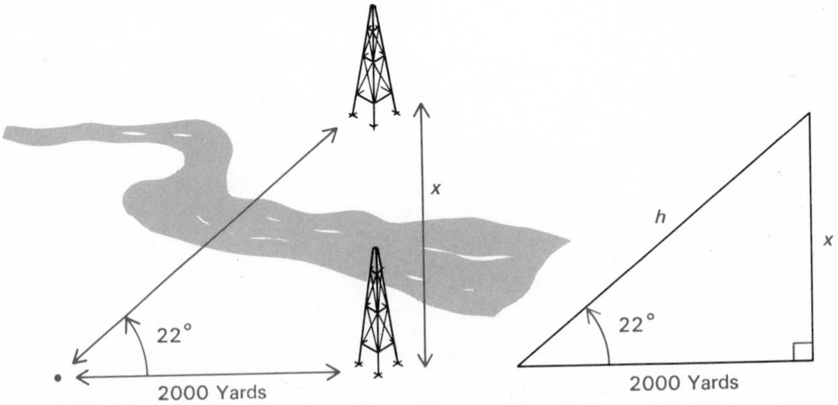

on the opposite side of the river makes an angle of 22°. How far apart are the two towers?

SOLUTION: The sketch in Figure 8.20 contains all of the given information for this problem and a drawing of the right triangle that is the mathematical model of the problem. Let the distance between the towers be called x. If we knew the length of the hypotenuse of this triangle, then we could determine the length x by using the equation

$$x = (\text{length of hypotenuse})[\sin(22°)].$$

But we were not given the length of the hypotenuse. Call this length h. We can determine h by using the other information given by the problem. That is, we know that the length of the leg adjacent to the 22° angle is equal to the length of the hypotenuse times the cosine of 22°. Hence

$$2000 = (h)[\cos(22°)].$$

From Table 8–2, cos(22°) = .927, so

$$2000 = (h)(.927)$$

or

$$h = \frac{2000}{.927} = 2161 \text{ yards, approximately.}$$

Now that we know h, we can find x:

$$\begin{aligned} x &= (2161)[\sin(22°)] \\ &= (2161)(.375) \\ &= 810 \text{ yards, approximately.} \end{aligned}$$

We have found the distance between the towers indirectly. It would be difficult to find this distance without using trigonometry.

Exercises 8.6

1. A wire has been stretched from the top of a 1,676 foot tall TV tower to the ground. The length of wire required was 2,000 feet. The installer was supposed to measure the angle the wire makes with the top of the tower but he forgot. Can he determine this angle without climbing to the top of the tower?
2. A tree casts a shadow 92 feet long at a time of day when the elevation of the sun is 48°. How tall is the tree? (*Hint:* You will first have to determine the length of the line from the top of the tree to the end of the shadow.)
3. By making observations from earth it can be determined that the angle α shown in the drawing below is equal to about 1°. Assuming the radius of the earth is approximately 3,963 miles, what is the approximate distance

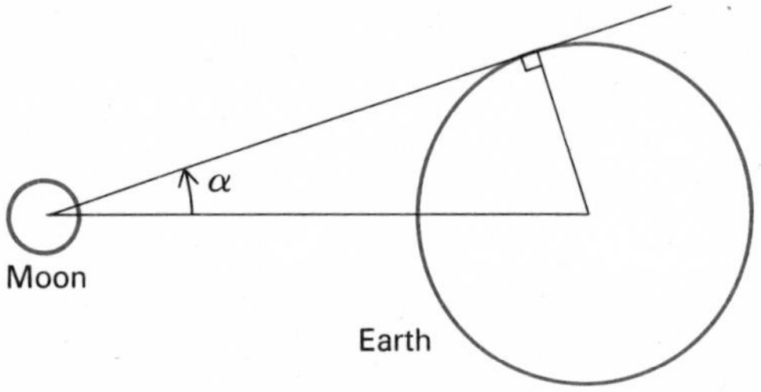

between the center of the earth and the center of the moon? Actually the true angle subtended is a bit less than 1°, so is the answer you got too big or too small?
4. A 300-foot radio tower has been installed and it is necessary to run a supporting cable from the top of the tower to a point on the ground 80 feet away from the base of the tower. In order to install the ground anchor for this cable it is necessary to know the angle the cable will make with the ground. What is this angle? (*Hint:* First compute the length of cable using the Pythagorean Theorem. Then use either the sine or cosine function and the appropriate table of values to find the approximate angle.)
5. At exactly 10 A.M. on a certain day a tree 60 feet tall casts a shadow 24 feet long. What was the angle of elevation of the sun at that time?
6. The leaning tower of Pisa is about 179 feet high and is about 16.5 feet out of plumb. Find the angle the tower is off from vertical.

9 The Theory of Probability

IT IS ALWAYS difficult to establish just when a particular part of mathematics got its start, but the theory of probability is generally given the birth-year of 1654. In this year a gambler, Chevalier de Mere, asked the mathematician Blaise Pascal (French, 1623–1662) about a certain dice game that was giving him trouble. Pascal corresponded with Fermat and the theory of probability stems from their correspondence concerning this dice game and related ideas. Today the theory is an important part of mathematics and has significant applications to all fields of science.

This story about the origin of probability is pleasant enough, and it may even be true. At any rate, it is frequently found in the literature. It is true that probability spent its early years in gambling casinos. In fact, it still spends a part of its time there in the sense that gambling problems provide excellent illustrative examples to use in discussing elementary probability. We shall employ such games of chance throughout our discussion of probability.

Related to the theory of probability, but occupying a place of its own in mathematics, is statistics. Even an elementary study of statistics requires preparation in areas of mathematics that we have not even touched upon, and so we shall tread very carefully around the edges of the subject and restrict our remarks to the most general.

9.1 A Priori and Statistical Probability

There are two kinds of probability and you have had informal experience with both of them. They are called "a priori probability" and "statistical (or a posteriori) probability." In this section we shall differentiate between the two and begin a study of a priori probability.

Blaise Pascal (1623–1662)

The difference between a priori and statistical probability can perhaps best be illustrated by looking at some examples. Consider these two problems, each of which has to do in some way with probability.

Problem 1: A coin is tossed and caught. What is the probability that the coin will come up heads?

Problem 2: What is the probability that a person born in 1968 in Toledo will live to be 80 years old?

You will surely agree that each of these problems has to do with probability, but that these are two very different kinds of probability problems. Pretty clearly, in order to answer Problem 2, we would have to collect evidence of some kind—we would have to examine birth and death records or something of this sort. This problem cannot be answered in a purely mathematical way. But Problem 1 does admit a purely mathematical solution: There are exactly two ways the coin can come up when it is tossed. Each of these two ways is equally likely. Exactly one of these two ways will result in a head. Therefore, the chances of tossing a head are 1 in 2. The mathematician expresses this by saying that the a priori probability of tossing a head is 1/2. The prefix words *a priori* mean "valid independently of observation" and this is the way we solved Problem 1. We did not need to find a coin and actually toss it many times in order to determine the probability. But in Problem 2, no such purely mathematical solution is possible. Problem 2 can be solved only through observation. The kind of probability we are talking about in Problem 2 is *a posteriori* ("based upon actual observation or upon experimental data") or *statistical* probability.

We should remark that under certain conditions we might feel it important to regard Problem 1 as a problem in statistical probability. For example, if we felt that the coin being tossed might be biased, then we would want to experiment with the coin in order to determine the probability. If we tossed the coin, say, 1000 times and found that it came up heads only 100 times, then we would be strongly tempted to disregard the a priori probability as being not applicable to this biased coin and use the statistical probability of $\frac{100}{1000}$ instead. Generally, however, we regard coins and the like as being unbiased and apply a priori probability.

To introduce the various terms that we shall be working with in our study of a priori probability, let us consider the throwing of a single die. (A **die** is a perfect cube the faces of which are inscribed with the digits 1 through 6.) When the die is thrown, there are six possible **outcomes**: that a 1 will come up, that a 2 will come up, and so on. These possible outcomes are called **mutually exclusive** because it is impossible for more than one of them to occur at the same time. Also, under the assumption that the die is perfect, these six different outcomes are **equally likely**. This means that the die has been constructed in such a way that no one number will come up more often than any other number over a long series of throws. If the die were loaded, then the possible outcomes would not be equally likely, although they would still be mutually exclusive. We shall always assume in our work with a priori probability that the die is unaltered. We refer to the throwing of a die as an **experiment**.

Another example of an experiment the outcomes of which are mutually exclusive and equally likely is the tossing of a coin. Still another example is the dealing of a card from a well shuffled deck of cards.

Suppose now that we are going to perform some experiment and that we have already identified each of the (finitely many) possible outcomes. Then the **a priori probability** that a given event will occur as the result of the experiment is given by the quotient f/n where n represents the total number of possible outcomes of the experiment and f represents the total number of these that are favorable to the event occurring. Here are some examples that will help to clarify this definition.

Example 1: What is the probability that in throwing a die an even number will come up?

SOLUTION: The total number of possible outcomes is six. The event we are talking about is that an even number will come up and there are three outcomes that are favorable to this event occurring. These are the outcomes that a 2 will come up, that a 4 will come up, and that a 6 will come up (see Figure 9.1). All the other outcomes are unfavorable. Hence the probability is 3/6 or 1/2.

Figure 9.1

Example 2: An American roulette wheel[1] contains the numbers 1 through 36 (evenly divided into red and black numbers—see Figure 9.2) and the two green numbers 0 and 00. What is the probability that when the wheel is spun, the little white ball will fall into a green number?

Figure 9.2

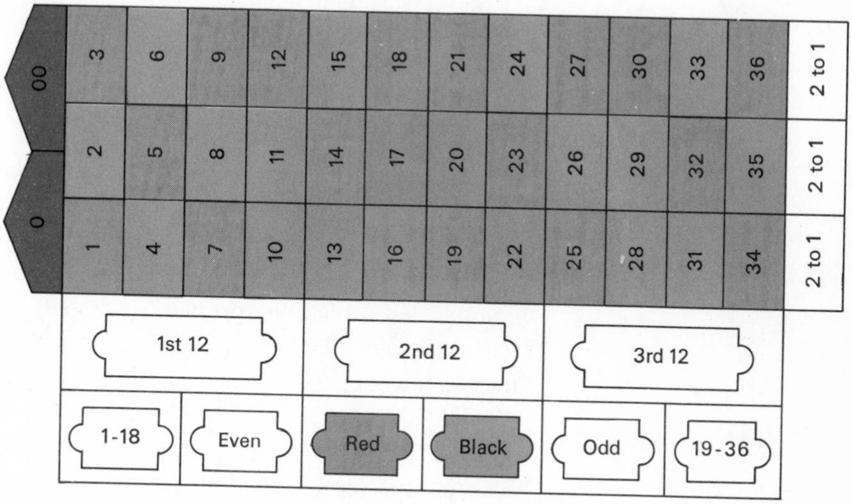

American Roulette Layout

Solution: There are a total of $36 + 2 = 38$ outcomes that may result from the experiment of spinning the wheel. Of these 38 outcomes, exactly two are favorable to a green number being selected (the outcomes 0 and 00). Hence, the probability of getting a green number is $2/38 = 1/19$.

Example 3: The cards A♠, 2♠, 3♠, and 4♠ are removed from the standard deck. What is the probability that if a fifth card is dealt, it will be the 5♠?

Solution: The experiment consists of dealing a card from the 48-card deck that remains after the four specified cards have been removed. Of the 48 possible outcomes of such a deal only one, the 5♠, will be favorable. Hence, the probability is 1/48. Incidentally, this kind of hand is called a "straight flush" in poker.

[1] The American wheel differs from the European wheel in that the European wheel contains only one green number, 0.

Example 4: What is the probability of completing the hand 2♠, 3♠, 4♠, and 5♠ to make a flush? (*Note:* A "flush" in poker is a hand consisting of five cards all of the same suit.)

SOLUTION: We have depleted the deck by four spades so there are only nine spades left in the 48-card depleted deck. Hence the probability of drawing a fifth spade is 9/48 or 3/16. That is, there are 48 ways of dealing off the fifth card, but only nine of them are favorable to dealing off a spade.

The extreme limits of a priori probabilities are 0 (impossibility) and 1 (certainty). All other probabilities lie somewhere between these limits. The nearer a probability is to 0 the less likely it is that the event will occur and the nearer the probability is to 1 the more likely it is that the event will occur.

The examples of this section were all rather simple. In order to work more complicated probability problems, we shall have to develop some counting techniques. We shall do this in Section 9.3. First, however, we pause to discuss the connection between a priori probability and the real world.

Exercises 9.1

1. Compute these probabilities having to do with the rolling of two dice by listing all possible outcomes and listing all favorable outcomes.
   (a) What is the probability that a number less than six will be rolled?
   (b) What is the probability that an even number will be rolled?
   (c) What is the probability that an even number less than six will be rolled?
   (d) What is the probability that either an even number or a number less than three will be rolled?
2. The following questions have to do with the American roulette layout shown in Fig. 9.2.
   (a) If you place your bet on the space marked "1–18" then you will win if any one of the numbers 1 through 18 comes up. What is the probability of this event occurring?
   (b) If you put your bet on the space marked "1st 12" you will win if any one of the numbers 1 through 12 comes up. What is the probability of this event occurring?
   (c) If you place your bet on one of the spaces marked "2 to 1" you will win if any one of the numbers in the column in which you have placed your bet comes up. What is the probability of this event occurring?

(d) Compare the probabilities for *red*, *black*, *odd*, and *even*. (*Note*: 0 and 00 are green numbers that are neither odd nor even.)

(e) It is possible to place your bet on the lower left corner of the square containing the number 1. By so doing you bet that one of the numbers 0, 00, 1, 2, and 3 will come up. What is the probability of winning with this bet?

(f) It is possible to place your bet on the common corner of the squares containing the numbers 22, 23, 25, and 26. By so doing you bet that one of these four numbers will come up. What is the probability of winning on this bet?

3. A single card is drawn from a deck. What is the probability that it is either a heart or a face card?

4. Would you rather bet the number 10 on an American or on a European roulette wheel? Explain using probability.

5. Describe the different possible outcomes of each of the following experiments. Are these outcomes mutually exclusive? Equally likely?
   (a) Selecting a card from a shuffled deck of cards.
   (b) Choosing a wife.
   (c) Asking a supermarket cashier for change for a quarter.
   (d) Dealing a card from a deck from which all the aces have been removed.

6. One way to alter the behavior of a die is to shave a small amount of surface material off the faces containing the six and the one. (These are on opposite sides of the die.) Such a die is called a *Six-Ace Flat*. Will the six possible outcomes of throwing a Six-Ace Flat be mutually exclusive? Which outcomes will be more likely and which will be less likely?

7. Before working these two problems try to predict how the answers will compare. Then work the problems by enumerating all possible outcomes and all favorable outcomes.
   (a) A man has two children one of which is a boy. What is the probability that the other is also a boy?
   (b) A man has two children the older of which is a boy. What is the probability that the younger is also a boy?

8. The cards K♡, Q♡, 6♡, and 7♡ are removed from a deck and this four-card partial deck is well shuffled. Each of two players is dealt two cards. One of the players, Ethelred, says, "I have a face card in my hand." At another table another couple has gone through exactly the same procedure and one of these players, Ethelbert, says, "I have the king of hearts in my hand." Which of these two players, Ethelbert or Ethelred, is

more likely to have two face cards in his hand? Try to predict which has the greater probability before working the problem. (*Hint:* First list all of the possible hands: K ♡ and Q ♡, K ♡ and 6 ♡, K ♡ and 7 ♡, and so forth.)

9. You have two cards, one of which is red on both sides and the other of which is red on one side and white on the other side. You close your eyes and someone mixes up the cards and places one of them on the table. Then you open your eyes and see that the face-up side of the card on the table is red. What is the probability that the other side of this card is also red? (*Hint:* The answer is *not* $\frac{1}{2}$.)

9.2 The Law of Large Numbers

The Law of Large Numbers lies at the heart of the theory of probability and is one of the fundamental theorems in this subject. We shall discuss the theorem informally, without giving a precise statement of it.

We know that the a priori probability of tossing a head with a perfect coin is 1/2. When we say this, we must clearly appreciate that all we mean is that of the two possible outcomes of the toss, one of them is favorable to a head being tossed. The **Law of Large Numbers** is a theorem that relates this purely mathematical statement of the a priori probability to what might actually happen when a coin is tossed a great many times. The law consists of two parts. The first part states simply that by tossing the coin sufficiently many times, we can make the ratio of heads to total tosses be as near to the a priori probability of 1/2 as we desire. That is, if we let N denote the total number of tosses and h_N denote the total number of heads obtained in these N tosses, then by making N large enough we can assure that the ratio h_N/N will be as near to 1/2 as we desire. For example, suppose that we want to make the ratio h_N/N be within .001 of 1/2. We can make this happen if we toss the coin sufficiently many times—if we make N sufficiently large. Note that we have not said how many times we must toss the coin before the ratio of heads to total tosses will be in the range .499 to .501; we have only said that there exists some number of tosses such that, after that many tosses, the ratio will be in the range .499 to .501. It is impossible to predict how many tosses might be required. We could not make a statement such as, "After one trillion tosses the ratio h_N/N will be in the range .499 to .501." The reason we could not make such a statement is obvious: It is conceivable that in the first trillion tosses a tail would be tossed every time. The probability that this would happen is very small indeed, but there is a definite nonzero probability that it could happen.

This first part of the Law of Large Numbers is often called the **law of averages.**

The second part of the Law of Large Numbers deals with the difference between the number of heads actually obtained after N tosses and the number of heads we would be led to anticipate on the basis of the a priori probability. Since the a priori probability of tossing a head is 1/2, we might expect that after N tosses, we would have obtained $N/2$ heads. But we know that in actual practice it is unlikely that we would obtain $N/2$ heads after N tosses. The actual number of heads could be less than $N/2$ or greater than $N/2$. That is, the difference $N/2 - h_N$ might be positive, actually equal to zero, or negative. The second part of the Law of Large Numbers says that this difference will fluctuate around 0, but that as the total number of tosses gets larger and larger, this difference will fluctuate more and more wildly between positive and negative values. The graph in Figure 9.3 shows in a general way how the difference $N/2 - h_N$ jumps up and down as N becomes larger and larger and how these jumps reach lower lows and higher highs.

Figure 9.3

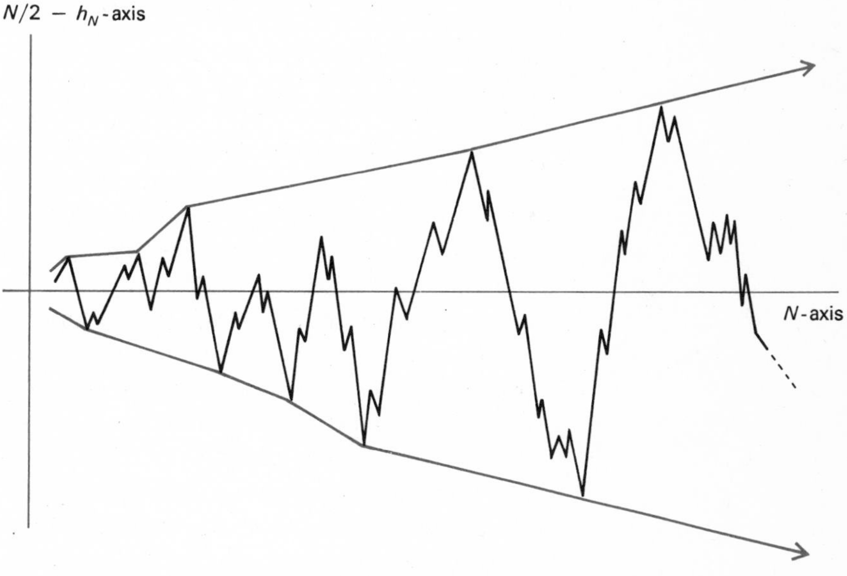

The conclusion we draw from this fluctuation of the difference $N/2 - h_N$ is that as N becomes larger and larger, there will occur longer and longer runs of tails and longer and longer runs of heads. The longer and longer runs of tails are what make the graph attain higher and higher highs as N gets larger.

The longer and longer runs of heads are what make the graph attain lower and lower lows as N gets larger and larger.

Thus we see that the Law of Large Numbers (Part 2) anticipates long runs of heads and long runs of tails. When such runs occur, we should not really be surprised, because we know that they are bound to occur eventually. For example, betting the red and black on roulette is much the same as betting heads or tails on the flip of a coin. The longest run of one color that we know about was a run of 32 red numbers at Monte Carlo. This event caused considerable commotion at the casino, as indeed it should have. Such long runs happen very rarely. But we should not think that their happening is something truly extraordinary, because the Law of Large Numbers tells us that they are bound to happen. Provided this world lasts long enough, the Law of Large Numbers tells us that there will sometime be a run of, say, 2000 red numbers at Monte Carlo. The sun may explode and turn Monte Carlo into a cinder four billion years before the event is to take place, but if we last long enough it will happen.

The Law of Large Numbers is often misused. To illustrate these misuses, suppose that we were to undertake a series of coin-tossing experiments and that we recorded the results of each toss. Suppose also that on each of the first 32 tosses we got a head. How would you react to this? Very likely you would be surprised that this run of heads happened right at the beginning of the test. After recovering from your shock, you would prepare to make the 33rd toss. What about this 33rd toss? Do you have any strong feelings as to what will or ought to happen? There are different points of view here; let us examine each of them.

First, there is the opinion held by a fellow named Skeptic. Skeptic reacts to this series of tosses by stating that he cannot believe that the coin we are using is an unbiased coin. Somehow, Skeptic feels, this coin has been constructed so that it will come up heads every time. Skeptic is reacting to this unusual situation by claiming that, in his opinion, the statistical evidence is such that he for one cannot accept the coin as being perfect. Therefore he must apply statistical probability rather than a priori probability to this situation, and he concludes that the chances are very high that a head will come up on the 33rd toss. This is a reasonable attitude to take, but we shall ignore Skeptic because we insist that the coin being used is unbiased—it is either perfect or so nearly perfect that no bias is detectable.

The second attitude is held by Lawyer. Lawyer predicts in no uncertain terms that a tail is much more likely to come up on the 33rd toss than a head.

Lawyer claims that in the long run the number of heads will equal the number of tails and, since heads have come up 32 times so far, according to the law of averages it is tails' turn to come up. Lawyer knows that after sufficiently many tosses of the coin, the ratio of heads to total tosses (h_N/N) will be close to 1/2. This ratio now stands at 32/32 or 1. Lawyer feels that the law of averages is going to make this ratio begin its return to 1/2 *right now*! But this is patent nonsense. The law of averages says no such thing. The law of averages would not be disturbed if heads came up on each of the first million tosses. All the law of averages says is that after a sufficiently large number of tosses, this ratio will be near 1/2. How large "sufficiently large" is we do not know and cannot know. In this particular series of tosses, it might be that it will take millions and millions of tosses to get the ratio of heads to total tosses near to 1/2.

The third attitude is held by Gambler. Gambler knows that the second part of the Law of Large Numbers tells him to expect long runs of heads. He thinks that so unusual a happening as a run of 32 heads must indicate that we are now in the middle of one of these long runs of heads. So he predicts that heads will come up on the 33rd toss. But Gambler is making the same kind of mistake that Lawyer made. Gambler is trying to draw information about one particular toss of the coin from the Law of Large Numbers and this simply cannot be done. He and Lawyer are just working opposite sides of the same street.

The last attitude is held by Uninterested. Uninterested is completely bored by the question of what is going to happen on the 33rd toss, and while Lawyer and Gambler are arguing and pounding the table to lend credence to their arguments, Uninterested has gone to sleep. He knows that the a priori probability of getting a head on any one toss of the coin is exactly the same as the a priori probability of getting a tail. Hence the coin is just as likely to come up heads as it is to come up tails on the 33rd toss and there is no way to use probability theory to come to a definite conclusion as to what will happen. Uninterested knows that the coin tossings are independent experiments in the sense that no one toss is in any way effected or controlled by what happened on earlier tosses. He knows that the coin cannot remember that it has come up heads 32 times already. Perhaps if the coin could remember it would be properly chagrined and would try very hard to come up tails the 33rd time, but such speculation is wasted. Uninterested is disgusted by Lawyer's and Gambler's attempts to draw information concerning what is going to happen on one particular toss of the coin from the Law of Large

Numbers. He correctly understands that this law will give him information only as to what will happen after a sufficiently large number of tosses, but he also knows that he cannot predict how large "sufficiently large" might be.

Now that we have a good idea of the role played by a priori probabilities, let us go on to consider some counting techniques that we can use to compute probabilities in less trivial situations than coin tossings.

Exercises 9.2

1. We asserted in the text that tossing a coin for heads and tails is very nearly the same as spinning a European roulette wheel for red and black, but these are not really the same experiments. How does the probability of tossing a head differ from the probability of spinning red on a European roulette wheel?
2. Here are the results of 200 coin tossings:

THHTT	HTHTT	HTHTH	THHTH	TTTTH	THHHT	TTTHH	HTHTH
TTTHT	HTHHT	THTHH	TTHTT	HTHTH	TTTTH	HHHTH	TTHHH
HHHTH	HTHTH	THHHH	THTTT	THHTH	HTTHH	HTHTH	THTHH
HTHTT	HHHTH	HHTHT	HHHTH	HHHTT	TTTHH	HTTHH	HHHHT
HHHTH	TTTHH	HHTHH	TTHTT	THHHT	TTTHH	HHHHT	HHTTH

Starting with $N = 5$, compute the number $N/2 - h_N$ for each value of $N = 5, 10, 15, 20, 25, \ldots, 2000$, and plot the corresponding points $(N, N/2 - h_N)$ as in Fig. 9.3. To what extent does this graph resemble the graph shown in Fig. 9.3? Are heads occurring in the way that you would expect them to occur?

3. Repeat Exercise 2 by making 200 coin tossings yourself. How do your results compare with those of Exercise 2? (You can save time by tossing a number of coins at once.)
4. You have been dealt the cards 2♡, K◇, J♠, and 9♣ from a shuffled deck. What is the probability that the next card dealt to you will give you a pair? (A *pair* is two cards of the same rank.)
5. In poker a *straight* consists of five cards whose ranks are in order, for example, 2, 3, 4, 5, and 6. Ace counts high and low. If from a complete deck you have been dealt the cards shown below, what is the probability that upon being dealt a fifth card you will fill to a straight? (We shall ignore suits in this problem.)

   (a) A, 3, 4, 5. **(b)** A, 2, 3, 4. **(c)** 2, 3, 5, 6.
6.* If the probability that an event E will occur as the result of some experiment is f/n, then the probability that the event will *not* occur is $1 - f/n$.

Use this principle to solve the following problems.

(a) A die is tossed four times. What is the probability that at least one six will be rolled? (*Hint:* First compute the probability that no six will be rolled.)

(b) A coin is tossed three times. What is the probability that at least one head will be thrown? At most two heads?

9.3 Some Counting Problems

In this section we shall discuss some counting techniques that can be used to simplify the computation of probabilities. These methods will be used in the next section to compute probabilities in less trivial situations than we encountered in Section 9.1.

All counting techniques are based upon the following **counting principle**: Suppose that two tasks are to be performed. If the first task can be done in n different ways and the second task can then be performed in m different ways, then the two tasks can be performed (in order) in nm different ways. This counting principle can be extended in the obvious way to apply to any finite number of tasks to be performed in order.

Example 1: How many license plates can be made of the form

Letter-Letter-Letter-Digit-Digit?

SOLUTION: There are 26 ways to fill in the first letter; then there are 26 ways to fill in the second letter; then there are 26 ways to fill in the third letter; then there are ten ways to fill in the first digit; and, finally, there are ten ways to fill in the second digit. Hence there are $26 \cdot 26 \cdot 26 \cdot 10 \cdot 10 = 14{,}576{,}000$ different license plates that can be made of this form.

Example 2: How many license plates can be made of the form

Letter-Letter-Letter-Digit-Digit

if no letter or digit is to be repeated?

SOLUTION: There are 26 ways to fill in the first letter. But after this letter has been chosen there remain only 25 letters to use in filling in the second letter. Then there are only 24 ways to fill in the third letter. The first digit can be filled in in any one of ten ways. But then the second digit can only be filled in in only nine different ways. Hence there are only $26 \cdot 25 \cdot 24 \cdot 10 \cdot 9 = 1{,}904{,}000$ license plates in which no letter or digit is repeated.

Note the difference between Examples 1 and 2. In Example 1 each task to be performed (each filling in of a space) was independent of the tasks that were done previously. But in Example 2 the second task was dependent upon what happened as a result of the first task. That is, what could happen as a result of the second task was effected by what already had happened as a result of the first task. Then what could happen as a result of the third task depended upon what already had happened as a result of each of the first and second tasks. As we see illustrated in Example 1, if the tasks to be performed are independent, then the number of ways a series of such tasks can be performed is simply the product of the ways the individual tasks can be performed. But, if the tasks are dependent, then the number of ways the series of tasks can be performed is the product of the numbers of ways each individual task can be performed, assuming that the preceding tasks have already been performed.

Example 3: The Morse Code is a device by means of which the 26 letters and ten digits can be symbolized by dots or dashes. Is it possible to devise a code similar to the Morse Code which does not involve any blocks of five or more dots or dashes?

SOLUTION: No. There are two blocks containing exactly one dot or dash. There are $2 \cdot 2 = 4$ blocks containing two dots or dashes. There are $2 \cdot 2 \cdot 2 = 8$ blocks containing exactly three dots or dashes. There are $2 \cdot 2 \cdot 2 \cdot 2 = 16$ blocks containing exactly four dots or dashes. Hence there are $2 + 4 + 8 + 16 = 30$ blocks containing not more than four dots or dashes. Since there are 36 characters to be represented, there must be six blocks containing at least five dots or dashes.

Many counting problems may be reduced to the following "common denominator" kind of problem. Given a finite set containing n $(n > 0)$ objects, how many subsets does it possess that contain t $(0 < t \leq n)$ objects? If we can answer to this problem, then we can solve a wide variety of related counting problems.

Example 4: The set $\{a,b,c\}$ has three two-object subsets: $\{a,b\}$, $\{a,c\}$, and $\{b,c\}$.

Example 5: How many three-object subsets does the set $\{a,b,c,d,e\}$ possess?

SOLUTION: A complete list of the three-object subsets is:

$\{a,b,c\}$	$\{a,c,d\}$	$\{a,d,e\}$	$\{b,c,d\}$	$\{b,d,e\}$	$\{c,d,e\}$
$\{a,b,d\}$	$\{a,c,e\}$		$\{b,c,e\}$		
$\{a,b,e\}$					

These are all of the three-object subsets and so $\{a,b,c,d,e\}$ contains ten three-object subsets.

Solving such problems by listing the subsets is tedious and would be difficult if n were very large. There is a formula that conveniently answers this general problem, a formula that expresses the number of t-object subsets. This formula is most often expressed in terms of the **factorial notation.**[2] If n represents a nonzero whole number, then the symbol $n!$ (read "n factorial") is used to abbreviate the product of n and all the nonzero whole numbers less than n. Thus $1! = 1$, $2! = 2 \cdot 1 = 2$, $3! = 3 \cdot 2 \cdot 1 = 6$, $4! = 4 \cdot 3 \cdot 2 \cdot 1 = 24$, $5! = 5 \cdot 4 \cdot 3 \cdot 2 \cdot 1 = 120, \ldots, 10! = 9 \cdot 8 \cdot 7 \cdot 6 \cdot 5 \cdot 4 \cdot 3 \cdot 2 \cdot 1 = 3{,}628{,}880$, and so on. The symbol $0!$ is used as another name for 1. We shall point out the reason for this in a moment.

Using this factorial notation, the number of t-object subsets of a set containing n $(n > 0)$ objects is given by the expression

$$\frac{n!}{t!(n-t)!}.$$

We shall represent this number by $C(n,t)$, and so we can write the formula

$$C(n,t) = \frac{n!}{t!(n-t)!}.$$

For example, the number of two-object subsets of a set containing 6 objects is

$$C(6,2) = \frac{6!}{2!4!} = \frac{6 \cdot 5 \cdot 4 \cdot 3 \cdot 2 \cdot 1}{2 \cdot 1 \cdot 4 \cdot 3 \cdot 2 \cdot 1} = 15.$$

[2] This symbol was invented in 1808. Its only purpose is to make typesetting easier.

The reason we defined $0!$ to be another name for 1 was so that this formula would work when $n = t$. When $n = t$, we are asking for the number of n-object subsets of a set containing n objects and there is only one of these (namely, the set itself). So we see that $C(n,n) = 1$. But according to the formula,

$$C(n,n) = \frac{n!}{n!0!} = \frac{1}{0!}.$$

Thus, in order for the formula to be correct when $n = t$, we must define the symbol $0!$ to be equal to 1.

Example 6: How many different five-card poker hands can be dealt from a standard deck?

SOLUTION: Reduced to its essentials, all we are asked here is, how many different five-object subsets does a set that contains 52 objects possess? Hence we are required to compute $C(52,5)$:

$$C(52,5) = \frac{52!}{5!47!} = \frac{52 \cdot 51 \cdot 50 \cdot 49 \cdot 48}{5 \cdot 4 \cdot 3 \cdot 2 \cdot 1} = 2{,}598{,}960.$$

Example 7: A class contains 27 students and the teacher wants to select five students to go to the board and work problems. In how many ways can he select these five students?

SOLUTION: We must compute $C(27,5)$:

$$C(27,5) = \frac{27!}{5!22!} = \frac{27 \cdot 26 \cdot 25 \cdot 24 \cdot 23}{5 \cdot 4 \cdot 3 \cdot 2} = 80{,}730.$$

Example 8: If you were a student in the class mentioned in Example 7, how many of the 80,730 five-student sets would contain you?

SOLUTION: We are asked for the number of five-student sets that can be constructed containing you. Starting with you as an object, such a set is formed by including four more students in the set. There are 26 students from which to draw these four, and so there are $C(26,4)$ different ways to complete a five-object set which already has you as its first object. There are 14,950 sets of five students which contain you.

The counting techniques discussed here will enable us to solve a surprisingly large number of probability problems, but there are many counting techniques besides these. The study of such techniques is called **combinatorial analysis**. Combinatorial analysis plays a large part in modern mathematics and is particularly important in probability and statistics. Loosely speaking, we may think of combinatorial analysis as the art of counting.

Exercises 9.3

1. How many different ways are there to deal a bridge hand from a standard deck?
2. You are to select three different numbers from each of the groups of numbers 1 through 37, 38 through 59, and 60 through 80. In how many different ways can you do this?
3. If we place no restrictions upon the internal characteristics of a "word", how many three-letter words are possible in the English language? Assuming that each three-letter word must contain at least one vowel, how many such words can there be? Assuming that no three-letter word contains fewer than one or more than two vowels, how many such words can there be?
4. How many divisors does the whole number $2^a \cdot 3^b \cdot 5^c \cdot 7^d \cdot 11^e$ possess? How many divisors does 3,300 possess? List all of these divisors.
5. Let us assume that every nation has a flag consisting of one, two, or three of the colors red, white, yellow, blue, green, black, and gold, but that no two nations employ the same combination of colors in their flag. How many nations may be represented by flags of one color? Of two colors? Of three colors? Of three or fewer colors?
6. A man witnessed a hit-and-run accident. Although he was not able to identify the complete license number of the car, he did recognize that the license was of the form

   Letter-Letter-Letter-Digit-Digit-Digit,

   that the license contained the letter K in some position, and that the license involved the combination of digits 17 next to each other in some position. If the police had to check all cars with licenses fitting this description, how many cars would they have to check?

7. Use the counting principle and the notion of prime factorization to prove the following two theorems.
   (a) If a whole number is a perfect square, then it has an odd number of divisors.
   (b) If a whole number is not a perfect square, then it has an even number of divisors.
8. For each whole number value of n from 2 through 8 compute the number $(n - 1)! + 1$. For which values of n does n divide $(n - 1)! + 1$? Make a conjecture and test your conjecture by computing a few more values of $(n - 1)! + 1$.
9. Six lines are drawn in the plane so that no three of them intersect at the same point and no two of them are parallel. How many triangles are contained in this configuration of lines? (*Hint:* Each set of three lines forms a triangle.) How many triangles are formed if exactly two of the lines are parallel?

9.4 Computing Probabilities

We shall continue our study of probability with the study of certain gambling games. It is from such games that the theory derived historically and they still serve as efficient tools with which to learn probability.

We have already discussed the relatively simple game of roulette. So let us begin here with the dice game called craps. The rules for craps are quite simple: One begins by rolling two dice. If either a 7 or an 11 is obtained in the first roll, the shooter wins. If one of the numbers 2, 3, or 12 is obtained, then the shooter loses. If some other number, say a 5, is obtained on the first roll, then the number becomes the shooter's "point." On subsequent rolls (and the shooter must continue to shoot until he either wins or loses), the shooter wins if he rolls his "point" before he rolls a 7. Otherwise he loses.

Example 1: What is the probability that the shooter will win on the first roll? That he will lose on the first roll? That he will neither win nor lose on the first roll?

SOLUTION: The shooter is using two dice, either of which can come up in six different ways. Accordingly, there are $6 \cdot 6 = 36$ different ways these two dice can be thrown. The winning and losing ways to throw the dice on the first roll are shown below. Hence the probability of winning on the first

Ways to Win		*Ways to Lose*	
Die 1	*Die 2*	*Die 1*	*Die 2*
1	6	1	1
2	5	1	2
3	4	2	1
4	3	6	6
5	2		
6	1		
5	6		
6	5		

roll is 8/36 and the probability of losing on the first roll is 4/36. Thus on the first roll the shooter is twice as likely to win as to lose. The probability of neither winning nor losing on the first roll is

$$\frac{36 - (8 + 4)}{36} = 24/36 = 2/3.$$

Next, consider a couple of card games. Of all card games, perhaps the most famous is poker. Draw poker is played by first dealing five cards to each player. After some betting and exchanging of cards and then more betting, the players remaining in the game compare their hands. The possible hands are ranked from highest to lowest. The highest ranking hand wins.

Example 2: A high-ranking poker hand is one that consists of five cards, all of the same suit. Such a hand is called a "flush." What is the probability of being dealt a flush?

SOLUTION: There are a total of $C(52,5)$ different five-card poker hands that can be dealt from the standard deck. There are $C(13,5)$ flushes in any one suit and there are four suits. Hence the probability of being dealt a flush is[3]

$$\frac{4C(13,5)}{C(52,5)} = \frac{5{,}148}{2{,}598{,}960} \text{ or about } 1/505.$$

[3] This count includes both straight and royal flushes.

Example 3: A very fine draw-poker hand is one consisting of three cards all of the same rank and two cards both of another rank. Such hands are called *full houses.* (An example of a full house is the hand 6♣, 6♠, 6◇, 4◇, 4♣.) What is the probability of being dealt a full house?

SOLUTION: Let us first work with a particular full house, the one consisting of three aces and two kings. There are $C(4,3)$ ways to deal off three aces from the four aces in the deck and there are $C(4,2)$ ways to deal off two kings from the four kings in the deck. Hence there are $C(4,3) \cdot C(4,2) = 24$ different ways to deal off a full house consisting of three aces and two kings. More generally, if R_1 and R_2 are any two of the 13 ranks, then there are 24 ways to deal off a full house consisting of three cards of rank R_1 and two cards of rank R_2. But we can select the rank R_1 in 13 different ways, and after that we can select the rank R_2 in 12 different ways. So there are $24 \cdot 13 \cdot 12 = 3744$ different full houses that can be dealt. Thus the probability of being dealt such a hand is 3,744/2,598,960, or about 1/694.

Because the probability of being dealt a full house is less than the probability of being dealt a flush, full houses rank higher than flushes in draw poker.

Another popular card game is bridge. Thirteen cards are dealt to each of four players and the game begins.

Example 4: What is the probability of being dealt a 13-card hand consisting of all spades? (This is very nearly the best bridge hand that can be dealt.)

SOLUTION: The total number of ways to deal 13 cards is $C(52,13)$. Of all of these hands, only one consists of all spades. Hence the probability of being dealt all spades is

$$\frac{1}{C(52,13)} = \frac{1}{635{,}013{,}559{,}600}.$$

Example 5: The worst bridge hand that you can be dealt is called a "yarborough." This is a hand that does not contain any cards higher than a nine. What is the probability of being dealt such a hand?

SOLUTION: To deal a yarborough, we would have first to remove the 10's, J's, Q's, K's, and A's from the deck. This would leave 32 cards in the deck from which to deal the yarborough. There are $C(32,13)$ bridge hands that can be dealt from this depleted deck and so the probability of being dealt a yarborough is

$$\frac{C(32,13)}{C(52,13)} = \frac{5,394}{9,860,459} \text{ or about } 1/1828.$$

Keno is a form of lottery and is played in many different ways. One way to play the game is for you to select eight numbers of your choice from the 80 numbers 1 through 80. After you have made your selection, the house selects 20 numbers at random. You win according to how many of your eight numbers are included in the 20 numbers chosen by the house. The popularity of this game is due to the fact that it is possible to win as much as $25,000 on as small a bet as $1.20.

Example 6: You select eight numbers from the numbers 1 through 80. Then the house selects 20 numbers at random. What is the probability that all eight of your numbers are chosen by the house?

SOLUTION: There are a total of $C(80,20)$ ways for the house to choose their 20 numbers. How many of these will include your eight numbers? Starting with your eight numbers, we need to fill out a total of 20 numbers from the 72 numbers remaining after you choose your eight. Hence there are $C(72,12)$ ways to fill out your eight numbers to make 20. Thus the probability of having all eight of your numbers chosen by the house is

$$\frac{C(72,12)}{C(80,20)} = \frac{51}{11,680,845} \text{ or about } 1/229,036.$$

Finally let us mention a principle that applies to problems in which two or more events are to take place in succession. If an event E has a probability of p and, after the event E has occurred, a second event F has a probability of q, then the probability that event E will occur followed by the occurrence of event F is pq.

Example 7: What is the probability that red will come up twice in a row on an American roulette wheel?

SOLUTION: The first event is that red will come up and the second event is the same. The probability that the first event will occur is 18/38. Assuming that the first event has now occurred, the probability that the second event will occur is also 18/38. Hence the probability asked for is $(18/38)^2$ or about 1/90.

Example 8: What is the probability of dealing two spades from a shuffled deck?

SOLUTION: The probability of dealing off one spade is 13/52. Assuming that this event takes place, the probability of dealing off a second spade is 12/51. Hence the probability of dealing off two spades is (13/52) (12/51) or 1/17.

Exercises 9.4

1. What is the probability of dealing five spades from a standard deck? What is the probability of dealing five spades from a deck from which there have already been ten cards dealt, four of which were spades?
2. What is the probability of dealing the cards J ◇, Q ◇, K ◇, and A ◇ in that order from a shuffled deck? What is the probability of dealing these four cards in any order at all?
3. How many ways are there to deal two cards from a shuffled deck? What is the probability of dealing off a spade and then a heart from the deck? A spade, then a heart, and then a club? A spade, then a heart, and then another spade?
4. If in playing Keno you mark only one number from the eighty available before the house draws their twenty numbers, what is the probability that your number will be drawn? If you mark two numbers, what is the probability that exactly one of your numbers will be drawn? That at least one of your numbers will be drawn?
5. What is the probability of being dealt a five-card poker hand consisting of four cards all of the same rank and a fifth card? Compare this probability with that of being dealt a full house and decide which of the two hands should be the higher ranking.
6. At the University of Kansas a coed is supposed to have been dealt a bridge hand consisting of A ♠, K ♠, Q ♠, A ♡, K ♡, Q ♡, A ◇, K ◇, Q ◇, J ◇, A ♣, K ♣, and Q ♣. (This is a perfect seven no trump hand.) What is the probability of being dealt thirteen cards consisting of four aces, four kings, four queens, and one jack?

7. The newspaper that carried the story of the bridge hand described in Exercise 6 captioned it, "Once in a lifetime." Assuming that the coed played twenty games of bridge every day of every year, how long would it take (on the basis of the a priori probabilities) for her to expect a hand like this one? One lifetime?
8. We remarked in an earlier section that red had once come up 32 times in a row at Monte Carlo. What is the probability of this event?
9. Russian roulette is played by two players as follows: One bullet is placed into the empty cylinder of a six-gun and the cylinder is spun. The first player holds the gun to his head and pulls the trigger. If he dies, then the second player wins automatically. If he draws a blank, then the second player takes his turn by spinning the cylinder, putting the gun to his head, and pulling the trigger. If he dies the first player wins. If he does not die, then the game is played again. Would you rather go first or second in this game? (*Hint:* Compute the probability that the first player will die. Then, assuming that the first player did not die, compute the probability that the second player will die.)
10. Hungarian roulette is played just like Russian roulette except that if the second player has to take a turn he does not spin the cylinder before he pulls the trigger. Would you rather go first or second in this game?
11. Bulgarian roulette is played by putting two bullets into the cylinder at random. The first player spins the cylinder, puts the gun to his head, and pulls the trigger. If he dies, the second player wins. If he lives, then the second player *without spinning the cylinder* puts the gun to his head and pulls the trigger. Do you want to go first or second or don't you care? Is the situation changed by having the second player spin the cylinder before pulling the trigger?
12. A dart thrower has one chance in three of hitting the bull's eye. What is the probability that he will hit the bull's eye if he throws three darts? (*Hint:* Compute the probability that he will miss on each throw and use Exercise 6, Section 9.2.)

9.5 Mathematical Expectation

One of the important uses of probability is in decision making. In this section we shall introduce the notion of mathematical expectation and point out some of the ways that this idea can be used to aid in making decisions.

Let us marshal the facts that we shall need. Suppose that we are interested in a certain game (such a roulette or craps) that has a finite number of mutually exclusive outcomes represented by $O_1, O_2, \ldots, O_n$. Suppose that the probability of an outcome O_k occurring is p_k, and that in the event that an outcome O_k does occur you will receive W_k dollars. Then we define the **mathematical expectation** of this game to be the number

$$p_1 W_1 + p_2 W_2 + \cdots + p_n W_n.$$

This number represents the average amount of money you should expect to receive after a sufficiently large number of games have been played. If this number is greater than the amount you must pay in order to play the game, then in the mathematical sense the game is not a game at all, it is simply a sure-fire way to make money. If the mathematical expectation is less than the amount you must pay in order to play the game, then again the game really is not a game, it is just a way of throwing money away. The only true games are those for which the mathematical expectation is equal to the cost of playing the game. In such games the amount you win or lose is not predetermined by the a priori probabilities involved and you will win or lose according to whatever it is that we call "luck."

The easiest game to analyze is roulette, and so we shall begin with this game. But first let us comment on the two ways that the payoffs for games can be announced. A bet that has a payoff rate of "8 to 1" is one in which when you bet \$1 and win, you are paid \$8 winnings and are also given your \$1 bet back. Hence if the payoff rate is 8 to 1, then you receive a total of \$9. Another way to announce the same payoff rate is to say that you are paid off at the rate of "9 for 1" if you win. This means that you bet your \$1 and, if you win, you are given \$9 in return for the \$1 you bet. Similarly, the payoff rates of 36 *for* 1 and 35 *to* 1 are identical. In either case you pay \$1 in order to play and if you win you receive \$36 in return.

Example 1: If you bet \$1 on a single number in roulette, say the number 15, and if that number comes up, then you will win a total of \$36. (The payoff rate here is 35 to 1 or 36 for 1.) What is the mathematical expectation of this bet?

SOLUTION: There are 38 possible outcomes in a roulette game and since these outcomes are equally likely, each has a probability of $\frac{1}{38}$. If the outcome is the number 15, then you receive \$36; otherwise you receive nothing. Hence, there is only one nonzero summand in the mathematical expectation and that is $\frac{1}{38}(36)$ or 36/38. This means that over a long period of play you should expect to receive (on the average) \$36/38 each time you play the number 15. But do not forget that it costs you \$1 to bet on this number and so you should expect to lose \$2/38 or $5\frac{5}{19}$¢ each time you bet \$1.

In Example 1 we say that the house has an *edge* of $5\frac{5}{19}$ percent on this particular bet. It can be shown that with one exception (see Exercise 1) every bet that you can make on the roulette table (and there are a great many different kinds of bets possible) has the same expectation. Thus no matter how you place your bets at roulette (with the one exception) you should expect to lose about $5\frac{5}{19}$¢ for each \$1 that you bet. Since there are other games that give the house less of an edge, roulette is one of the worst gambling games.

It should be clearly understood that when we say you will lose $5\frac{5}{19}$¢ for each dollar that you wager, we mean that if you were to play roulette over a very long period of time then you would tend to lose money at this rate. The Law of Large Numbers guarantees this and so is working against you at roulette. By the same token the Law of Large Numbers is working for the house and so while the house may suffer heavy loses over short periods of time, in the long run they will tend to profit by $5\frac{5}{19}$¢ for every dollar wagered on their tables. In any game in which the mathematical expectation is less than the amount of money you must pay in order to play the game, the Law of Large Numbers works against you and in favor of the house.

You have probably heard people talk about "systems" for beating roulette. Any system that requires continued play over a long period of time must buck the Law of Large Numbers and the house's edge. Since the Law of Large Numbers is immutable, no roulette system that requires extended play is possible. The only way to avoid the consequences of the Law of Large Numbers is to play for so short a time that the Law of Large Numbers does not get a chance to begin working against you. One system of this kind is called the "Bold Strategy" or the "Big Bang Strategy." To gamble on roulette using this strategy simply walk up to the table and bet everything you want to gamble on a single number. Win or lose, you then leave the table and do not continue to play.

Next, let us examine one of the more popular bets on the craps table. This is the *field bet*. The field is the set of numbers 2, 3, 4, 9, 10, 11, and 12. You can make this bet at any time during the play and if one of these seven field numbers comes up on the next throw of the two dice, then you win. The payoff rate for the numbers 2 and 12 is 3 for 1 and is 2 for 1 for the other numbers.

Example 2: What is the mathematical expectation of a field bet of $1?

SOLUTION: If on one roll of the dice any one of the numbers 2, 3, 4, 9, 10, 11, or 12 results, then you win. If any other number comes up you lose. The probabilities of these seven favorable outcomes are given below. Therefore

Outcome	*Ways can occur on the two dice*	*Probability of occurring*	*Payoff rate*
2	1–1	1/36	3 for 1
3	1–2, 2–1	2/36	2 for 1
4	2–2, 1–3, 3–1	3/36	2 for 1
9	4–5, 5–4, 3–6, 6–3	4/36	2 for 1
10	5–5, 4–6, 6–4	3/36	2 for 1
11	5–6, 6–5	2/36	2 for 1
12	6–6	1/36	3 for 1

the mathematical expectation of the field bet is

$$\frac{1}{36}(3) + \frac{2}{36}(2) + \frac{3}{36}(2) + \frac{4}{36}(2) + \frac{3}{36}(2) + \frac{2}{36}(2) + \frac{1}{36}(3)$$

or 34/36. This means that you should expect (on the basis of the a priori probabilities involved) to receive $34/36 each time you bet $1 on the field. But it costs you $1 to play, so you should expect to lose $2/36 or $5\frac{5}{9}$¢ each time you bet $1. This is an even worse bet than the roulette game.

Next, let's look at the lottery game Keno. This is a real sucker game. One way to play the game (a way that is relatively easy to work with here) is to pick in any way that you desire five numbers from the total of 80. (Such a selection is called a "five spot.") Then the house selects 20 numbers at random. Let us suppose that you have paid $28.20 for the privilege of selecting your five numbers. If all of your five numbers are included in the twenty numbers chosen by the house, then you will win $25,000.[4]

Example 3: How much should you expect to win or lose by betting $28.20 for a five-spot Keno selection?

[4] The bet of $28.20 is the smallest bet you can make on a five spot ticket and win the limit, $25,000.

SOLUTION: We must compute the probability of having your five numbers chosen by the house. There are $C(80,20)$ ways for the house to choose their 20 numbers. Starting with your five numbers, we can fill out a selection of 20 numbers by drawing 15 numbers from the 75 that remain from the original 80 after you have selected your five. Hence there are $C(75,15)$ ways to fill out your five numbers to a total of 20 numbers. The probability of having all five of your numbers chosen by the house is therefore $C(75,15)/C(80,20)$ or about 1/1503. Each time this happens, you receive \$25,000 (and otherwise you receive nothing) so the mathematical expectation of this bet is (1/1503)(25,000) or about 16.7. So you should expect (on the average) to receive about \$16.70 each time you make this bet. But the bet costs \$28.20 to make and so you should expect to lose \$11.50 each time you play. This works out to a house edge of 40.8 per cent![5]

In our discussion of mathematical probability as it applies to games of chance, all the probabilities were definitely established a priori probabilities and all of the payoffs were definite. In other less exotic situations to which mathematical expectation might be applied to help one decide on the best course of action, neither the probabilities nor the payoffs are likely to be so definitely established. Here is an example of one of these more ordinary problems where mathematical expectation can be used to aid in decision making.

Example 4: A man in Seattle wants to open either a Brauhaus or a Biergarten. He knows that it rains a good deal in Seattle and that on rainy days the Biergarten will not do nearly as good as a business as the Brauhaus. But on sunny days the Biergarten will do a fine business. He estimates that the probability of rain on the average day in Seattle is 2/5. Further, he estimates that he would receive net profits according to the following table:

	Biergarten	*Brauhaus*
Rain (2/5)	\$50	\$500
Sun (3/5)	\$450	\$100

[5] If only three of your numbers are drawn you will win \$23.50 and if four are drawn you will win \$235. (This works out to a mathematical expectation of \$20.83 per game and means a per game loss of \$7.27 and a house edge of 26 per cent.) We ignored these smaller winnings in order to simplify the computations.

The dollar amounts in this table represent net profit. For example, the net profit from the Brauhaus on a rainy day would be \$500. Should the man open a Brauhaus or a Biergarten?

SOLUTION: Before reading this solution you might like to come to a decision for yourself based upon the evidence given above.

Let's apply mathematical expectation and see what we might conclude. The net profits play the role of the payoff rates in our discussions of gambling games. Hence the mathematical expectation of the Biergarten is

$$\frac{2}{5}(50) + \frac{3}{5}(450) = 20 + 270 = 290,$$

while the mathematical expectation of the Brauhaus is

$$\frac{2}{5}(500) + \frac{3}{5}(100) = 200 + 60 = 260.$$

We conclude, therefore, that we can expect a profit of \$290 a day from the Biergarten and a \$30 smaller daily profit from the Brauhaus. Hence, according to this analysis, the man should definitely open the Biergarten. If he stays in business a long time, he will tend to make more money with the Biergarten than with the Brauhaus.

Exercises 9.5

1. We remarked in the text that all bets on roulette except one yield the same house percentage. This exception is the bet (placed on the lower left hand corner of the square containing the number 1) on the set of numbers $\{0, 00, 1, 2, 3\}$. The payoff rate for this bet is 7 for 1. Is this a better bet than the other bets or is it worse?
2. If you place \$1 on the square marked "1st 12" you are betting that one of the numbers 1 through 12 will come up. The payoff rate for this bet is 3 for 1. Show that the mathematical expectation for this bet is the same as betting on a single number.
3. If you place \$1 on the square marked "2 to 1" next to the square containing the number 34 then you are betting that one of the numbers $1, 4, 7, 10, \ldots, 31$, or 34 will come up. The payoff rate for this bet is 2 to 1. Show that the mathematical expectation for this bet is the same as for betting on a single number.

4. Suppose that the winner of a lottery will receive a prize worth \$500. Each ticket is to cost \$1. How many tickets should be sold in order that the lottery be completely fair?

5. You toss a die and are paid an amount in dollars equal to the number you have tossed. What is the minimum amount of money you should expect to have to pay in order to play this game?

6. It is permissible to mark only one number on a Keno game. If you pay \$1.20 for the privilege of marking one number and if your single number is among the twenty numbers chosen by the house, then you will win \$3.60. How much should you expect to lose each time you bet \$1.20 on this game?

7. *Chuck-a-Luck* is a game played with three dice. You play by placing your bet on any one of the numbers 1 through 6. The three dice are thrown and you are paid off as follows:

If your number comes up on exactly one die: 2 for 1.
If your number comes up on exactly two dice: 3 for 1.
If your number comes up on exactly three dice: 4 for 1.

How much should you expect to lose every time you bet \$1 on the number 1? How does Chuck-a-Luck compare with roulette, Keno (betting eight numbers), and the field bet at craps?

8. Why can't Chuck-a-Luck be "beaten" by betting \$1 on each of the numbers 1 through 6? That is, you will lose money even if you bet \$1 on each of the six numbers. Why?

9. A man buys an item costing \$6.00. He tells the salesgirl that he has four dollar bills in his pocket together with two five dollar bills and two ten dollar bills. He offers to reach into his pocket and pull out two bills at random and give them to the girl in return for the item he is buying. Should the salesgirl consider this proposition?

10. The kingdoms of Klutz and Smorg are engaged in an arms race the cost of which is getting out of hand. The king of Klutz has placed "desirability ratings" upon various contingencies connected with the disarming of the Kingdom of Klutz. The king figures that the desirability factor of disarming is -10 if Smorg invades as a consequence of the disarming and is $+10$ if Smorg does not invade. On the other hand, the desirability factor of continuing the arms race is $+5$ if Smorg has plans to invade Klutz and is $+2$ if Smorg does not intend to invade. If the chances of Smorg's invading Klutz are 40 per cent, should Klutz arm or disarm? If this percentage is 30, what should Klutz do?

9.6 Statistics

When most people use the word statistics they are referring to lists of numbers such as the lengths of bridges or the population of countries. To a mathematician or scientist, however, the word has a completely different and much more profound meaning. In this section we shall discuss in a very general way that part of mathematics which is called statistics.

Suppose that beef stew is being made and that the cook has put into a pot 20 pieces of meat and 20 hunks of potato. After the stew has cooked and been placed on the table, father dips in and pulls out a ladle of meat and potatoes. Now what would you say about the sample of the stew that he has in this ladle? What do you think might be the proportion of meat and potatoes? On the basis of a priori probability, we would probably conclude that there should be about an equal number of pieces of meat and potatoes since meat and potatoes are equally present in the pot itself. This is the kind of problem with which a priori probability deals. Given a known population (in this case the population of pieces of meat and potatoes in the pot), what conclusions can you draw about a particular sample (the ladle full of stew) of that population?

The opposite problem could be described like this. You go to a friend's home for dinner and are served stew from a great black pot. You dip the ladle in and pull out a serving that you find consists of six pieces of potatoes and one piece of meat. Do you draw any conclusions about the contents of the pot? Here we know the composition of the sample and we would like to use that knowledge to draw conclusions about the composition of the contents of the pot. This is the kind of problem that statistics is designed to answer. Given an unknown population, what conclusions about that population can you draw from a known sample of that population? It should be clear, then, that statistics is the mathematical science of inductive inference. Statistics has been called "the science and art of making wise decisions in the face of uncertainty."

If we need to give a beginning for statistics, we might take the year 1763, an English clergyman named Thomas Bayes, and a theorem called Bayes' theorem. We shall not state Bayes' theorem (it is too technical), but here is what the theorem is designed to do for us. Suppose that we are concerned with an unknown population.[6] Suppose also that for some reason we have formed a definite opinion about the characteristics of this population. (Just how we went about forming these opinions is not important—we have formed them.) Now we take a sample of that unknown population and examine this sample to determine its characteristics. It is possible that the characteristics of the sample will differ from our opinions as to the characteristics of the unknown population. In this event, Bayes' theorem tells us how to alter our previous opinions in light of the observed characteristics of the sample we have drawn. The fact that Bayes' theorem exists tell us that there is a mathematical way of altering our opinions about an unknown population by taking samples of that population. Basically, this is what statistics is all about.

We can state the central problem of statistics as follows: What conclusions can we draw, and how confident can we be in those conclusions, concerning an unknown population by studying samples of that population? This general question can be broken down into three slightly more specific questions which statistics attempts to answer:

1. Given a sample of an unknown population, what conclusions about the unknown population can be drawn from that sample?
2. How reliable are these conclusions? How confident can we be in them?
3. How can we most intelligently select samples from the unknown population in order to be able to draw the most reliable conclusions?

The first two of these questions suggest that a statistical answer to a problem concerning the probable characteristics of an unknown population will consist of two parts: some conclusions about those characteristics and an indication of how reliable these conclusions are. Thus the statistician will answer a question something like this. "The best conclusion that I can draw from the sample that you have given me is that . . . . You may be confident that this conclusion will be correct about . . . per cent of the time."

It should hardly be necessary to give examples of the variety of ways that statistics is used today. In fact, there is hardly a business or governmental activity that does not use statistical theory is essential ways. Election forecasts, market surveys, television ratings, and national defense postures are all derived from statistical inference. Of course, such statistical inferences

[6] The population need not be of people. It could be a population of light bulbs coming off an assembly line, a population of fruit flies in a jug, or any other set of objects.

sometimes give completely erroneous results. President Truman was very much amused by one set of statistical conclusions and the Ford Motor Company still feels embarrassed pangs whenever anybody mentions the Edsel. But in each of these instances the statistical inferences drawn from the samples were correct; it was the sampling procedures that were at fault. This indicates the vital importance of Question 3. If we do not draw samples intelligently, we are going to arrive at statistical conclusions that are worthless. If you wanted to determine how the people of Keokuk feel about movies, then you should not hold all your interviews in the lobby of one of the local movie houses. Neither should you wait until 9 p.m. and then conduct your interviews by phone.

The best way to take samples of unknown populations is in as random a way as you can devise. Suppose that you wanted to make a telephone survey of the people in a certain town concerning their opinions about fluoridation. There are 10,000 people in the town and you want to sample 1000 people. You could make yourself a ten-sided die and then, working from the telephone directory, you could go from name to name, tossing the die each time you came to a new name. Whenever the die came up 10, you would call the person whose name you were at. If the die came up any other number, you would go on to the next person and toss the die again. The a priori probability is that you would in this way select 1000 people to call and your selection will be based on a method as nearly random as anything you could easily devise.

One last remark about statistical conclusions. Generally speaking, the more precise the conclusions drawn from the samples, the less reliable those conclusions will be. Conversely, the less precise and more general are those conclusions, the greater will be their reliability. An example of this is the 1968 presidential election. The pollsters still had not forgotten their 1948 débacle and, as election day grew near, there was a certain amount of doubt in the pollster's camps. As it turned out, the last predictions that were announced just a few days before the election were tagged with such a large possible margin of error that no result (short of Wallace's being elected) would have contradicted their conclusions. Rather than do as they did in 1948 and make rather firm conclusions (with an attendant drop in reliability), they decided in 1968 to make more general conclusions, thereby increasing the reliability of those conclusions.

10 Limits of Sequences

IN CHAPTER 6 we listed a number of fundamental properties of the system of real numbers. The last of these, the completeness property, has a character quite different from the rest of the properties, and it is from this last property that the really deep results follow. We shall discuss the property and some of its consequences in this chapter. We shall derive the familiar formulas for the circumference and area of a circle and see how the completeness property plays an essential role in the derivations of these formulas. We shall conclude the chapter with a brief examination of some of the ideas of integral and differential calculus.

The calculus was invented almost simultaneously by Isaac Newton (1642–1727) in England and Gottfried Leibniz (1646–1716) on the continent, but many of the central ideas had been around a long time before these famous mathematicians did their work. The central idea of integral calculus can be traced back to the ancient Greeks, and the central idea of differential calculus has roots in the work of Fermat and others (about 1629). The main deficiency in Newton's and Leibniz's work was a lack of rigor, and it was not until over a hundred years later that Augustin-Louis Cauchy (French, 1789–1857) through his work with limits of sequences turned calculus into a rigorous part of mathematics. (Cauchy is regarded by many as the father of rigor in mathematics.) In fact, the calculus as it is taught in many schools today is still in substantially the same form as it was laid down by Cauchy in the early nineteenth century.

Isaac Newton (1642–1727)

10.1 Sequences of Real Numbers

Sequences of real numbers play fundamental roles in most parts of mathematics. In this section we shall introduce this idea together with some notation and vocabulary. Sequences of real numbers form the basis for this entire chapter.

By an **infinite sequence of real numbers** (henceforth simply **sequence**), we mean an arrangement into some definite order of the objects of a countably infinite set of real numbers. Examples of such sequences are

Gottfried Wilhelm Leibniz (1646–1716)

$$1, 2, 3, 4, 5, \ldots$$

$$0, 2, 4, 6, 8, \ldots$$

$$\frac{-1}{1}, \frac{-1}{2}, \frac{-1}{3}, \frac{-1}{4}, \frac{-1}{5}, \ldots$$

$$3, 3, 3, 3, 3, \ldots$$

The individual numbers in the sequence are called the **terms** of the sequence. In the above examples we have written out the first few terms of each sequence and have then indicated that the terms are to continue in the manner indicated by the first few terms by using the ellipsis symbol. But it is better if we insert what is called the **general term** of the sequence. For example, when the sequences above are written with the general term included, they are written as

$$1, 2, 3, 4, 5, \ldots, n, \ldots$$

$$0, 2, 4, 6, 8, \ldots 2n - 2, \ldots$$

$$\frac{-1}{1}, \frac{-1}{2}, \frac{-1}{3}, \frac{-1}{4}, \frac{-1}{5}, \ldots, \frac{-1}{n}, \ldots$$

$$3, 3, 3, 3, 3, \ldots, 3, \ldots$$

The general term can be thought of as an expression that generates the terms of the sequence as n is replaced by each of the numbers $1, 2, 3, 4, 5, \ldots$, in turn. We shall write a general sequence as

$$a_1, a_2, a_3, a_4, a_5, \ldots, a_n, \ldots.$$

Each of the terms is understood to be a real number, and the subscript on each term indicates its position in the sequence. If the general term would be excessively complicated, then we shall amend a phrase to the listing of the first few terms to make definite how the sequence is formed.

In our work in this chapter we shall restrict our attention to two particular kinds of sequences. We shall work mostly with increasing sequences. We call a sequence $a_1, a_2, a_3, a_4, a_5, \ldots, a_n, \ldots$ an **increasing sequence** if each term (after the first) is greater than its predecessor. Thus the sequence is increasing provided that $a_{n-1} < a_n$ for each $n = 2, 3, 4, \ldots$. We call this sequence **nondecreasing**, provided that each term (after the first) is greater than or equal to its predecessor: $a_{n-1} \leq a_n$ for each $n = 2, 3, 4, 5, \ldots$. Note that an increasing sequence is also nondecreasing.

Example 1: Which of the following sequences are increasing? Which are nondecreasing?

(a) 1, 1, 2, 3, 3, 4, 5, 5, 6, 7, 7, 8, 9, . . . , in which each odd positive integer is repeated twice.

(b) $1, -2, 3, -4, 5, -6, 7, -8, \ldots,$ in which the general term is the positive integer n if n is odd and is the negative integer $-n$ if n is even.

(c) $\frac{-1}{2}, \frac{-1}{3}, \frac{-1}{4}, \frac{-1}{5}, \frac{-1}{6}, \ldots, \frac{-1}{n+1}, \ldots.$

(d) $\frac{1}{2}, \frac{1}{3}, \frac{1}{4}, \frac{1}{5}, \ldots, \frac{1}{n+1}, \ldots.$

(e) $\frac{1}{2}, \frac{1}{2}, \frac{1}{3}, \frac{1}{3}, \frac{1}{4}, \frac{1}{4}, \frac{1}{5}, \ldots,$ in which each rational number appears twice.

(f) $1, 1, 1, 1, \ldots, 1, \ldots.$

(g) $\frac{1}{2}, \frac{2}{3}, \frac{3}{4}, \frac{4}{5}, \frac{5}{6}, \ldots, \frac{n}{n+1}, \ldots.$

SOLUTION: Sequences (a), (c), (e), (f), and (g) are nondecreasing. (Sequence (d) is called a *decreasing sequence.*) Sequences (c) and (g) are increasing. Sequence (f) is called a **constant sequence**.

We call a nondecreasing sequence **bounded** if there is some real number b such that $a_n \leq b$ for each $n = 1, 2, 3, 4, \ldots$. Such a real number b is called an **upper bound** for the sequence.

Example 2: The sequence $1, 2, 3, 4, 5, \ldots, n, \ldots$ is unbounded because there is no real number b which is greater than or equal to every term of this sequence. This sequence has no upper bounds at all. In Example 1, sequence (c) is bounded by the real number 0 since each term of this sequence is negative and hence less than or equal to 0. Zero is an upper bound for this sequence. Sequence (f) is bounded by 1 since every term of that sequence is less than or equal to 1. Sequence (g) is also bounded by the real number 1.

It should be clear that if a sequence is bounded, then it has infinitely many upper bounds. For if b is one such upper bound, then each of the numbers $b + 1, b + 2, b + 3, \ldots$ is also an upper bound for the sequence. Thus a sequence either has infinitely many upper bounds or else it has no upper bounds at all.

It is often helpful to think of the terms of a sequence as being points on the number line and we shall frequently want to do this. A number b is an upper bound for a sequence (see Figure 10.1) if and only if no point of the sequence lies to the right of the number b. In effect, the upper bound b is a kind of barrier to the right of which none of the terms of the sequence can go.

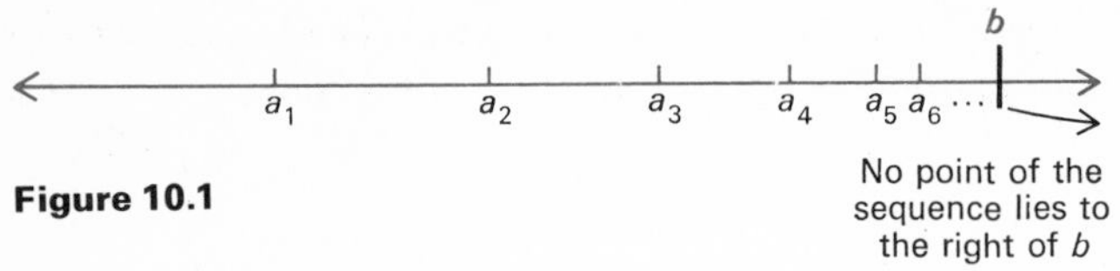

Figure 10.1

An upper bound for a sequence may or may not be itself a term of the sequence. For example, the sequence $1, 2, 3, 4, 5, 5, 5, \ldots, 5, \ldots$ is constant from the fifth term on, has 5 as an upper bound, and 5 is a term of the sequence. The sequence $\frac{1}{2}, \frac{2}{3}, \frac{3}{4}, \frac{4}{5}, \ldots, n/n + 1, \ldots$ is bounded by many upper bounds, but none of these is a term of the sequence. If a sequence is increasing, then no term of the sequence can be an upper bound for the sequence. If an upper bound for a sequence is also a term of the sequence, then from some term on, the sequence must be constant. That is, if b is an upper bound for a sequence $a_1, a_2, a_3, \ldots, a_n, \ldots$, and if b is a term of the sequence, then there is some subscript k such that $b = a_k = a_{k+1} = a_{k+2} = a_{k+3} = a_{k+4} = \cdots$.

Exercises 10.1

1. Write out the first six terms of the sequence whose general terms are given below.

(a) $\dfrac{n^2 - 1}{n^2 + 1}$. **(c)** $\dfrac{(-1)^n}{n}$.

(b) $\dfrac{n^2 - 1}{n}$. **(d)** $n^2 - n$.

2. Which of the following sequences are increasing? Which are nondecreasing?

(a) $1, 3, 5, 7, 9, 11, \ldots, 2n - 1, \ldots$.

(b) $0, 1, 1, 2, 2, 3, 3, 4, 4, \ldots, \left[\!\left[\dfrac{n}{2}\right]\!\right], \ldots$.

(c) $2, \dfrac{5}{2}, \dfrac{10}{3}, \dfrac{17}{4}, \ldots, \dfrac{n^2 + 1}{n}, \ldots$.

(d) $\dfrac{3}{2}, \dfrac{4}{3}, \dfrac{5}{4}, \dfrac{6}{5}, \ldots, \dfrac{n + 2}{n + 1}, \ldots$.

3. By studying part (b) of Exercise 2 very carefully you may be able to see how to use the greatest integer function to express the general term of the sequence 0, 0, 1, 1, 1, 2, 2, 2, 3, 3, 3, 4, 4, 4, ... Can you?

4. Give an upper bound for any of the sequences in Exercise 1 that are nondecreasing and bounded.

5. In the figure we have located the first few terms of an increasing sequence and a few other points (P, Q, R, and S) none of which is a term of the sequence.

(a) If R is an upper bound for the sequence, what can you say about S? Can you say anything about P and Q?

(b) If P is not an upper bound, can you conclude that Q is an upper bound? Can you conclude that S is an upper bound?

(c) If R is an upper bound but P is not an upper bound, then can you necessarily find a term of the sequence between Q and R? Between P and R? Between P and Q?

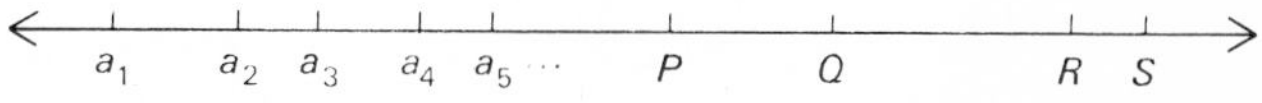

6. Is the sequence 1, 1.9, 1.99, 1.999, 1.9999, 1.99999, . . . a bounded sequence? If so, find three upper bounds for it.

7. Make up a sequence that has 3 as an upper bound. Make up a sequence that does not have 3 as an upper bound but does have 14 as an upper bound.

8. Find an expression for the general term of the sequence in Example 1, part (b). (*Hint*: Observe that when -1 is raised to an odd power the result is negative but when -1 is raised to an even power the result is positive.)

9. The general term for a sequence is a function whose domain is the set of positive integers and whose range is contained in the set of real numbers. Write out the first five terms of the sequences whose general terms are given by these functions.

(a) $f(x) = 5x^2$. **(b)** $f(x) = \dfrac{2}{x}$. **(c)** $f(x) = \sin x°$.

10.* Just as there are increasing and nondecreasing sequences there are decreasing and nonincreasing sequences. Drawing analogies from our definitions of increasing and nondecreasing sequences, define **decreasing sequence** and **nonincreasing sequence** and give three examples of each kind of sequence. What does it mean to say that a real number ℓ is a

lower bound for a nonincreasing sequence? Give an example of a sequence that is neither increasing, decreasing, nonincreasing, or nondecreasing.

11.* The sequence 1, 2, 3, 5, 8, 13, 21, ... is sometimes called the *Fibonacci sequence* after its discoverer. Each term of the sequence (after the first two) is the sum of its two immediate predecessors. These terms represent the number of pairs of rabbits on hand at the end of each month under the following circumstances: At the beginning of the first month a pair of productive rabbits are put into a cage. Each pair of productive rabbits is assumed to produce one new pair of baby rabbits each month and each pair of baby rabbits takes one month to become productive. So:

At the beginning of first month: 1 pair of adults.
At the end of first month: 1 pair of adults + 1 pair of babies.
At the end of second month: 2 pairs of adults + 1 pair of babies.

Continue this list determining the number of pairs of rabbits present in the cage at the end of each month for fifteen months. Compare these monthly totals with the first fifteen terms of the Fibonacci sequence.

10.2 The Completeness Property

At the end of Chapter 6 we listed the fundamental properties of the real number system, the last of which is called the "completeness property." Most of the really deep results concerning the real numbers stem from this important property and we shall discuss it in this section. In subsequent sections we shall discuss some of the applications of this property.

Let $a_1, a_2, a_3, a_4, \ldots, a_n, \ldots$ be a bounded nondecreasing sequence of real numbers. In Figure 10.2 we have located a few of the terms of such a sequence on the number line (green points), and also have located a few of the upper bounds for this sequence (black points). Let U denote the set of *all* the upper

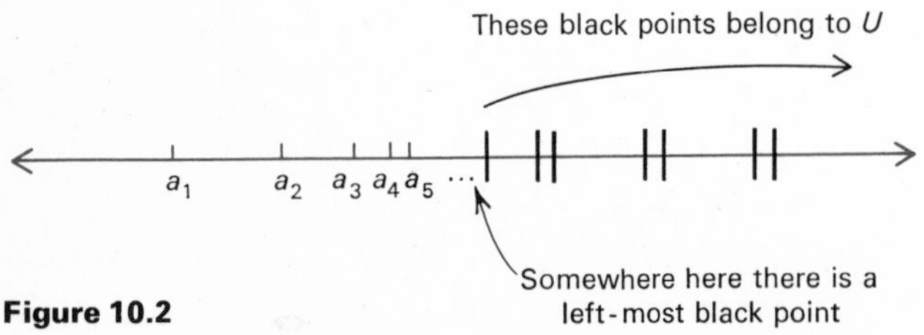

Figure 10.2

bounds for this sequence. Then the **completeness property** for the real numbers states that among the numbers in the set U of all upper bounds, there is one particular upper bound that is less than all the other upper bounds. This particular upper bound is called the **least upper bound** of the given sequence. In terms of the number line, this means that there is some particular black point (upper bound) that lies to the left of all the other black points. This left-most black point is the least upper bound in the set U. No green point lies to the right of this least upper bound and no black point lies to the left of it.

We have defined the least upper bound of a sequence to be the least number in the set of all upper bounds and have also defined it to be the left-most green point on the number line. Here is a definition of least upper bound phrased in terms of the given sequence.

Definition of the Least Upper Bound of a Sequence. *A real number l is the least upper bound of a sequence $a_1, a_2, a_3, a_4, \ldots, a_n, \ldots$, provided that l has the following two properties:*

1. $a_n \leq l$ *for each* $n = 1, 2, 3, 4, \ldots$.
2. *If x is any real number less than l, then there is at least one term of the sequence, say a_k, such that $a_k > x$.*

Property (1) implies that l is an upper bound for the sequence, and property (2) implies that no number x, less than l, can be an upper bound so that l must be the least one.

We can translate the language of this definition into the language of the number line (refer to Figure 10.3). To say that a point L is the least upper

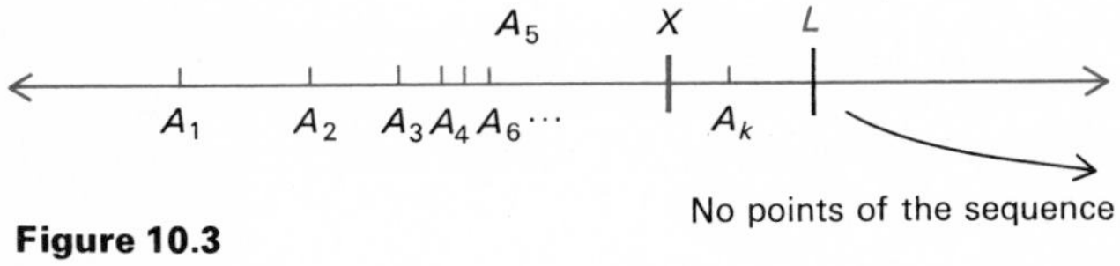

Figure 10.3

bound of a nondecreasing sequence of points $A_1, A_2, A_3, A_4, \ldots, A_n, \ldots$ means that the point L has these two properties:

1. No point of the sequence lies to the right of L.
2. If X is any point lying to the left of L, then there is at least one point of the sequence, say the point A_k, which lies to the right of X.

Property (1) implies that the point L is an upper bound for the sequence of points, and property (2) implies that no point X lying to the left of L can be an upper bound. Hence L is the left-most or the least upper bound for the sequence of points.

Example 1: The sequence

$$\frac{1}{2}, \frac{2}{3}, \frac{3}{4}, \frac{4}{5}, \frac{5}{6}, \frac{6}{7}, \ldots, \frac{n}{n+1}, \ldots$$

is increasing. When located on the number line, each term of this sequence (after the first) lies to the right of its predecessor and, consequently, there is no right-most term of this sequence. No matter which term of this sequence you look at, the next term lies to the right of that one. In Figure 10.4 we have pictured the first few terms in such a sequence (green points). Also we have indicated by the black points a few of the upper bounds for this sequence.

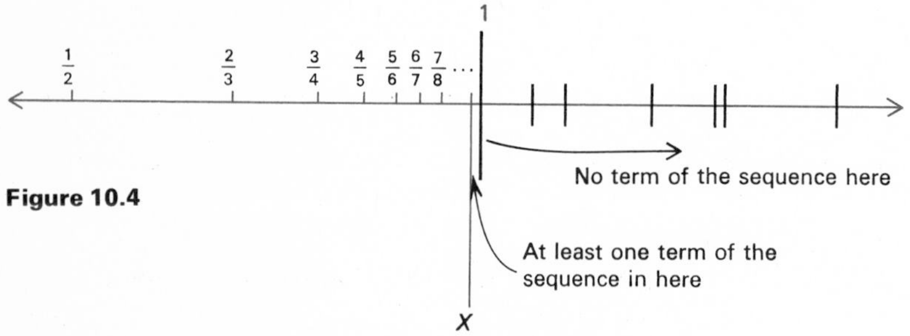

Figure 10.4

According to the completeness property, this sequence has a least upper bound. It can be proved that this least upper bound is the real number 1. That is,

1. No term of the sequence lies to the right of the number 1 on the number line, and
2. No matter which point X lying to the left of the number 1 you look at, there is a term of the sequence lying to the right of that point. That is, there is a term of the sequence between that point and the number 1.

Suppose, for example, that we were to look at the point .9997 lying to the left of the least upper bound 1. Then, according to what we have said, we can find a term of this sequence which lies to the right of .9997. Can you find one such term? Since .9997 lies to the left of .9999 and $.9999 = \frac{9999}{10000}$ is one of the terms of this sequence (it is a_{9999}), this term lies to the right of the number .9997. We could do the same sort of thing no matter which number less than 1 we were given.

Exercises 10.2

1. The least upper bound of the bounded increasing sequence

$$\frac{1}{2}, \frac{2}{3}, \frac{3}{4}, \frac{4}{5}, \frac{5}{6}, \ldots, \frac{n}{n+1}, \ldots$$

is 1.

(a) This means that .986 is not an upper bound for this sequence and so there is at least one term that lies to the right of .986. Find three such terms.

(b) Since $.9999 < 1$, there must be a term in the sequence that lies to the right of .9999 on the number line. Find four such terms.

(c) Try to prove that 1 is an upper bound for this sequence by examining the general term.

2. Since each term of the sequence

$$-1, -\frac{1}{4}, -\frac{1}{9}, -\frac{1}{16}, -\frac{1}{25}, \ldots, -\frac{1}{n^2}, \ldots$$

is negative it is obvious that 0 is an upper bound for the sequence. Show that none of the following numbers is an upper bound for this sequence.

(a) $\frac{-1}{100}$. **(b)** $\frac{-1}{1000}$. **(c)** $\frac{-1}{10000}$.

Generalizing on these results we conclude that none of the numbers $-\frac{1}{100}, -\frac{1}{1000}, -\frac{1}{10000}, -\frac{1}{100000}$, and so on, is an upper bound. It then follows that 0 must be the least upper bound. Why?

3. Consider the sequence

$$\frac{1}{2}, \frac{4}{5}, \frac{9}{10}, \frac{16}{17}, \frac{25}{26}, \ldots, \frac{n^2}{n^2+1}, \ldots.$$

What kind of sequence is this? Is it bounded? Can you spot the least upper bound? Find a term of the sequence that lies to the right of the number .9999.

4. What kind of a sequence is the sequence 1, 1.9, 1.99, 1.999, 1.9999, 1.99999, ...? Does this sequence have any upper bounds? If so, name five. If it has an upper bound, then it must have a least upper bound. Can you tell what this least upper bound must be? Find a term of the sequence that lies to the right of $\frac{249}{125}$.
5. Make up an increasing sequence that has the number 3 for a least upper bound. Then construct an increasing sequence that has 14 as its least upper bound.
6. The least upper bound for the bounded increasing sequence

$$\frac{5}{3}, \frac{5}{9}, \frac{17}{9}, \frac{33}{17}, \ldots, \frac{2^{n+1}+1}{2^n+1}, \ldots$$

is greater than 1.99. Prove this by showing that 1.99 is not an upper bound for this sequence. That is, find a term of the sequence which is greater than 1.99.
7. Show that 1.999 is not an upper bound for the sequence in Exercise 6.
8. Use the equation $2^{n+1} + 1 < 2^{n+1} + 2$ to deduce that the general term in the sequence in Exercise 6 is less than 2. Conclude from this that 2 is an upper bound for that sequence.
9. Generalizing the results of Exercises 6 and 7 and using Exercise 8, what can you conclude is the least upper bound of the sequence in Exercise 6?
10. Prove that the sequence .4, .44, .444, .4444, .44444, . . . does not have $\frac{5}{9}$ as a least upper bound by computing the differences between each of these terms and $\frac{5}{9}$ and observing that each of these differences will be at least as large as $\frac{1}{9}$. Conclude that there is an upper bound for this sequence that is less than $\frac{5}{9}$.
11. In the figure the first few terms of a sequence have been located on the number line. The points P, Q, R, and S are not points of the sequence.

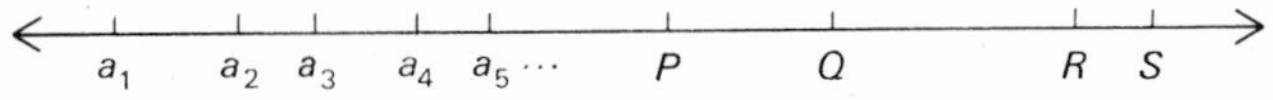

(a) If P is the least upper bound for the sequence, what can you say about Q, R, and S?
(b) If Q is the least upper bound for the sequence, what can you say about P? About R and S?

(c) If P is not an upper bound for the sequence but R is an upper bound, which of these four points might conceivably be the least upper bound for the sequence?

10.3 Limits and Convergence of Sequences

This section is a continuation of the ideas in the previous section.

Let $a_1, a_2, a_3, a_4, \ldots$ be a bounded nondecreasing sequence of real numbers whose least upper bound is the number ℓ (refer to Figure 10.5). What can you say about the way the terms of the sequence are "behaving" with respect to this least upper bound? Many students would answer that the terms of the sequence are getting *closer and closer* to the least upper bound. This is true, but is not sufficiently precise, because this is true of every upper bound for the sequence. That is, a number is an upper bound for the sequence

Figure 10.5

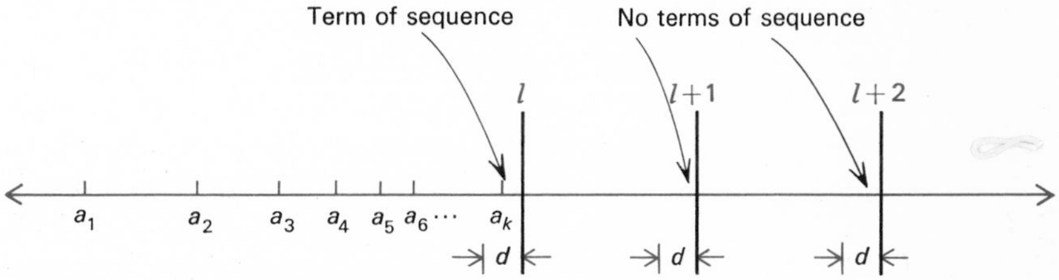

if and only if the terms of the sequence get closer and closer to that number. How are the terms behaving with respect to the least upper bound ℓ that they are not behaving, for example, with respect to the least upper bound $\ell + 1$? In the jargon of mathematics, we say that the terms of the sequence are not only getting closer and closer to ℓ but that they are getting **arbitrarily close** to ℓ. By this we mean that if we were given a distance d to the left of ℓ, then no matter how small this distance might be, there is a term of the sequence, say a_k, whose distance from ℓ is less than d. The least upper bound ℓ is the only number with this property.

Example 1: The sequence

$$\frac{-1}{2}, \frac{-1}{3}, \frac{-1}{4}, \frac{-1}{5}, \frac{-1}{6}, \frac{-1}{7}, \ldots, \frac{-1}{n+1}, \ldots$$

is an increasing sequence which has 0 as its least upper bound. Thus the terms of the sequence are getting arbitrarily close to 0. Given the distance .003, find a term of the sequence which is within this distance of 0.

SOLUTION: Since $.003 = \frac{3}{1000}$ and $\frac{1}{1000} < \frac{3}{1000}$, the term $-\frac{1}{1000}$ is within .003 of the least upper bound 0. See Figure 10.6.

Figure 10.6

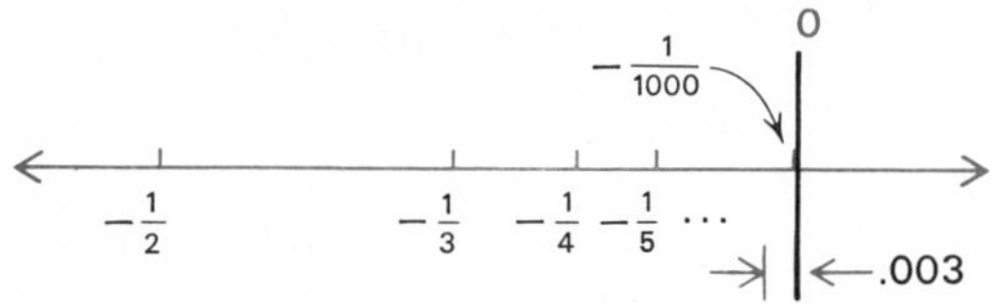

Suppose that the number ℓ is the least upper bound of a nondecreasing sequence $a_1, a_2, a_3, a_4, a_5, \ldots, a_n, \ldots$. Then we call ℓ the **limit** of this sequence and say that the terms of the sequence are **converging** to this limit ℓ. The sequence is called a **convergent sequence** because it has a limit.

Example 2: The limit of the sequence in Example 1 is 0 since 0 is the least upper bound for this sequence. The terms of the sequence are converging to 0—they are getting arbitrarily close to 0. Because it has this limit, the sequence itself is convergent. The sequence $1, 2, 3, 4, 5, \ldots, n, \ldots$, on the other hand, is not a convergent sequence (it is called *divergent*) because it has no limit—it has no least upper bound. The terms of the sequence get larger and larger without bound and do not get arbitrarily close to any real number.

To express the fact that a real number ℓ is the limit of a sequence $a_1, a_2, a_3, a_4, a_5, \ldots, a_n, \ldots$, we write

$$\text{limit } a_n = \ell.$$

To express the fact that 0 is the limit of the sequence in Example 1, for instance, we would write

$$\text{limit } \frac{-1}{n+1} = 0.$$

We should stress that all we have been saying is that there are many different ways to express the fact that a real number ℓ is the least upper bound for a given sequence. The following statements are all equivalent.

1. ℓ is the least upper bound for the sequence.
2. ℓ is the limit of the sequence.
3. The terms of the sequence are converging to ℓ.
4. The terms of the sequence are getting arbitrarily close to ℓ.

Using the idea of the limit of a sequence, we can phrase the completeness property in the following convenient form.

The Completeness Property for Real Numbers. *Every bounded nondecreasing sequence of real numbers has a limit.*

The idea of the limit of a sequence had caused a good deal of trouble since the time of Greek mathematics because it was so poorly understood. It was Augustin-Louis Cauchy (French, 1789–1857) who first approached this idea in a mathematically rigorous way. Cauchy, in about 1821, described the limit of a sequence of real numbers like this: "When the successive values attributed to a variable approach indefinitely a fixed value so as to end by differing from it by as little as one wishes, this last is called the limit of all the others." By "the successive values attributed to a variable" Cauchy was referring to the successive values taken on by the general term a_n as n ranges over the positive integers. The "fixed value" referred to is the least upper bound of the sequence, and the phrase "so as to end by differing from it by as little as one wishes" refers to the fact that the terms of the sequence get arbitrarily close to this least upper bound; that is, they are converging to this least upper bound.

Exercises 10.3

1. Since the sequence in Example 1 converges to 0, it should be possible to find a term of that sequence whose distance from 0 is less than .0001. Find three such terms.

2. Consider the sequence $1, \frac{3}{2}, \frac{5}{3}, \frac{7}{4}, \frac{9}{5}, \ldots$.

(a) Find an expression for the general term of this sequence.

(b) Prove that 2 is an upper bound for this sequence by showing that no matter which positive integer n represents the general term can be written as the difference between 2 and a positive real number.

(c) In fact, not only is 2 an upper bound but it is also the least upper bound—it is the limit of the sequence. Illustrate that the terms of the sequence are getting arbitrarily close to 2 by finding a term within .001 of 2. By finding a term within .00001 of 2.

3. Consider the sequence

$$0, \frac{1}{6}, \frac{2}{9}, \frac{3}{12}, \ldots, \frac{n-1}{3n}, \ldots.$$

(a) Prove that every term of this sequence is less than $\frac{1}{3}$. (*Hint*: Write the general term as the difference of $\frac{1}{3}$ and something else.)

(b) In fact, $\frac{1}{3}$ is the limit of this sequence. Find a term of the sequence that is within .001 of $\frac{1}{3}$. That is within .00001 of $\frac{1}{3}$.

4. Suppose that $a_1, a_2, a_3, a_4, \ldots, a_n, \ldots$ is a nondecreasing sequence that converges to the limit A. Then we can regard the terms of this sequence as approximations for the limit A. That is, from the terms of this sequence we can obtain as accurate an approximation for the number A as we desire. Explain this.

5. Suppose it is known that a sequence $a_1, a_2, a_3, \ldots, a_n, \ldots$ converges to a real number A and that another sequence $b_1, b_2, b_3, \ldots, b_n, \ldots$ converges to a real number B. Do you think that the sequence $a_1 + b_1$, $a_2 + b_2, a_3 + b_3, \ldots, a_n + b_n, \ldots$ converges? If so, to what does it converge? Using sequences we have discussed either in the text or in the exercises, give an example to illustrate your answer.

6.* We saw in Chapter 6 that $.55555\cdots = \frac{5}{9}$. The **partial sums** of this decimal numeral are the terminating numerals .5, .55, .555, .5555, .55555, ... Illustrate that the sequence of partial sums of $.55555\cdots$ converges to $\frac{5}{9}$ by

(a) Showing that .555, .5555, and .55555 are all less than $\frac{5}{9}$.

(b) Showing that there is a term of the sequence within the distance .0001 of $\frac{5}{9}$ and that there is a term of the sequence within .000001 of $\frac{5}{9}$.

7.* Illustrate that the sequence of partial sums of the nonterminating numeral $.4545454545\cdots$ converges to $\frac{5}{11}$ by

(a) Showing that .4545 and .454545 are less than $\frac{5}{11}$.

(b) Showing that there is a term of the sequence whose distance from $\frac{5}{11}$ is less than .0001 and that there is a term whose distance from $\frac{5}{11}$ is less than .0000001.

10.4

The Circumference of a Circle

It was known as early as 500 B.C. that there was a special relationship between the circumference of a circle and the length of its diameter. Its quotient

$$\frac{\text{circumference}}{\text{length of diameter}}$$

was proved to be the same for all circles. The most important method for determining the numerical value of this quotient (the number we call π) is the method of exhaustion. This method is generally mentioned in connection with Archimedes (*c.* 287 B.C.) but it was used earlier by another Greek, Antiphon (*c.* 430 B.C.). In this section we shall describe this method and show how it can be used to find the circumference of a circle whose diameter is given.

Antiphon's method of exhaustion is basically this: The finding of the circumference of a circle is intrinsically a very difficult problem, but finding the perimeter of a polygon is relatively easy (since the perimeter of a polygon is simply the sum of the lengths of its sides). So by inscribing a polygon with a great number of sides inside the circle, it is at least possible to obtain an approximation to the circumference of the circle. The more sides this inscribed polygon has, the better the approximation will be. For example, in Figure 10.7 we have shown an equilateral triangle, a square, a regular pentagon, a regular hexagon, and a regular heptagon inscribed in a circle.

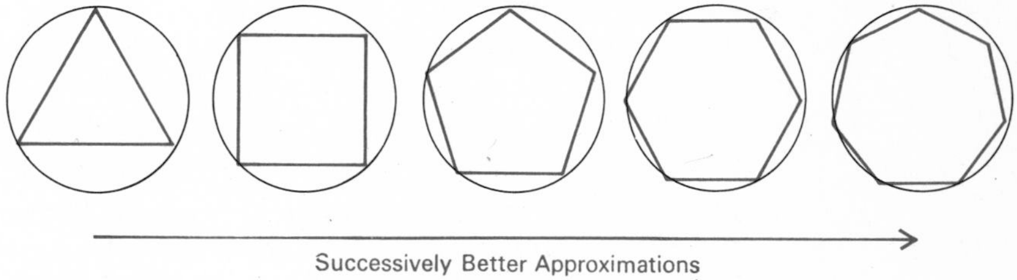

Observe that the perimeter of the triangle is a poor approximation to the circumference of the circle, but as we increase the number of the sides of the inscribed polygon the perimeter becomes a better and better approximation. If we inscribed a regular polygon of, say, 720 sides in the circle we would find that its perimeter is a very good approximation to the circumference of the circle. The idea is that as the number of sides of the regular n-gons increase, their perimeters "exhaust" the circumference of the circle. According to a manuscript dated about 335 B.C., Antiphon was supposed to have begun this exhaustion process with an inscribed square. He then used this square to construct an inscribed regular octagon, which he then used to construct an inscribed regular 16-gon, an inscribed regular 32-gon, and so on. By constructing polygons of more and more sides, the circumference of the circle was supposed to be "exhausted." Then (quoting from the manuscript): "He concluded that in this manner a polygon would be inscribed in the circle, the sides of which, on account of their minuteness, would coincide with the circumference of the circle." Antiphon's basic idea of inscribing regular polygons of more and more sides was a very excellent one, but the quoted statement above is absolutely false. No one of the inscribed regular polygons, no matter how many sides it may have, will ever coincide with the circle. It is possible that Antiphon imagined somehow that he would eventually obtain a polygon with infinitely many "one-point sides" which would coincide with the circle. Of course this is nonsense. What is needed to make Antiphon's argument complete is the notion of a sequence and the completeness property for the real numbers. Let us see how this argument can be completed.

Suppose that, within a circle of radius r, there are inscribed regular polygons with 3 sides, 4 sides, 5 sides, and so on. Let p_3 denote the perimeter of the regular 3-gon, p_4 denote the perimeter of the inscribed regular 4-gon, and so on. We obtain a sequence of real numbers $p_3, p_4, p_5, p_6, \ldots, p_n, \ldots$. It should be clear that this sequence is increasing and that it is bounded. (Construct a square containing the circle. The perimeter of this square is an upper bound for the sequence of perimeters.) Hence, according to the completeness property, this sequence has a limit. We *define* the circumference of the circle to be this limit. Thus, by definition, when we speak of the circumference of a circle, we are referring to the limit of a sequence of perimeters of inscribed regular polygons. What is not true is that any of these perimeters is equal to the circumference of the circle as Antiphon suggested, but that instead these perimeters are converging upon this circumference as their limiting value. Thus

$$\text{limit } p_n = \text{circumference}.$$

Antiphon's error was that he thought that since this sequence was converging to the circumference, this meant that some number in the sequence actually had to be equal to this limiting value.

There are a number of methods by means of which we may compute the perimeters of these inscribed regular polygons. However, all of these require computations that are lengthy and somewhat involved and so we shall not present any of them here. (See, however, Exercise 3.) Instead, let us simply list the results. In the following table, we have computed approximate values for the perimeters of regular n-gons inscribed inside a circle of radius r. Each of these perimeters is written as a real number multiple of the diameter ($2r$) of the circle.

Number of sides	*Perimeter*	*Number of sides*	*Perimeter*
3	2.5980762($2r$)	18	3.1256176($2r$)
4	2.8284273($2r$)	36	3.1376052($2r$)
5	2.9389265($2r$)	45	3.1390475($2r$)
6	3.0000000($2r$)	90	3.1409550($2r$)
7	3.0356137($2r$)	180	3.1414320($2r$)
8	3.0614672($2r$)	360	3.1415400($2r$)
9	3.0781809($2r$)	720	3.1415760($2r$)
10	3.0901700($2r$)		

The limit of the sequence of numerical coefficients of these perimeters is denoted by the Greek letter π. That is, the coefficients (2.5980762, 2.8284273, and so on) are converging to a real number, and we denote this real number by the letter π. Note that the coefficient given by the perimeter of the inscribed regular 720-gon gives an approximation for π, 3.1415760, which is correct to four decimal places. By computing more and more perimeters, we can obtain more and more coefficients and so can obtain better and better approximations to π, but we can never hope to be able to find the complete decimal numeral for this irrational number.

Exercises 10.4

1. Archimedes used a procedure similar to ours and found that π is a number between $3\frac{1}{7}$ and $3\frac{10}{71}$. To how many decimal places is Archimedes' approximation accurate?

2. Explain why the perimeter of the inscribed regular 6-gon is equal to six times the radius of the circle. (*Hint*: Decompose the 6-gon into six triangles.)

3. You can use trigonometry to find approximate values for the perimeters of the inscribed polygons as follows. (For simplicity let us assume that the radius of the circle is 1.) Let O be the center of the circle and let $\overline{AB}$ be one of the sides of the n-gon. By decomposing the triangle OAB into two right triangles it is possible to use the sine function to find the length of one-half the side $\overline{AB}$. Then the perimeter of the polygon can be easily determined. Use this procedure to find the approximate perimeter of the inscribed regular
(a) 36-gon. **(b)** 180-gon.

10.5 The Area of a Circle

We can use the method of exhaustion to find the area of a circle. To do this we consider the areas of inscribed polygons.

Let a circle of radius r be given. Just as in the last section, consider a sequence of regular n-gons ($n = 3, 4, 5, 6, \ldots$) inscribed inside the circle. Let A_3 denote the area of the inscribed regular 3-gon, A_4 denote the area of the inscribed regular 4-gon, and so on. We thus obtain a sequence of real numbers $A_3, A_4, A_5, A_6, \ldots, A_n, \ldots$, which is increasing and bounded. (These areas are all bounded, for instance, by the area of a square which completely contains the given circle.) According to the completeness property, then, this sequence of polygonal areas has a limit, and we *define* the area of the circle to be this limit:

$$\text{limit } A_n = \text{area.}$$

Thus as the number of sides of the inscribed regular n-gon gets larger and larger, the area, A_n, of this n-gon gets closer and closer to the area of the circle, and, in fact, gets arbitrarily close to the area of the circle. Antiphon would have said that the areas of the inscribed polygons were exhausting the area of the circle.

Once we know that the limit of the sequence of perimeters of these inscribed polygons is $\pi(2r)$, it is not difficult to compute the areas of the inscribed polygons and to determine their limit. So let us go through this computation. In Figure 10.8 we show a portion of the circle of radius r and one of the sides ($\overline{AB}$) of the inscribed regular n-gon. The point O is the center of the circle and the segment $\overline{OC}$ is drawn perpendicular to the side $\overline{AB}$.

Let the length of the segment $\overline{AC}$ be denoted by x. Then we have

$$p_n = 2nx.$$

Figure 10.8

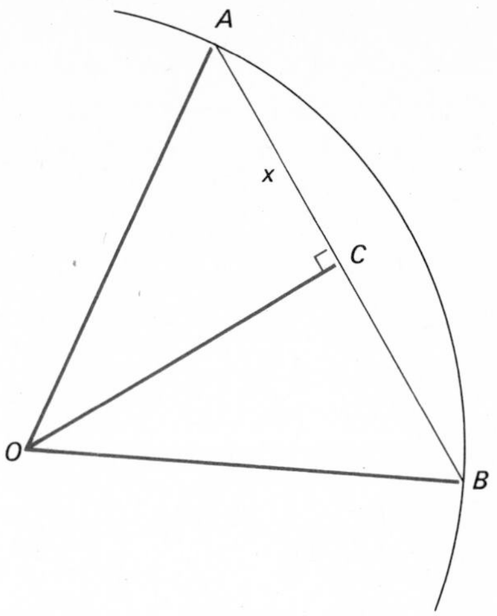

The length of segment $\overline{OC}$ is obtained by using the Pythagorean theorem applied to the right triangle OCA:

$$\text{length of } \overline{OC} = \sqrt{r^2 - x^2}.$$

Therefore the area of triangle OCA is

$$(\tfrac{1}{2})(x)(\sqrt{r^2 - x^2}),$$

so that the area of the entire polygon, A_n, is given by the equation

$$A_n = (2n)(\tfrac{1}{2})(x)(\sqrt{r^2 - x^2})$$

or

$$A_n = (nx)(\sqrt{r^2 - x^2})$$

But since $p_n = 2nx$, we can rewrite this equation in the form

$$A_n = \left(\frac{p_n}{2}\right)(\sqrt{r^2 - x^2})$$

We now have an expression for the general term in the sequence of areas $A_3, A_4, A_5, \ldots, A_n, \ldots$ and so if we can determine the number to which this general term gets arbitrarily close as n gets larger and larger, we shall have determined the limit of this sequence of polygon areas. Examine the expression for A_n very closely. Study each of the two factors separately. The first factor, $p_n/2$, converges to $\pi(2r)/2$ or πr as n gets larger and larger since p_n converges to $\pi(2r)$. (We showed this in the last section.) What happens to the factor $\sqrt{r^2 - x^2}$ as n gets larger and larger? As n gets larger and larger, the length $\overline{AC}$, being one half the length of one side of the inscribed n-gon, converges to 0. Therefore as n gets larger and larger, $\sqrt{r^2 - x^2}$ converges to $\sqrt{r^2 - 0}$ or $\sqrt{r^2}$ or just r. Thus as n gets larger and larger, A_n converges to the product of πr and r or πr^2. This limit, πr^2, is by definition the area of the circle of radius r.

Exercises 10.5

1. The most extensive record we have of very ancient mathematics is contained in the *Ahmes Papyrus*. Ahmes was an Egyptian scribe who copied the contents of the papyrus about 1650 B.C. Among many other things the papyrus contains the statement that the area of a circle of radius $\frac{9}{2}$ units is equal to the area of a square of side 8 units. Is this correct? How good an approximation does this provide for the area of a circle of radius 9 units? How good a value of π does this provide?
2. Below you are given the general term a_n of a nondecreasing bounded sequence and a real number. You are to explain why the sequence with this general term converges to this real number by examining what happens to the general term as n gets larger and larger.

   (a) $3 - \dfrac{1}{n}$; 3. **(b)** $\sqrt{16 - \dfrac{1}{n}}$; 4. **(c)** $\dfrac{n-1}{5n}$; $\dfrac{1}{5}$.

3. Find the limit of the sequence whose general term is given by examining this general term in order to see to which real number it converges as n gets larger and larger.

   (a) $\dfrac{-2}{n^3 + 4}$. **(c)** $\dfrac{-7}{5^n}$.

   (b) $1 - \dfrac{1}{n^2 + 5}$. **(d)** $\dfrac{n+1}{1 - n^2}$. (*Hint:* Rewrite the denominator.)

4. Illustrate the correctness of your answers to Exercise 3 by finding a term of each sequence that is within .001 of the limit you found there.

10.6 The Integral of a Function

The method of exhaustion may be used to find areas of regions other than circular regions. In fact, if $\mathscr{R}$ is a region that is bounded by a simple closed curve, then it may be possible to inscribe polygons inside the region in such a way as to obtain a sequence of real numbers whose limit is the exact area of the region. We shall illustrate this procedure in this section.

In Figure 10.9 we have sketched that portion of the graph of the function $f(x) = 11 - x^2$ that lies between $x = 0$ and $x = 3$. This curve together with

Figure 10.9

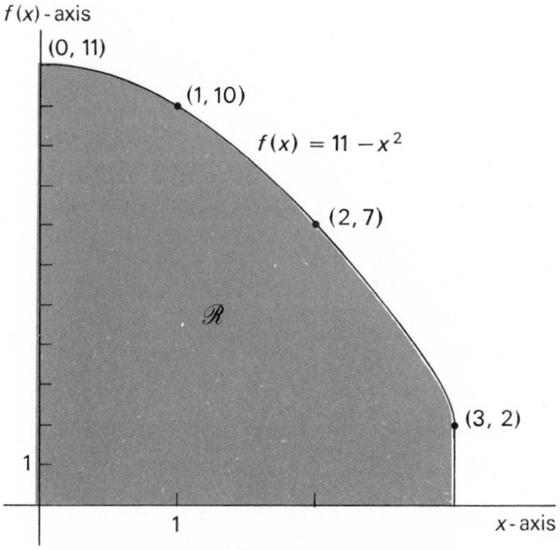

the lines $y = 0$, $x = 0$, and $x = 3$ bounds a region $\mathscr{R}$ whose area can be expressed as the limit of a sequence of real numbers. The terms of the sequence are the areas of polygons inscribed in the region. The technique for constructing these inscribed polygons is simple. Begin by subdividing the segment from 0 to 3 on the x-axis into n ($n = 1, 2, 3, 4, 5, \ldots$) equal subsegments. Above each of these subsegments, construct a rectangle whose height is as large as possible without going outside the region $\mathscr{R}$. These n rectangles taken together form a polygon which is inscribed in the region $\mathscr{R}$. In Figure 10.10 we have shown the inscribed polygons that would be constructed by subdividing the segment from 0 to 3 into 1, 2, 3, and 4 equal subsegments.

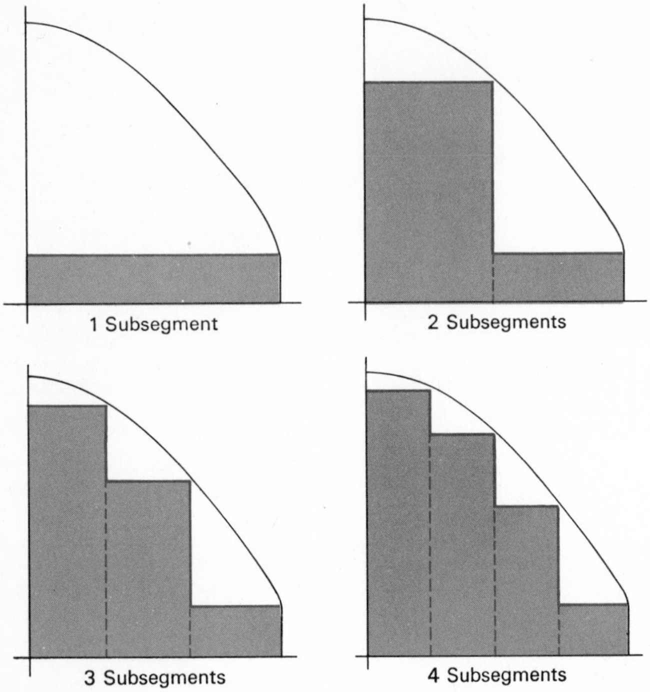

Figure 10.10

Our reason for inscribing polygons of this shape inside the region $\mathscr{R}$ is that these polygons have areas which are easy to determine; each such area is the sum of a finite number of rectangular areas. We denote the area of the inscribed polygon built upon a subdivision of the segment from $x = 0$ to $x = 3$ into n equal subsegments by A_n.

Since we can construct an inscribed polygon corresponding to each positive integer value of n, we can obtain a sequence of real numbers $A_1, A_2, A_3, A_4, A_5, \ldots$. This sequence is increasing and bounded (why?) and so, according to the completeness property, has a limit. We define the area of the region $\mathscr{R}$ to be this limit. That is, when we speak of the area of the region $\mathscr{R}$, we are referring to the limit of the polygonal areas A_n:

$$\text{limit } A_n = \text{area of } \mathscr{R}.$$

Example 1: Let us compute A_3, the area of the polygon constructed when the segment from 0 to 3 on the x-axis is subdivided into three equal subsegments.

The bases of the three rectangles formed from this subdivision of the x-axis are of length 1 (3 divided by the number of equal subsegments). The heights of the rectangles are determined by the values of the function $f(x) = 11 - x^2$ at the subdivision points. We have included all pertinent information in Figure 10.11. Then we can compute the value of A_3 as follows:

$$\begin{aligned} A_3 &= 1[f(1)] + 1[f(2)] + 1[f(3)] \\ &= 1[10] + 1[7] + 1[2] \\ &= 19. \end{aligned}$$

Figure 10.11

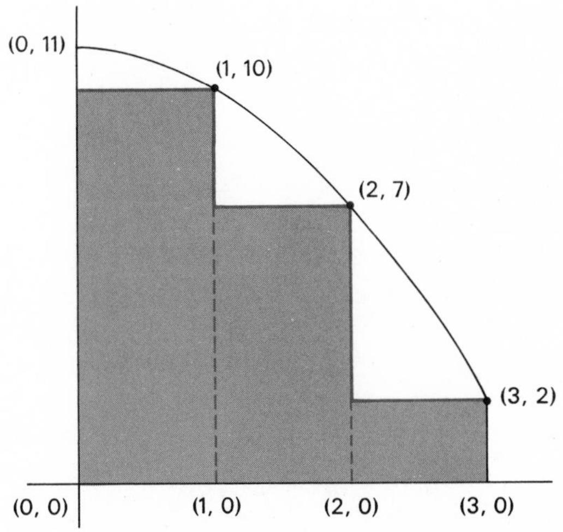

We could obtain a better approximation to the area of region $\mathscr{R}$ by computing the value of, say, A_{100}. This would be tedious, however, and since we shall be able to determine the exact area of the region $\mathscr{R}$, there is no point in computing more of these A_n's.

In order to determine the exact value of the area of region $\mathscr{R}$, we would find an expression for the general term A_n and then examine this expression to see if we could discover the number to which A_n gets arbitrarily close as n gets larger and larger. We could determine (but we shall omit the details of this calculation) that the area A_n of the polygon built on top of a subdivision of the segment on the x-axis from 0 to 3 into n equal subsegments is given by the formula

$$A_n = 24 - \frac{27}{2n} - \frac{9}{2n^2}.$$

(You should verify that this formula gives the correct value for A_n when $n = 3$.) Now the limit that we are seeking is the number to which this quantity, $24 - 27/2n - 9/2n^2$, gets arbitrarily close as n gets larger and larger. We observe that as n gets larger and larger, each of the summands $27/2n$ and $9/2n^2$ converges to 0. This means that as n gets larger and larger, $24 - 27/2n - 9/2n^2$ gets arbitrarily close to $24 - 0 - 0$ or 24. Hence 24 is the limit of the sequence of A_n's and so is the exact area under the curve.

In integral calculus, we denote the area A of the region $\mathscr{R}$ by the symbol[1]

$$\int_0^3 (11 - x^2)\,dx.$$

This symbol is called "the integral of $f(x) = 11 - x^2$ from 0 to 3." We have just seen that

$$\int_0^3 (11 - x^2)\,dx = 24.$$

If we simplify things a good deal, then we can say that the central problem of integral calculus is to find areas of regions bounded by curves. The usefulness of doing this lies in the fact that many different kinds of problems from mathematics, physics, astronomy, chemistry, and other sciences, can be translated into problems of area and then solved by using the methods of integral calculus. Thus a student in a beginning course in integral calculus learns two things. He learns how to evaluate certain elementary kinds of integrals (that is, how to find the areas of regions bounded by certain elementary classes of curves) and how to translate problems dealing, for example, with centers of gravity, moments of inertia, velocity and acceleration, and so on, into problems of area.

[1] The integral sign $\int$ is derived from the letter S which stands for *sum* and has to do with the fact that each polygon is expressed as the sum of rectangular areas. This notation is due to Leibniz.

Exercises 10.6

1. Continuing Example 1, compute the value of A_4, the area of the polygon built upon a subdivision of the interval from $x = 0$ to $x = 3$ into four equal subsegments. Then verify that your value is correct by using the formula for A_n given following that example.

2. Find a value of n for which the real number $A_n = 24 - 27/2n - 9/2n^2$ is within .1 of 24.

3. Consider the region in the plane bounded by the graph of the function $f(x) = \frac{1}{2}x^2 + 1$ between $x = 0$ and $x = 2$, the x-axis, the y-axis, and the vertical line $x = 2$.

(a) Sketch this region and sketch the inscribed polygons that are obtained by subdividing the segment from $x = 0$ to $x = 2$ on the x-axis into 1, 2, 3, 4, and 5 equal subsegments.

(b) Compute the areas of each of the inscribed polygons in (a).

(c) It can be proved using advanced methods that the area of the region under the curve is $\frac{10}{3}$. Find a value of n for which a subdivision of the segment from $x = 0$ to $x = 2$ results in a polygon whose area differs from $\frac{10}{3}$ by not more than 1.

4. Each of these integrals represents the area of a certain region in the plane. Sketch this region and then find the value of the integral by using elementary techniques from geometry rather than by using sequences of inscribed polygons.

(a) $\int_0^4 x\,dx = ?$ (This is the area of the region under the graph of the function $f(x) = x$ between $x = 0$ and $x = 4$ and above the x-axis.)

(b) $\int_1^5 3\,dx$. (The function is the constant function $f(x) = 3$.)

(c) $\int_{-1}^1 |x|\,dx$.

5.* The integral of a polynomial function of degree two is given by the following formula.

$$\int_a^b (cx^2 + dx + e)\,dx = \left[\frac{c}{3}(b)^3 + \frac{d}{2}(b)^2 + e(b)\right] - \left[\frac{c}{3}(a)^2 + \frac{d}{2}(a)^2 + e(a)\right].$$

(a) Use this formula to verify that the integral of the function in Exercise 2 between $x = 0$ and $x = 2$ is $\frac{10}{3}$.

(b) Use this result to verify the value 24 for the integral discussed in Example 1.

(c) Use this result to find the area under the graph of the function $f(x) = 8x^2$ between $x = 1$ and $x = 4$. Then very carefully sketch the graph of this function on squared paper and get as good an approximation to the area under this curve as you can by counting squares. Compare your approximate answer with the answer given by the formula.

10.7 The Derivative of a Function

We have seen how integral calculus derives from the ancient idea of the method of exhaustion. Thus, in effect, the central problem of integral calculus derives from antiquity. The other half of the calculus, called differential calculus, stems from ideas originating in about the fifteenth and sixteenth centuries and has to do with finding the slope of a curve at a point. In this section we shall discuss this idea.

Before we introduce the idea of the derivative of a function, we must say what we mean by the slope of a curve at a point and to do this we need the notions of the slope of a line and limit. Consider the curve $\mathscr{C}$ shown in Figure 10.12. The point P is a point belonging to this curve, and we want to

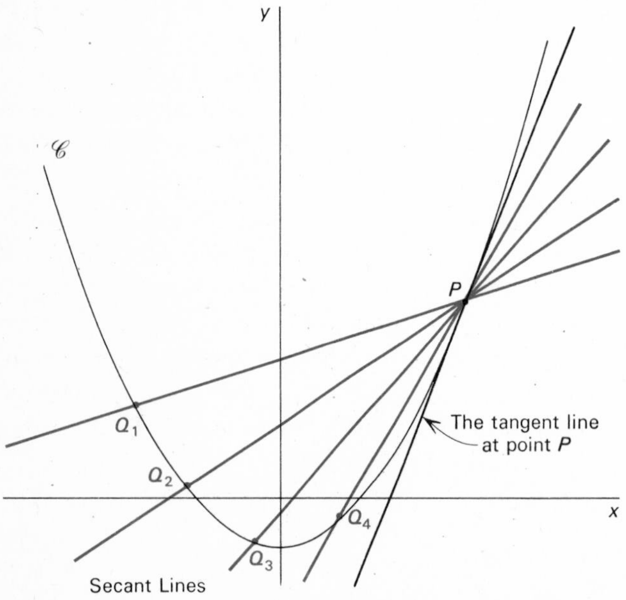

Figure 10.12

define the slope of the curve $\mathscr{C}$ at the point P. Let $Q_1, Q_2, Q_3, \ldots$ be an infinite sequence of points of the curve which are converging to the point P. That is, the distances measured along the curve between P and these points are converging to zero. Now consider the secant lines determined by these points and the point P (these are the green lines in Figure 10.12). Each of these secant lines is nonvertical and so has a slope. We shall denote the slopes of these secant lines by $m_1, m_2, m_3, \ldots$. It is this sequence of slopes that we must consider.

First of all, from the geometry of Figure 10.12, it should be fairly clear that the sequence $m_1, m_2, m_3, \ldots$ is an increasing sequence of real numbers. This is because each secant line is more nearly vertical than its predecessor and so has greater slope than its predecessor. Also this sequence is bounded. (Why? Can you find an upper bound for this sequence of slopes?) Hence, according to the completeness property, this sequence of slopes has a limit and we shall denote this limit by m. That is,

$$\text{limit } m_n = m.$$

This number m is called the **slope of the curve $\mathscr{C}$ at the point P**. The line passing through the point P and having this limit m for its slope is called the **tangent line to the curve $\mathscr{C}$ at the point P**. The tangent line can be regarded as the limit of the sequence of secant lines in the sense that as n gets larger and larger, the secant lines come nearer and nearer to coinciding with the tangent line. The slope of the tangent line is the limit of the slopes of the secant lines.

Example 1: The curve we showed in Figure 10.12 is the graph of the function $f(x) = x^2 - 1$ and the point P in that illustration is the point $(3, 8)$. We can compute the slope of this curve $\mathscr{C}$ at this point by finding an expression for the general term m_n in the sequence of slopes and by examining this expression to see if we can determine the real number to which m_n converges as n gets larger and larger. So let Q_n be the general point in the sequence of points (refer to Figure 10.13) and let (x_n, y_n) be the coordinate of Q_n. Then the slope of the secant line $\overleftrightarrow{Q_nP}$, m_n, is given by the equation

$$m_n = \frac{8 - y_n}{3 - x_n}.$$

Since (x_n, y_n) is a point of the graph of $f(x) = x^2 - 1$, we know that

Figure 10.13

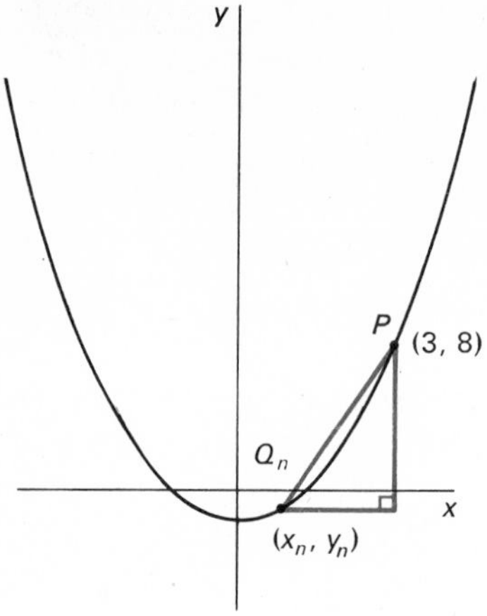

$y_n = x_n^2 - 1$ so that

$$m_n = \frac{8 - (x_n^2 - 1)}{3 - x_n} = \frac{9 - x_n^2}{3 - x_n} = \frac{(3 + x_n)(3 - x_n)}{3 - x_n} = 3 + x_n.$$

Now as n gets larger and larger, the point Q_n converges to the point P and so the x-coordinate of Q_n converges to the x-coordinate of P. That is, as n gets larger and larger, x_n converges to 3. Therefore, as n gets larger and larger, $3 + x_n$ converges to $3 + 3$ or 6. This shows that the slope of the tangent line to the graph of $f(x) = x^2 - 1$ at the point (3, 8) is equal to 6. That is, the slope of the graph at (3, 8) is 6.

Now we are ready to define the derivative of a function. Suppose that $f(x)$ is a function and that a is a number in the domain of this function. Then by the **derivative of the function f(x) at x = a** we mean the slope of the graph of this function at the point for which $x = a$. For example, the derivative of the function $f(x) = x^2 - 1$ at $x = 3$ is the number 6. We denote this derivative by the symbol $f'(a)$ so that if $f(x) = x^2 - 1$ and $a = 3$, then $f'(3) = 6$.

Differential calculus is the study of methods by means of which the derivatives of functions may be found and the study of ways in which the derivative of a function can be used to solve other problems. Many mathematical and physical problems which can be rephrased in such a way that their solution consists of determining the derivative of a function at some point. For example, there are many problems whose solution involves determining maximum or minimum values of a particular function. Consider the curve in Figure 10.14 which we shall assume is the graph of some function whose maximum value we would like to determine. How could we use

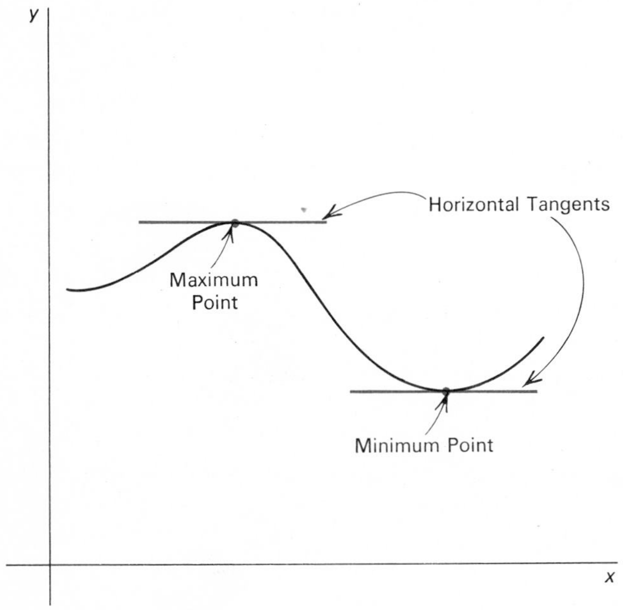

Figure 10.14

the notion of the slope of a curve at a point (the notion of a derivative) to help us in determining this maximum value? We use the fact (which is proved in differential calculus) that the tangent line to a curve at either a maximum or minimum point has slope 0 (is horizontal). To find maximum and minimum points, therefore, we need to be able to find the values of x for which the derivative of a function is equal to 0. Here is an example.

Example 2: In differential calculus, it is proved that the derivative of the function $f(x) = 3x^2 + 6x - 1$ (refer to Figure 10.15) is given by the formula $f'(x) = 6x + 6$. That is, the derivative of this function at any point x is $6x + 6$. So to find any maximum or minimum values of this function, all we need to do is to find the values of x which make the derivative equal to 0. At these values of x, the graph of the function has zero slope and so among them

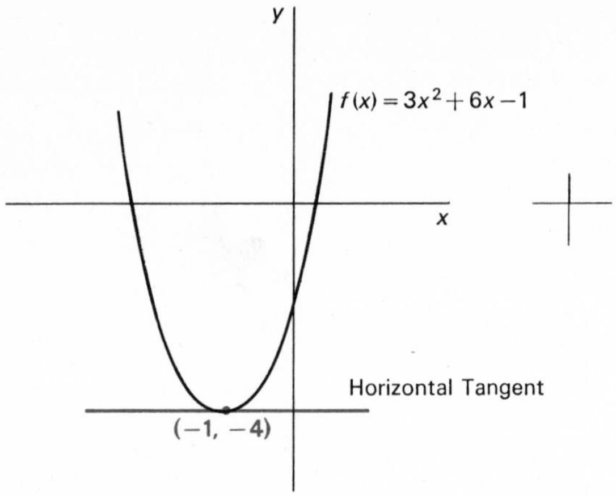

Figure 10.15

will be all the maximum and minimum points of the function. Setting $6x + 6$ equal to 0 and solving for x, we get the value $x = -1$. Hence, when $x = -1$, this function has either a maximum value or a minimum value. Since $f(-2) = -1$, $f(-1) = -4$, and $f(0) = -1$, we conclude that the function has a minimum when $x = -1$ and that this minimum value of the function is -4. In other words, the point $(-1, -4)$ is a minimum point of the graph of the function.

Exercises 10.7

1. It was asserted that the sequence of slopes of the secant lines in Figure 10.12 was bounded. Can you find a line through the point P whose slope is an upper bound for the sequence of slopes of the secant lines? Could your line be the vertical line through P?

2. In the manner of Example 1, find the derivative of the function $f(x) = x^2 - 1$ when $x = 1$.

3. Consider the graph of the function $f(x) = x^2 - 2x - 5$ and the point (5, 10) belonging to that graph. By selecting a point very near to (5, 10) and computing the slope of the line through that point and the point (5, 10) we can get some kind of approximation to the derivative of this function when $x = 5$. Do this.

4.* It can be proved in differential calculus that the derivative of the second-degree polynomial function $f(x) = ax^2 + bx + c$ at a point $(x, f(x))$ is given by the formula $f'(x) = 2ax + b$.

(a) Use this result to prove that the derivative of the function $f(x) = 3x^2 - 6x + 5$ when $x = 2$ is equal to 6.

(b) Use this formula to verify the answer given in Example 1 in the text and the answer you got in Exercise 2.

(c) Use this result to obtain the exact value of the slope of the function in Exercise 3 at the point (5, 10). Did your approximation come close? If it didn't, then you didn't select a point close enough to (5, 10).

5. The graph of the function $f(x) = x^2 - 2x - 5$ is a parabola that opens upward. Hence this curve has a minimum point at which the slope of the curve is 0. Using the formula of Exercise 4, find the coordinate of this minimum point. (*Hint:* Find the derivative of this function and set that derivative equal to 0 and solve for x.)

6.* It can be proved in differential calculus that if $f(x) = ax^3 + bx^2 + cx + d$, then the derivative of this function at a point $(x, f(x))$ is given by the equation $f'(x) = 3ax^2 + 2bx + c$.

(a) The graph of the function $f(x) = x^3 - 3x^2 - 4x + 10$ (refer to Exercise 1, Section 8.3) has one minimum point and one maximum point. Use this formula to find the exact coordinates of these maximum and minimum points.

(b) In Section 8.4 we used graphing methods to find the maximum value of the function $V(x) = (20 - 2x)(20 - 2x)(x)$. (Refer to Example 2 of that section.) If we rewrite this equation in the form $V(x) = 4x^3 - 80x^2 + 400x$ then we can find this maximum value exactly by using the above formula. Do this and show that this maximum value is obtained exactly when $x = 3\frac{1}{3}$. (*Hint:* You will need to know that $(3x - 10)(x - 10) = 3x^2 - 40x + 100$.)

Answers to Selected Exercises

Some of the answers that follow are complete and others are only partially complete. Frequently a hint is given instead of the answer. Many exercises have more than one correct answer and so answers different from the ones given here may nevertheless be correct. Many times you can verify your answers for yourself and whenever this is possible you should do it. To work an exercise without verifying as completely as you can that your answer is correct is the same thing as only working half the exercise.

Section 1.3

2. **(a)** I do not like school and I do not like to study. **(e)** It is false that I like school and don't like to study. **3.** b and c. **6.** Column under statement is T-T-F-F. Choose p to be any false statement and q to be any statement at all.

Section 1.4

2. They are the same. They are different. **4.** **(a)** If $x \neq 4$, then $x + 3 \neq 7$. **(c)** If the ground stays dry, then it will not have rained. **6.** a and b. **9.** **(a)** Either $2 \nless 3$ or $2 \ngtr 3$.

Section 1.5

1. **(a)** $4 < 5$. **(c)** s. **2.** No. "If $x + 3 = 5$, then $x + 1 = 3$." The hypothesis "$x + 3 = 5$." **3.** **(a)** $2 + 2 \neq 5$. **4.** **(a)** Cows fly. **5.** **(a)** $x = 0$. **(c)** $x = 0$.

Section 1.6

2. **(a)** There exists a number that is not greater than 0. **3.** **(a)** Every implication is either true or false. **7.** No, we are not.

Section 2.1

1. a, e, and f express relations; the others express operations. **3.** *Is two less than.* 5. 9. Yes; 2. No. **8.** The result of the operation performed on x and y is the product of the square root of x and the number y. $5 \cdot 36 = 180$. No. Upon 36 and 25 it is $6 \cdot 25 = 150$. **10.** For example, conjunction, disjunction, and implication operations. True for conjunction and disjunction ($p \wedge q \leftrightarrow q \wedge p$ and $p \vee q \leftrightarrow q \vee p$), but not true for implication ($p \rightarrow q \not\leftrightarrow q \rightarrow p$).

Section 2.2

1. No; it has none of the three properties. **2.** The symmetric property. **4.** Yes. **6.** Reflexive only. **9.** For example, *has greater area than.*

Section 2.3

1. *b*, *d*, and *g*. **3.** The average of the scores on the two exams he did take. **5.** **(a)** It is a diamond. **6.** Yes. Yes. **9.** *b*, *d*, and *e*. **11.** K♦, 3♣, and 5♣.

Section 2.4

1. **(a)** Commutative. **(c)** Associative. **3.** **(a)** Associativity and commutivity of multiplication. **4.** **(d)** 4, 8, 16, and 20. **6.** Yes; using truth tables can show that $(p \wedge q) \wedge r \leftrightarrow p \wedge (q \wedge r)$. Yes. **10.** Yes. Draw a line through entries $a * a$ and $d * d$. The table is symmetric with respect to this line. That is, fold the table along this line and the entries match up.

Section 2.5

1. 3♠ $*$ 5♦ $\neq$ 3♠. **2.** Yes; it has infinitely many. Every true statement is an identity for conjunction. **4.** Only *d* and *g* are correct. (In *e* and *f* the canceled quantity might have been equal to zero.) **8.** *a* is not an equivalence because when *p*, *q*, and *r* are all false the left side is false and the right side is true. *b* is an equivalence. Show this by truth tables. **9.** (1) Right. (2) Left. (3) Left. (4) Associative property of addition. (5) Transitive.

Section 2.6

3. **(a)** $x = 0$. **(b)** $x = 1, 4$. **6.** Additive inverse of 0 is 0, of 1 is 5, of 2 is 4, of 3 is 3, of 4 is 2, and of 5 is 1. **8.** $2 < 3$ since $2 \oplus 1 = 3$. $3 < 2$ since $3 \oplus 5 = 2$. **9.** Row 4 is 4–0–1–2–3 and column 3 is 3–4–0–1–2. **11.** **(a)** No solution. **(c)** $x = 0, 2$.

Section 2.7

2. **(a)** $x = 1, 5$. **(c)** No solution. **6.** No; the multiplicative inverse of 1 is 1 and of 5 is 5 and no other objects have inverses. **7.** Row 3 is 0–3–1–4–2 and column 2 is 0–2–4–1–3. **9.** Yes; the multiplicative inverse of 1 is 1, of 2 is 3, and 3 is 2, and of 4 is 4.

Section 3.2

1. **(a)** $3 < 5$ because $3 + 2 = 5$ and $2 \neq 0$. **(b)** $5 > 3$ because $3 < 5$. **4.** Each is transitive, none is symmetric, and $\leq$ and $\geq$ are reflexive. **6.** (1) Hypothesis. (2) Definition of $<$. (4) Distributive property. (5) $d > 0$ and $z > 0$. (6) Definition of $<$. **9.** (1) Hypothesis. (2) Definition of $<$. (4) Associativity of addition. (5) $d > 0$ and $e > 0$ imply $d + e > 0$. (6) Definition of $<$.

Section 3.3

3. Only *b* and *d* are true. **4.** **(a)** Use Theorem C. **(c)** Use Theorems D and E. **5.** **(a)** 0, 1, 2, 3, and 4 are solutions. The analog of Theorem A and Theorem C were used. **6.** Commutative. Multiplication. Definition of division.

Section 3.4

1. **(a)** Only solution in the system of whole numbers is 2. **2.** In going from (5) to (6) we inadvertently canceled 0 thus destroying the validity of the argument.

Section 3.5

1. **(a)** $2^2 \cdot 3^3$. **2.** **(a)** $2^6 \cdot 3^5 \cdot 5^4$. **5.** 2. 2^2. 2^3. 2^4. 2^5. 126. **6.** 10^1, 10^2, 10^3, 10^4, and 10^5. 56 0's. 10^0.

Section 3.6

1. The divisors of 144 are 1, 2, 4, 8, 16, 3, 6, 9, 12, 18, 24, 36, 48, 72, and 144. **3.** There are 30 such pairs. **6.** **(a)** 1, 2, 4, 8, and 16. **(b)** 0, 16, 32, 48, 64, ... **(c)** Yes; every number. **(d)** Yes. **(e)** For example, 4 is a divisor of 8 but 8 is not a divisor of 4. **9.** Of any two successive whole numbers one of them must be even. The only even prime is 2 and so of two successive primes one of them must be 2. Hence the only pair of successive primes is 2, 3.

Section 3.7

3. 58. **5.** It is a perfect square if and only if all its exponents are even. **6.** It is square-free if and only if all the exponents are 1. **8. (a)** $2^3 \cdot 3^3 \cdot 5$. **(c)** $2 \cdot 3^4 \cdot 17$.

Section 3.8

1. (a) GCD $= 2 \cdot 3$. LCM $= 2^2 \cdot 3 \cdot 5$. **(c)** GCD $= 2 \cdot 3^2$. LCM $= 2^4 \cdot 3^2 \cdot 11$. **5. (a)** Yes. **(c)** Yes. **6. (a)** Yes. **(b)** Yes. Yes. **(c)** No. **(d)** No. For example, take $x = 12$, $y = 8$, and $z = 2$. **8.** No. For example, 12 is divisible by 6 and by 4 but not by their product. The trouble is that 6 and 4 are not relatively prime. If x and y are relatively prime and each divides n, then their product will also divide n.

Section 3.9

3. $28 = 1 + 2 + 4 + 7 + 14$ and $496 = 1 + 2 + 4 + 8 + 16 + 31 + 62 + 124 + 248$. 8128 is a perfect number because $8128 = (2^7 - 1)(2^6)$ and $2^7 - 1$ is a prime number.

Section 4.1

6. (b) For example, the set of all statements p such that $p \vee \sim p$ is false. **7.** $\varnothing$ has no objects at all while $\{\varnothing\}$ contains exactly one object. **9. (a)** $\{0,2,4,6,8\}$. **(c)** $\{1,3,5,7,9\}$. **10. (a)** $\{3,4\}$.

Section 4.2

2. The paradox involved is that the least number not nameable with less than 22 syllables is nameable with 19 syllables. **3.** If the barber were male, then no matter what he did he would be breaking the law. So the barber must be female. **5.** $(x - 1)(x + 1) = (x - 1)(1)$ does not necessarily imply $x + 1 = 1$ since $x - 1 = 0$.

Section 4.3

2. The proper subsets are a, b, and c. The disjoint sets are c and g. The only equal set is e. The subsets are a, b, c, and e. **2.** A set with n objects has 2^n subsets. **6.** There are 8 such subsets (including $\varnothing$). **7.** Yes; the empty set is disjoint from every set and is also a subset of every set. **11.** $a \leftrightarrow c$; $b \leftrightarrow d \leftrightarrow g$; $e \leftrightarrow f$.

Section 4.4

1. (a) $\{2,3\}$. **(d)** $\{2,3\}$. **2.** A. A. B. **5.** $a \leftrightarrow d$ and $b \leftrightarrow c$. **7.** Yes. For example, take $A = \{1\}$, $B = \{2\}$, and $C = \{1,2\}$. Tells you that the operation of union does not possess the cancellation property. Yes. Intersection does not have the cancellation property. **10.** Yes; $\varnothing$. Yes; the universal set. **11. (a)** $\{1\}$, $\{1,2,3\}$, and $\{1,2,3\}$. **(c)** $A \subseteq B$.

Section 4.5

1. (a) There are 2. **(b)** There are 24. **(c)** There are none.

Section 4.6

2. There are six different one-to-one correspondences between this set and $\{1,2,3\}$. **3. (a)** Cardinal. **(d)** Ordinal. **5.** $a_0 \leftrightarrow 0$, $b_0 \leftrightarrow 1$, $a_1 \leftrightarrow 2$, $b_1 \leftrightarrow 3$, ... In general, a_i corresponds to the even whole number $2i$ and b_i corresponds to the odd whole number $2i + 1$. **7.** $P(S)$ has $2^2 = 4$ objects; $P(P(S))$ has $2^4 = 16$ objects; $P(P(P(S)))$ has $2^{16} = 75{,}536$ objects.

Section 4.7

3. $n \times \aleph_0 = \aleph_0 + \aleph_0 + \cdots + \aleph_0 = \aleph_0$. **4.** $\aleph_0 \times \aleph_0 = \aleph_0$.

Section 5.1

4. b, c, and e are true. **8. (a)** No. **(c)** No. **(e)** Yes. **11.** First two are convex. First and third only. **12.** Circular region. No.

Section 5.2

6. It was either a rotation whose center was a point of the triangle or a reflection about a line cutting the triangle in one point. **7.** It was a reflection about the line determined by the two fixed points. **10.** Translation only. Translations and rotations for the other three kinds of figures.

Section 5.3

3. It stretches it. It shrinks the figure. It leaves the figure unchanged. **4.** The lines are parallel. **6.** They are congruent. The location of the center of the homothety is not significant; no matter where the center is located the resulting figures are congruent. **7.** 1. It left all points of the figure fixed.

Section 5.4

1. *a, c, d, e, f, h, i*, and *j* are both. *b* and *k* are only congruence invariants. *g* is neither. **3.** Congruence and Euclidean. **4.** Yes. No. Yes. Yes.

Section 5.5

2. Yes. Yes. **3.** *a, b*, and *g* are topologically equivalent. *c* and *h* are equivalent. *d, e*, and *f* are equivalent. **7.** Only *d* and *e*. **9.** No. An annular region. **11.** Yes. Yes. No. Yes.

Section 5.6

1. **(a)** 2 sides and 1 edge. **(b)** 1 side and 2 edges. **(c)** 1 side and 2 edges. **(d)** 1 side and 2 edges. **6.** 2 sides and 2 edges. They are the same figures as the original. **7.** 1 side and 1 edge. You get a large loop with a knot tied in it. 1.

Section 6.1

1. -7 is the only number which when 7 is added to it results in 0. **11.** **(a)** $xz < yz$. **(b)** $xz > yz$. **12.** **(c)** negative. **13.** $\aleph_0$. No; the cardinal numbers of these two sets are equal.

Section 6.2

1. **(a)** Yes. α. Itself. Itself. **3.** ◆ does not define a group because β is the identity and α has no inverse with respect to this identity. ▲ and ● are not groups by Exercise 2. ■ is not a group because β has no inverse with respect to the identity α. **5.** The proof: (1) $x * z = y * z$. (2) $(x * z) * z^{-1} = (y * z) * z^{-1}$. (3) $x * (z * z^{-1}) = y * (z * z^{-1})$. (4) $x * i = y * i$. (5) $x = y$. **6.** According to the changed table, $c * d = e * d$. If this were a group, then by Exercise 5 we would have to conclude that $c = e$, which is absurd.

Section 6.3

3. **(a)** 41/56. **(c)** 35/24. **5.** No; given any positive rational number x/y, $x/(y+1)$ is still positive but is smaller. Yes; 1. No. Yes; -1. **7.** **(a)** $ad + bc$. **8.** **(a)** $1/7 + 1/8 + 1/56$. **(b)** $1/7 + 1/8 + 1/56 + 1/9 + 1/72 + 1/57 + 1/3192$.

Section 6.4

2. All hold except 2D. For example, 2 has no inverse with respect to 4-multiplication. **3.** Yes. Because property 4B does not hold (although 4A and 4C do hold).

Section 6.5

1. **(b)** 428/99. **(d)** 4507/3300. **3.** Yes. Yes. Yes. Not necessarily. **4.** Nothing except that it would whir for a while and then produce 4.5. It would whir and produce 2.5. It would whir and whir and whir and whir.

Section 6.6

3. Assume such a triangle existed with legs of length x and hypotenuse of length y. Then $x^2 + x^2 = y^2$ or $y/x = \sqrt{2}$. Since x and y are integers this is a contradiction. **6.** *b, c*, and *d* are rational. **7.** The repeating block has some definite length, say n. Go out in the numeral until you get to $2n$ zeros in a row. The repeating block is contained somewhere in this segment of zeros. Hence the repeating block contains no ones. Contradiction.

Section 7.1

1. **(a)** $\sqrt{61}$. **2.** $y > 0$. $y < 0$. $x < 0$. $x > 0$. **6.** It is not: $(\sqrt{32})^2 + (\sqrt{41})^2 \neq (9)^2$. **8.** No. (8,5) and $(-4,-11)$ belong to the same circle and $(-6,2)$ belong to another.

Section 7.2

1. **(b)** $2x + y = 2$. **4.** **(a)** $(0, -1/2)$ and $(1/4, 0)$. **6.** It passes through the origin.

Section 7.3

1. **(a)** -2. **4.** $x + 2y = 5$. **8.** $9x + 10y = -16$. **9.** 46.

Section 7.5

1. **(b)** $(x + 3)^2 + (y + 5)^2 = 18$. **3.** $y^2 + 6y - 4x = -13$. **4.** **(a)** Hyperbola opening left and right. Cuts the x-axis at $(2,0)$ and $(-2,0)$. **(b)** Ellipse cutting the x-axis at $(5,0)$ and $(-5,0)$ and cutting the y-axis at $(0,3)$ and $(0,-3)$. **(c)** Parabola opening to the right and passing through the origin.

Section 8.1

3. **(a)** For each input there are infinitely many different outputs. Every simple closed curve would be an output. **4.** Yes. This is called a *constant* box. **5.** **(a)** The inputs are the non-vertical lines.

Section 8.2

3. x is some real number greater than or equal to 2 and less than 3: $2 \leq x < 3$. **5.** For example, $(8,2)$ and $(5,-1)$. **7.** **(a)** No; no polygon has zero perimeter. No. **(c)** One; the 4 by 4 square. **8.** **(d)** For example, the greatest integer function: $f(x) = [\![x]\!]$.

Section 8.3

1. The total number of maximum and minimum points is one less than the highest power of x appearing in the function. **2.** Except for a they are all asymptotic to the negative x-axis from above. They all pass through the point $(0,1)$. The greater the base number the more steeply the graph rises as x gets larger and larger. **5.** **(a)** This graph is called a *step-graph.* It consists of segments whose right-hand endpoints have been removed.

Section 8.4

1. Largest area is when $x = 25$. Then the area is 625. **3.** $A(x) = 2x^2 + 256/x$. Dimensions should be 4 by 4 by 4.

Section 8.5

2. These values are so close together that if rounded off to three places they would appear to be equal. **3.** Exactly the same as it did between 0° and 360°. The graph repeats itself every 360°. **6.** Use Fig. 8.13 and the Pythagorean Theorem.

Section 8.6

1. Cos $\alpha = .838$, where α is the angle at the top of the tower. From the table cos 33° = .839. So α is approximately equal to 33°. **2.** Approximately 102 feet. **3.** Approximately 233,118 miles. Too small.

Section 9.1

1. **(d)** 2/3. **2.** **(d)** They are all equal to 9/19. **3.** 25/52. **5.** **(c)** Outcomes are different collections of coins whose total is 25¢. They are mutually exclusive. They are not equally likely. For example, 10¢–10¢–5¢ is more likely than 1¢–1¢–···–1¢. **7.** **(a)** 1/3 since the possibilities are BB, BG, and GB. **(b)** 1/2 since the possibilities are only BB and GB. **9.** There are 3 ways to lay down a card so that a red side shows. Of these 3 ways, 2 are favorable to the other side of the card being red. Hence the probability is 2/3.

Section 9.2

4. 12/48. **5.** **(a)** 1/6. **6.** **(a)** $1 - (5/6)(5/6)(5/6)(5/6)$.

Section 9.3

3. $(26)^3$. $(26)(26)(5) + (26)(5)(26) + (5)(26)(26) = 10{,}140$. $10{,}140 + (26)(5)(5) + (5)(26)(5) + (5)(5)(26)$. **5.** 7. 21. 35. 63. **6.** $6[(26)(26)(10)]$. **9.** $C(6,3)$. $C(6,3) - 4$.

Section 9.4

2. (1/52)(1/51)(1/50)(1/49). 1/C(52,4). **4.** C(79,19)/C(80,20). C(78/19)/C(80,20). 1 − C(78,20)/C(80,20). **9.** Probability that first player will die is 1/6. Probability that second player will die is (5/6)(1/6) = 5/36 < 1/6. **12.** Probability of no hits = (2/3)(2/3)(2/3). So answer is 1 − 8/27.

Section 9.5

5. $21/6. **7.** ME = (75/216)(2) + (15/216)(3) + (1/216)(4) = .921. **9.** ME = (6/28)(2) + (8/28) × (6) + (8/28)(11) + (1/28)(10) + (4/28)(15) + (1/28)(20).

Section 10.1

1. (a) 0, 3/5, 8/10, 15/17, 24/26, 35/37, ... **(c)** −1, 1/2, −1/3, 1/4, −1/5, 1/6, ... **3.** $a_n = [\![n/3]\!]$. **5. (a)** S is an upper bound. No. **(c)** No. Yes. No. **8.** $a_n = (-1)^n/(n+1)$.

Section 10.2

1. (a) For example, 999/1000. **(b)** For example, 99999/100000. **(c)** Since $n < n + 1$ for all n, $n/(n+1) < (n+1)/(n+1) = 1$. So all the terms are less than 1 and so 1 is an upper bound. **9.** 2 is an upper bound but, since each of the numbers 1.9, 1.99, 1.999, 1.9999, etc., is not an upper bound, 2 must be the least upper bound. (This is an informal argument.) **10.** The differences are 14/90 > 10/90 = 1/9, 104/900 > 100/900 = 1/9, etc. So 5/9 − 1/9 is also an upper bound. (In fact it is the least upper bound.)

Section 10.3

2. (a) $a_n = (2n - 1)/n$. **(b)** $(2n - 1)/n = 2n/n - 1/n = 2 - 1/n$. So $(2n - 1)/n < 2$ for all n. **(c)** When $n = 1001$, $(2n - 1)/n$ differs from 2 by 1/1001 (using part b). So take a_{1001}. **3. (a)** $(n - 1)/3n = 1/3 - 1/3n$. So for every n, $a_n < 1/3$. **6. (a)** .5555 = 5555/10000 < 5555/9999 = 5/9. **(b)** 5/9 − .5555 = .55555··· − .5555 = .000055555··· < .0001.

Section 10.4

1. $3\frac{1}{7}$ = 3.14285 (approximately) and $3\frac{10}{71}$ = 3.14084 (approximately). So he was correct to two decimal places. **3. (a)** One half the angle AOB is $180/n$. So $\overline{AB}$ = 2[sin(180°/36)] = .174. So perimeter is 6.264.

Section 10.5

2. (a) Since $1/n$ converges to 0, expression converges to 3. **(c)** Write general term in the form $1/5 - 1/5n$ first. **3. (d)** $(n + 1)/(1 - n^2) = (n + 1)/(1 + n)(1 - n) = 1/(1 - n)$. Limit is 0.

Section 10.6

3. (b) A_3 = 74/27. **(a)** A_3 will do. **5. (a)** Integral equals $[(1/3)(1/2)(2)^3 + (1/2)(0)(2)^2 + (1)(2)] - 0$. **(c)** Integral equals $[(1/3)(8)(4)^3 + 0 + 0] - [(1/3)(8)(1)^3 + 0 + 0] = 504/3$.

Section 10.7

2. $m_n = (0 - y_n)/(1 - x_n) = (1 - x_n^2)/(1 - x_n) = 1 + x_n$. The derivative at $x = 1$ is 2. **4. (a)** $f'(x) = (2)(3)(x) - 6$, so $f'(6) = 6$. **(b)** In Exercise 2, $f'(x) = 2x + 0$. So $f'(1) = 2$. **5.** $f'(x) = 2x - 2$. Set $2x - 2 = 0$ and get $x = 1$. So the point (1, −6) is a minimum point of the graph.

Index